A Handbook Series on Electromagnetic Interference and Compatibility

Volume 6

Electromagnetic Interference Test Methodology and Procedures

Edwin L. Bronaugh
William S. Lambdin

Interference Control Technologies, Inc.
Gainesville, Virginia

Interference Control Technologies, Inc.
Route 625, Gainesville, VA 22065
TEL: (703) 347-0030   FAX: (703) 347-5813

Library of Congress Catalog Card Number: 88-81459
ISBN: 0-944916-06-6

Acknowledgement

The authors wish to thank all of the people who made this book possible. Our indebtedness to Don White is most obvious in that his original editions of this volume and, to a lesser extent, his companion volume, *EMI Test Instrumentation and Systems,* provided both the framework on which this present volume is built and much of its contents. Our respect for the massive effort required of him to create the original text grew steadily as our work on this present volume progressed.

We wish to acknowledge the manufacturers of EMC instrumentation and accessories who furnished us with photographs and data on their products for use in the book. Although they are identified throughout the book wherever their material is used, we wish to express our sincere thanks as well for all of the material made available which we were not able to incorporate. We owe special thanks to Electro-Metrics and Vito Greco, its General Manager, for the use of their facilities in reproducing both the final manuscript and various interim drafts as the work progressed.

And, finally, we wish to dedicate this book to our respective wives, Gerrie Bronaugh and Betty Lambdin, whose patience, tolerance and encouragement sustained us. We thank them for overlooking all the household tasks that had to be postponed and all the social activities that had to be missed.

Other Books in the 12-Volume Series

VOLUME 1
Fundamentals of Electromagnetic Compatibility

VOLUME 2
Grounding and Bonding

VOLUME 3
Electromagnetic Shielding

VOLUME 4
Filters and Power Conditioning

VOLUME 5
EMC in Components and Devices

VOLUME 6
EMI Test Methodology and Procedures

VOLUME 7
EMC in Telecommunications

VOLUME 8
EMI Control Methodology and Procedures

VOLUME 9
United States Commercial Standards

VOLUME 10
European and International Commercial Standards

VOLUME 11
Military EMC Standards

VOLUME 12
Supporting Military EMC Standards

Contents

Preface

The twofold purpose of this new edition of *EMI Test Methodology and Procedures* is to update the earlier edition in light of current practices and to strengthen the usefulness of the volume both as a tutorial source and as a reference handbook. The implementation of these goals is discussed more fully in the accompanying section entitled, "How to Use This Handbook."

Despite the authors' awareness of well-intentioned campaigns to restrict the use of the term "electromagnetic interference (EMI)" to those levels of electromagnetic emissions which actually produce some adverse effect in a receptor, they have chosen to continue the practice of applying the term to cover any level of electromagnetic energy which **potentially** can cause such a problem. Their choice of this convention was based partly on its entrenched acceptance, but also on the realization that levels of emissions classified as innocuous today might have to be redefined as harmful in the future as additional or more sensitive devices are introduced into the electromagnetic environment.

How to Use This Handbook

This handbook is designed to be used either as a basic textbook to introduce an inexperienced reader to the subject of EMC testing or as a reference book for the experienced EMI professional to recall particular aspects of the discipline.

For the reader who is relatively unfamiliar with EMI testing, the first two chapters should prove particularly valuable. A quick reading of Chapter 1 can provide a perspective which justifies and encourages the further acquisition of knowledge on the subject. Without some acquaintance with the background in this first chapter, which covers the numerous entities which mandate and guide EMI testing, some of the procedures discussed in later chapters could appear arbitrary and mutually conflicting.

The inexperienced reader will then find Chapter 2, covering the fundamentals of EMI testing, particularly worthwhile because it introduces all of the principles and conventions needed for a broad comprehension of the subject. Once the basic principles in this second chapter are understood, the more specialized information presented in the following chapters becomes both more accessible and more meaningful. The text of the entire volume is developed so that a study of all 13 chapters in sequence can provide a cumulative education on the subject of EMI testing.

For the reader who is already experienced in EMI testing, but who is faced with an unfamiliar EMI testing task, the book is intended to offer easy access to such procedures. Depending on the scope of the information required, either the table of contents or the index should provide the key to the pertinent pages. Frequent references throughout the text to related information, both in this volume and in outside publications, are intended to facilitate a deeper investigation of many aspects of EMI testing.

Each of the last four chapters, 10 through 13, is devoted to specific procedures used for one of the four basic categories of EMI testing: conducted and radiated emissions (CE and RE) and conducted and radiated susceptibility (CS and RS). However, before utilizing any of the procedures in these final four chapters, it is highly recommended that the complementary preparations for testing covered in Chapter 9 be reviewed and heeded.

Finally, it should be noted that, to make the test procedures in this volume as generic as possible, specific identification of them as CE, RE, CS, RS or unique methods (UM) of MIL-STD-462 has been minimized. However, Table 1.3 is provided to correlate each of the MIL-STD-462 test methods to its corresponding section in Chapters 10 through 13 as well as to sections elsewhere in the volume which contain directly pertinent background information. In addition, throughout the book it is clearly indicated whenever a subject being discussed is exclusively pertinent to either military- or civilian-oriented EMI testing.

Common Terms and Abbreviations in EMC Literature

Prefixes for Decimal Multiples

10^{12}	tera	T
10^9	giga	G
10^6	mega	M
10^3	kilo	k
10^2	hecto	h
10	deka	da
10^{-1}	deci	d
10^{-2}	centi	c
10^{-3}	milli	m
10^{-6}	micro	μ
10^{-9}	nano	n
10^{-12}	pico	p

Technical Terms

absolute	abs
alternating current	ac
American wire gage	AWG
ampere	A
ampere per meter	A/m
ampere-hour	Ah
amplitude modulation	AM
amplitude probability distribution	APD
analog to digital	A/D
analog-to-digital converter	ADC or A/D converter
anti-jamming	AJ
arithmetic logic unit	ALU
audio frequency	AF
automatic data processing	ADP
automatic frequency control	AFC
automatic gain control	AGC

average	avg
bandwidth	BW
binary coded decimal	BCD
bit	b
bit-error rate	BER
bits per second	bps
British thermal unit	Btu
broadband	BB
byte	B
bytes per second	Bps
centimeter-gram-second	cgs
central processing unit	CPU
characters per second	cps
common-mode coupling	CMC
common-mode rejection ratio	CMRR
complementary metal-oxide semiconductor	CMOS
conducted emission	CE
conducted susceptibility	CS
continuous wave	CW
coulomb	C
cubic centimeter	cm^3
decibel	dB
decibel above 1 milliwatt	dBm
decibel above 1 volt	dBV
decibel above 1 watt	dBW
degree Celsius	°C
degree Fahrenheit	°F
degree Kelvin	K
diameter	dia
differential-mode coupling	DMC
digital multimeter	DMM
digital to analog	D/A
digital voltmeter	DVM

digital-to-analog converter	DAC or D/A conv.	input/output	I/O
diode-transistor logic	DTL	inside dimension	ID
direct current	dc	instantaneous automatic gain control	IAGC
double pole double throw	DPDT	insulated-gate field-effect transistor	IGFET
double sideband	DSB	integrated circuit	IC
double sideband suppressed carrier	DSB-SC	interference-to-noise ratio	I/N
dual in-line package	DIP	intermediate frequency	IF
electric field	E-Field	joule	J
electromagnetic compatibility	EMC	junction field-effect transistor	JFET
electromagnetic interference	EMI	kilogram	kg
electromagnetic pulse	EMP	kilohertz	kHz
electromotive force	EMF	kilovolt	kV
electron volt	eV	kilowatt	kW
electronic countermeasures	ECM	kilowatt-hour	kWh
electrostatic discharge	ESD	lambert	L
emitter-coupled logic	ECL	large-scale integration	LSI
extremely high frequency	EHF	least significant bit	LSB
extremely low frequency	ELF	length	l
farad	F	length (of cable)	l_c
fast Fourier transform	FFT	line impedance stabilization network	LISN
field intensity	FI	line of sight	LOS
field intensity meter	FIM	liter	l
field-effect transistor	FET	local oscillator	LO
foot	ft or '	low frequency	LF
frequency	freq	lower sideband	LSB
frequency division multiplex	FDM	lumen	lm
frequency modulation	FM	lux	lx
frequency shift keying	FSK	magnetic field	H-Field
gauss	G	master oscillator power amplifier	MOPA
gram	g	maximum	max
ground	gnd	maxwell	Mx
ground loop coupling	GLC	mean time between failure	MTBF
ground support equipment	GSE	mean time to failure	MTTF
hazards of electromagnetic radiation to ordnance	HERO	mean time to repair	MTTR
henry	H	medium frequency (300 kHz to 3 MHz)	MF
hertz (cycles per second)	Hz	metal-oxide semiconductor	MOS
high frequency	HF	metal-oxide semiconductor field-effect transistor	MOSFET
high-power transistor-to-transistor logic	HTTL	metal-oxide varistor	MOV
high-speed complementary metal-oxide semiconductor	HCMOS	meter	m
		microfarad	μF
high-threshold logic	HTL	microhenry	μH
hour	hr	micro-ohm	$\mu\Omega$
inch	in or "	mile	mi
inch per second	ips	military specification	MIL-SPEC
industrial, scientific and medical	ISM	military standard	MIL-STD
infrared	IR	milliamp	mA

million instructions per second	MIPS	pulse position modulation	PPM
millisecond	ms	pulse repetition frequency	PRF
millivolt	mV	pulse-amplitude modulation	PAM
milliwatt	mW	pulse-code modulation	PCM
minimum	min	pulse-duration modulation	PDM
minimum discernable signal	MDS	pulse-width modulation	PWM
minute	min	quasi-peak	QP
modulator-demodulator	modem	radiation hazard	RADHAZ
most significant bit	MSB	radio frequency	RF
multilayer board	MLB	radio interference and field intensity	RI-FI
multiplex, multiplexer	mux	radio-frequency interference	RFI
nanofarad	nF	random access memory	RAM
nanohenry	nH	receiver	RX
nanosecond	ns	reference	ref
narrowband	NB	relative humidity	RH
negative	neg	resistance-inductance-capacitance	RLC
negative-positive-negative (transistor)	npn	return to zero	RTZ
negative-to-positive (junction)	n-p	revolutions per minute	rpm
newton	N	roentgen	R
noise equivalent power	NEP or P_n	root-mean-square	rms
		second	s
non-return to zero	NRZ	sensitivity time control	STC
N-type metal-oxide semiconductor	NMOS	shielding effectiveness	SE
		sideband	SB
nuclear electromagnetic pulse	NEMP	siemens	S
		signal-to-interference (ratio)	S/I
oersted	Oe	signal-to-noise (ratio)	S/N
ohm	Ω	silicon controlled rectifier	SCR
ohm-centimeter	Ωcm	single sideband	SSB
ohms per square	Ω/sq	square meter	m^2
ounce	oz	standing-wave ratio	SWR
outside dimension	OD	super high frequency	SHF
peak	pk	super low frequency	SLF
peak-to-peak	p-p	surface acoustic wave	SAW
phase lock loop	PLL	surface-mount technology	SMT
phase modulation	PM	surface-mounted component	SMC
positive	pos	surface-mounted device	SMD
positive-negative-positive (transistor)	pnp	television	TV
		temperature coefficient	TC
positive-to-negative (junction)	p-n	tesla	T
		time division multiplex	TDM
pound (sterling)	£	transistor-to-transistor logic	TTL
pound per square centimeter	p/cm^2	transverse electromagnetic	TEM
pound per square inch	psi	ultra high frequency (300 MHz to 3 GHz)	UHF
power factor	PF	ultraviolet	UV
printed circuit board	PCB	very high frequency (30 MHz to 300 MHz)	VHF
private branch exchange	PBX	very high-speed integrated circuit	VHSIC
P-type metal-oxide semiconductor	PMOS	very large-scale integration	VLSI
pulse per second	pps	very low frequency	

List of Abbreviations

(3 kHz to 30 kHz) .... VLF
volt V
volt meter .... VM
voltage standing wave ratio VSWR
voltage-to-frequency
   converter .... VFC
voltampere .... VA
volt-ohm meter .... VOM
watt .... W
waveguide beyond cuttoff . WGBCO
weber .... Wb
words per minute .... wpm
yard .... yd

Mathematical Functions and Operators

absolute value .... abs
approximately equal .... ≈
argument .... arg
cosine .... cos
cosine (hyperbolic) .... cosh
cotangent .... cot
cotangent (hyperbolic) .... coth
determinant .... det
dimension .... dim
exponential .... exp
imaginary .... im
inferior .... inf
limit .... lim
logarithm,
   common (base 10) .... log
logarithm,
   Napierian (base e) .... ln
sine .... sin
tangent .... tan
tangent (hyperbolic) .... tanh

Common Variables in EMC Equations

angle in degrees or radians Θ, ϕ
    or ψ
angular velocity = $2\pi f$
   radians per second .... ω
attenuation constant,
   absorption factor .... α
Boltzmann's constant
   $(1.38 \times 10^{-23}$ J/K .... k
capacitance (in farads) C
charge .... Q
coefficient of self-inductance L
conductance .... G
conductivity, propagation
   constant, leakage
   coefficient, deviation ...... σ

current I
dielectric constant,
   permittivity .... ϵ
frequency (in Hz) .... f
impedance .... Z
increment or segment ...... Δ
induced voltage .... E
inductance (in henrys) L
infinity .... ∞
length (coil turn, ground
   loop, etc.) l
length in millimeters .... l_{mm}
magnetic susceptibility ..... χ
magnetizing force .... H
parasitic capacitance .... C_p
permeability of free space μ_0
permeability of medium
   relative to μ_0 .... μ_r
permittivity .... ϵ
phase constant .... β
pulse width .... τ
radius .... r
relative permittivity .... ϵ_r
resistance (in ohms) .... R
rise time .... τ_r
shield thickness .... d
standard deviation .... σ
summation of indicated
   terms .... Σ
time .... t
time constant, transmission
   factor .... τ
velocity, volume V
voltage reflection coefficient Γ
wave number = $2\pi/\lambda$ .... β
wavelength .... λ

Terms Distinctive to This Volume

antenna factor .... AF
area, effective (of an
   antenna) .... A_e
average crossing rate (a
   statistical detection
   process) .... ACR
bandwidth, impulse .... B_i
bandwidth, random noise.. B_n
bandwidth at response 3 dB
   down (≈ 0.5 power) ...... B_3
bandwidth at response 6 dB
   down (≈ 0.5 voltage) ..... B_6
conducted emissions .... CE
conducted susceptibility .... CS
conical log spiral (antenna) CLS

current probe .... CP

electric field strength .... E

effective radiated power
(transmitted power times
antenna gain)..................... ERP

error .... ϵ

frequency range, high end of f_H

frequency range, low end of f_L

frequency of local oscillator f_{LO}

gain; as of an antenna or
   radiator .... g or G

height, effective, of an
   antenna .... h_e

impulse generator............. IG

internal noise level .... INL

industrial, scientific and
   medical (equipment) ...... ISM

inductance (basis unit is
   henry, H)...................... L

magnetic flux density (basic
   unit is tesla, T, which is
   preferred to **gauss**
   and **gamma**)................ B

noise amplitude distribution
   (a statistical detection
   process)......................... NAD

noise factor (a ratio) .... $\underline{F}$

noise figure (10 log $\underline{F}$)...... F

normalized site attenuation NSA

pulse duration distribution
   (a statistical detection
   process)......................... PDD

quality factor.................... Q

radiated emission.............. RE

radiated susceptibility....... RS

site attenuation................. A

spectrum amplitude (basic
   units are V/Hz or
   volt-seconds)................. S(f)

transfer impedance (of
   current probe; basic unit
   is ohm)......................... Z_T

transmitter antenna factor TAF

transverse electric
   (waveguide mode).......... TE

transverse electromagnetic TEM

transmitter .... TX

volts per hertz =
   volt-seconds (basic unit of
   spectrum amplitude)...... V/Hz

volts per meter (basic unit
   of electric field strength) V/m

Chapter 1

Rationale and Administration of EMI Testing

Throughout the world, thousands of engineers and technicians annually spend hundreds of millions of dollars for their employing companies and agencies testing for electromagnetic interference (EMI). This introductory chapter examines why this massive effort is necessary, how it is administered and why EMI testing methods are so numerous and diverse.

Although this chapter should be of greatest value to those relatively new to the subject of electromagnetic compatibility (EMC), it could also provide a renewed perspective to the more experienced EMC professional by examining questions such as:

1. Why are some military methods for EMI testing so different from those of civilian agencies?
2. What considerations affect the setting of limits for various stages and types of EMI testing?
3. What organized activities are in place to encourage a greater degree of standardization in EMI testing?

1.1 The Rationale of EMI Testing

1.1.1 Basis for EMI Testing

EMI testing is performed to determine whether the equipment under test (EUT) is compatible with the electromagnetic environment in which it is designed to operate. The two distinct aspects of this consideration are:

1. The EUT must not emit levels of electromagnetic energy which could deteriorate the operation of anything already present or permitted in its intended operating environment. **EMI emissions testing** is performed to determine the extent to which the EUT satisfies this criterion.
2. The EUT must not be susceptible to having its operation affected by levels of electromagnetic energy already present or permitted in its intended operating environment. **EMI susceptibility testing** is performed to determine the extent to which the EUT satisfies this criterion. Frequently in EMC literature the complementary term **immunity** is used instead of **susceptibility** when discussing the extent to which the EUT is vulnerable to EMI.

1.1.2 Determining EMI Test Methods and Limits

1.1.2.1 EMI Transmissions: Radiated and Conducted

From the earliest days of EMI testing (see "Background," Section 1.3.1.1), it has been recognized that two basic routes exist for transmission of EMI into or out of an EUT: **radiation** and **conduction**. As working definitions, it is posited that:

1. **Conducted EMI** is electromagnetic energy undesirably coupled out of an emitter or into a receptor via any of its respective connecting wires or cables.
2. **Radiated EMI** is electromagnetic energy undesirably coupled out of an emitter or into a receptor by means other than conduction.

The path for transmission of EMI between an emitter and a receptor is frequently neither purely conductive nor purely radiative, but a combination of both. For example, EMI can be conducted out of an emitter via its power lead, radiated from that power lead to a power lead from another independent power source, and then conducted via that lead into a receptor. In addition, public power lines often provide a direct, uninterrupted conduction path for EMI to be coupled between emitters and receptors.

1.1.2.2 Models for the EUT Environment

The electromagnetic environment in which a particular EUT is to operate is the key to determining how it should be tested for EMI and how stringently its emissions and susceptibility should be restricted. A computer terminal for operation in the crowded electromagnetic environment of a military aircraft requires EMI test methods and limits quite different from those required for comparable equipment designed to operate in a residential setting.

For military equipment, the basic EMC model assumes that the EUT is mounted on a metal platform and that it is spaced only one meter or less from other equipment with which it might interact electromagnetically. Such a model simulates the crowded electromagnetic environment typical within military tanks, aerospace vehicles and communication shelters. In this situation, any device operating within the enclosure potentially can interfere with any other device and thus compromise operation of the entire complex. EMI testing within a shielded enclosure with radiative transducers one meter or less from the EUT is thus quite appropriate for components and equipment of most military systems.

For civilian equipment, such as computing devices covered by Part 15J of the FCC Rules and Regulations, the basic EMC model assumes that the EUT is installed on a nonmetallic platform and that it is spaced 10 m from a device such as a television receiver with which it might interfere. This 10 m **protection distance** implies that the FCC is interested in protecting, for example, a television set in a neighboring apartment from an EMI source such as a personal computer; it is not interested in protecting a television set in the same apartment as the computer. Therefore, EMI testing of such a "computing device" is most appropriately performed on a test site which simulates this apartment-house relationship: an open-area test site or its equivalent, where there are no metallic barriers to radiated energy and where pickup devices can be situated to determine the radiated EMI level at the protection distance of 10 m from the EUT.

Additional aspects of matching EMI test methods and limits to the intended function of an EUT in its respective intended electromagnetic environment are discussed in later sections of this Chapter.

1.2 Stages and Types of EMI Testing

An enhanced perspective on the wide diversity of methods and limits applied to EMI testing can be gained by considering the three **stages** at which such testing is performed:

1. the **component** and **equipment** stage
2. the **system** or **vehicle** stage
3. the **environmental** stage

Figure 1.1 illustrates the three stages to show how they are successively more encompassing.

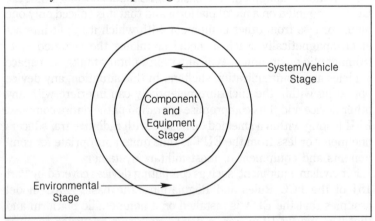

Figure 1.1—The Stages of EMI Testing

1.2.1 The Component and Equipment Stage

The basic component and equipment stage of EMI testing can be represented by the innermost circular area of Fig. 1.1. Two **types** of EMI testing occupy this first stage: **component** testing is performed on items prior to their integration into complete equipments or subsystems, while **equipment** testing is performed on items designed to stand alone as fully functional unto themselves. Many items of equipment successfully EMI-tested at this level are then pronounced electromagnetically compatible to perform their intended missions without further EMI testing, while other components and equipment, including subsystems, subsequently are further EMI-tested as constituent elements in the more encompassing stages of EMI testing discussed below.

EMI testing in accordance with MIL-STD-461* and MIL-STD-462* covers this basic stage of EMI testing for products with military applications, while EMI testing of computing devices for compliance to FCC Part 15J typifies this basic stage of testing for non-military products.

This basic stage of EMI testing also covers tests on filters used for EMI suppression and tests on shielded enclosures used to establish controlled and secure EMI test environments. Various standards and specifications applicable to this stage of EMI testing are discussed in Section 1.3.

1.2.2 The System/Vehicle Stage of EMI Testing

A more encompassing stage of EMI testing is the **system/vehicle stage**, represented in Fig. 1.1 as bounded by the intermediate circle. This stage of EMI testing is performed on a complete system or vehicle to determine that all of its constituent components and equipments, each presumably already individually EMI-tested at the basic component or equipment stage discussed above, are now able to cofunction in a state of electromagnetic compatibility. MIL-E-6051 covers EMI testing at this stage for military systems and vehicles.

An example of EMI testing of nonmilitary equipment at this stage is that of a modern passenger car to determine whether its many electronic controls and accessories are electromagnetically compatible on a vehicle level.

1.2.2.1 General Technique for System and Vehicle EMI Testing

This system/vehicle stage of EMI testing should be performed in a sterile electromagnetic environment so that test data is solely

---

*Throughout this book, any mention of a document not accompanied by a suffix letter or an issue date implies the latest issue of that document.

a result of any EMI interaction among the various elements which constitute the system or vehicle under test.

EMI tests at this stage consist basically of exciting and loading the system in a prescribed manner while monitoring all potentially susceptible receptors for any performance degradation or malfunction. In other words, the tests consist of determining if any intrasystem EMI exists, identifying the culprits involved in any resulting performance degradation, and establishing how much EMI hardening is needed to achieve EMC.

1.2.2.2 Mission Scenario

For the EMI testing to be meaningful, it is vital that the system or vehicle under test be stimulated and exercised in a manner corresponding closely to that expected during its mission. Specifically, the system/vehicle must be under load as in an actual mission, to the maximum extent feasible. Obviously, for some items, e.g. missiles, this loading must be simulated. In cases involving extremely complex systems, such as a large naval ship, 100 percent testing at this level is not feasible and is completed only by placing the ship in actual operation.

Section 1.3.1 discusses application of MIL-E-6051 to performance of this stage of EMI testing, while Chapter 9 covers factors affecting the mission scenario and other aspects of an appropriate test plan for this stage.

1.2.3 The Environmental Stage of EMI Testing

The **environmental stage** is the most encompassing and is performed to ascertain that a complete system or vehicle is electromagnetically compatible with the environment in which it is to operate. As represented by the additional area of Fig. 1.1, bounded by the outermost circle, this stage of EMI testing involves immersing the entire system or vehicle into electromagnetic environments typical of those it is expected to encounter when operational to determine whether any EMI interaction exists. Specifically, does any radiator in the environment degrade any aspect of system/vehicle operation or does the system/vehicle cause EMI to any receptor in the environment?

In general, the higher the stage of testing, the more complex and expensive the tests (and EMI controls) become. Closely related to this third stage of EMI testing are electromagnetic site surveys such as those performed prior to installations of communication centers or high-voltage power lines. Performing such surveys of the electromagnetic environment prior to final planning and installation of any system can facilitate its EMC design and thus reduce its potential cost.

1.2.4 Application of EMI Test Stages

Figure 1.2 illustrates the stages of EMI testing in the context of

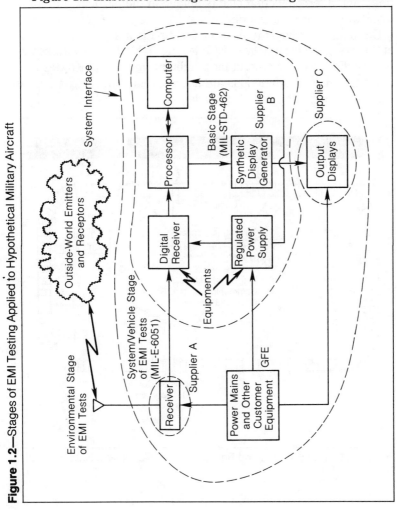

Figure 1.2—Stages of EMI Testing Applied to Hypothetical Military Aircraft

a hypothetical military aircraft, while Fig. 1.3 provides a framework for discussing them as they apply to a metropolitan automatic rapid transit system.

Everything in Fig. 1.2 within the outermost dashed line—the entire collection of housekeeping, avionics, weapon systems, special payloads, etc.—must operate in a state of EMC. The fact of each component or equipment having already complied with MIL-STD-461 increases the probability of EMC but, because of proximity and interconnection factors unique to the particular aircraft installation, does not guarantee it.

Defining what constitutes a malfunction is a key consideration at this system/vehicle stage of EMI testing. Table 1.1, showing some hypothetical scoring criteria for a military aircraft, illustrates the point that most malfunctions are not go/no-go, but are characterized by specific degrees of degradation.

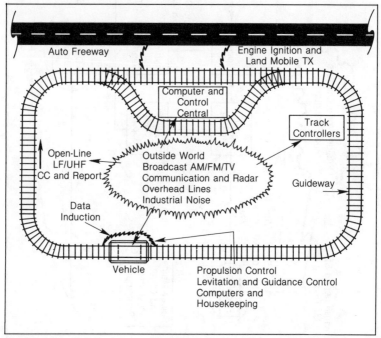

Figure 1.3—EMI Emitters and Receptors in an Automatic Rapid Transit System

**Table 1.1—Scoring Criteria for Hypothetical
Military Aircraft System**

System or Subsystem	Hypothetical Scoring Criteria		
	No Malfunction	Marginal	Malfunction
Navigation (DME)	< 0.2 mi.	0.2 to 0.5 mi.	> 0.5 mi.
Aircraft Control Surface Movement	< 0.8 mm	0.8 to 3.2 mm	> 3.2 mm
Digital Computer Bit Error Rate	$< 10^{-7}$	10^{-7} to 10^{-6}	$> 10^{-6}$
Voice Communication Word Intelligibility	> 95%	85 to 95%	< 85%
Engine Overheat Alarm Relay	no alarm	no alarm	alarm

Military systems and vehicles are tested for EMI at the environmental stage in accordance with MIL-STD-449, as discussed in Paragraph 1.3.1.7. An example from the civilian sector is the **in situ** testing of an automated rapid transit system serving a metropolitan area, as shown in Fig. 1.3.

Such a transit system includes one or more computer-automated central control stations, track guideway controllers and multiple vehicles, plus data communications. The vehicles pick up command and control signals from the guideway and decode them into vehicle speed and acceleration data, track routing and switching and other commands. The vehicles report back message receipt confirmation, periodic health status monitoring and other data. Each vehicle also contains its own subsystems for propulsion control, levitation, guidance and housekeeping.

A number of intrasystem, or system/vehicle stage EMI problems undoubtedly would have had to be solved. A few of these might include interaction between thyristors in the propulsion system and sensors used for levitation and guidance, transient noise induced from the vehicle rail shoes into telecommunications for the track guideway, and emissions into the central computer within the substation. Once all such system/vehicle stage problems were solved, a whole new set of problems would have to be faced when the transit system is installed in its operating environment. Examples of environmental stage problems would include:

1. radiated EMI coupling into the guideway telecommunications from automobile engine ignition systems and land mobile transmissions on the adjoining freeway
2. EMI to the telecommunications from out-of-band emissions from a nearby 5 MW UHF TV transmitter
3. EMI to the controlling computer from a nearby airport radar
4. EMI coupling into the vehicle sensor system as it passes under a noisy overhead electric power transmission line

1.3 Standards for EMI Testing

All standards and specifications for EMI testing can be classified into the following categories:

1. military
2. ANSI, VDE and other CISPR-based standards
3. FCC and other government regulations
4. IEEE, SAE and industry standards

The following review of the orientation of standards in each of these categories is provided as background for understanding their unique aspects when they are encountered in later chapters.[1]

1.3.1 Military Standards

1.3.1.1 Background

Documents were generated more than 50 years ago by the U.S. Army Signal Corps to cover suppression and measurement of interference from ignition systems of military vehicles to communication receivers. However, the earliest multi-service military EMI document was issued in June 1945 as Joint Army/Navy specification JAN-I-225. Although no interference limits were included, methods of measuring interference were prescribed over the relatively large frequency range of 150 kc (now kHz) to 20 mc (now MHz). This document was used in conjunction with AN-I-27, a specification for controlling interference in aircraft electrical systems. This, in turn, was superseded by AN-I-42 and later, in June 1950, by MIL-I-6181, which added susceptibility to the emissions tests previously specified, in addition to limits for both emissions and susceptibility.[2,3]

Radiated limits were specified in terms of equivalent input microvolts for particular measuring instruments and generally approximated the levels of minimum discernible signal of those instruments at each frequency of measurement. There was no differentiation to account for bandwidth of the EMI signal, and measurements were made using the widest available bandwidth position of the measurement receiver.

It should be noted that the scope of these early documents was deliberately narrow. They were intended to apply only to aeronautical equipment of the Army, Air Force and Navy and were directed specifically toward control of interference to voice communication receivers operating in the range of 2 to 30 MHz. Such a receiver was extremely vulnerable to interference picked up by the unshielded lead-in which was routed through the aircraft fuselage to connect it to an external long-wire antenna. Since little or no bypassing was applied to the receiver's power leads, conducted measurements of both emissions and susceptibility were needed. Since the antenna lead-in represented a high-impedance receptor for picking up EMI, a rod antenna was chosen as the most appropriate pickup transducer for radiated testing. Thus, even though the scope of this early EMI testing was relatively narrow, the foundation was laid for later military EMI test methods of much wider scope and application.

Progress was slow toward further tri-service coordination of EMI specifications, and a January 1953 draft of a proposed Military Standard 225 to standardize interference measurement techniques was never officially approved by all three services. However, this draft contributed heavily to MIL-I-16910, as issued by the Bureau of Ships, and to revision "B" to MIL-I-6181, as issued by the Air Force and Navy in May of 1953.

During the decade of the 1960s, the outstanding accomplishment in coordinated EMC activity among the three military branches was publication of the MIL-STD-460 series of specifications. Their release superseded numerous widely-used single-service and coordinated documents, including MIL-I-6181, MIL-I-11748 (Army), MIL-I-16910 (Navy), MIL-STD-826 (Air Force) and MIL-I-26600 (Air Force).

1.3.1.2 MIL-STD-461 and -462 for Component and Equipment EMI Tests

MIL-STD-461 entitled, "Electromagnetic Interference Characteristics, Requirements for Equipment," was issued in July 1967 and contained interference limits applicable to various EMI test methods. A companion document, MIL-STD-462, detailed the procedures to be used for each test method. The 460 series also included MIL-STD-463 to define terminology and MIL-STD-469 to detail EMC requirements pertaining to design of radar systems.[4-6]

The original version of MIL-STD-461 was superseded in August 1968 by its "A" revision, which was then widely used for the next decade. However, the role of the "A" revision as a true tri-service document was effectively terminated by the May 1, 1970 issuance by the Air Force of its Notices 2 and 3, which altered requirements drastically for all Air Force procurements.

Subsequent issuance of additional notices, especially Notice 4 by the Army, made it clear that a "B" revision was badly needed if the tri-service EMC concept was to survive. Although a version of MIL-STD-461B was being circulated for review and comments as early as 1970, it was not until April 1980 that its final version was officially released. In turn, in August 1986 it was superseded by a "C" revision. MIL-STD-461C made a number of relatively minor changes in addition to adding limits for three methods of testing susceptibility to the threat of electromagnetic pulse (EMP).[7,8]

The "B" and "C" revisions represented a significant change from the "A" version in several respects. Applicability of the various requirements for meeting levels of emissions and susceptibility was compartmentalized to apply to specific equipments in accordance with their respective types, functions, and intended missions. Also, a number of "Unique Methods" (UMs) were added to cover special requirements. The overall effect was to make the document much more flexible and more adaptable to unique requirements of each procuring Service. Despite the increased flexibility inherent in this approach, however, additional notices and revisions to MIL-STD-461 and -462 will always be needed to keep pace with the ever-changing needs of the defense establishment.

With the "B" issue of MIL-STD-461, requirements for EMI testing were divided into ten parts, applicable to equipment and subsystems installed or used as follows:

Part 1: generally applicable to all procurements

Part 2: in aircraft, or associated ground support

Part 3: aboard spacecraft, or associated ground support

Part 4: in surface facilities including tracked or wheeled vehicles
Part 5: in surface ships
Part 6: in submarines
Part 7: ancillary or support equipment in non-critical areas
Part 8: tactical and special vehicles and engine-driven equipment
Part 9: engine generators and power sets, etc., in critical areas
Part 10: commercial equipment, wherever used.

Table 1.2 shows the various EMI test methods of MIL-STD-462 corresponding to the limits applied by MIL-STD-461. Table 1.3 identifies the sections of this volume which directly pertain to proper performance of the respective test methods.

Table 1.2—MIL-STD-462 EMI TEST METHODS CORRESPONDING TO LIMITS IN MIL-STD-461

Method	Title Frequency Range
	Conducted Emission
CE01	Power and Interconnecting Leads, up to 15 kHz
CE03	Power and Interconnecting Leads, 15 kHz to 50 MHz
CE06	Antenna Terminals, 10 kHz to 26 GHz
CE07	Transients, Power Leads, Spikes, Time Domain
UM04	Power Leads, Engine Generators, Etc., 15 kHz to 50 MHz
UM05	Power Leads, Commercial Eqpt./Critical Areas, 50 kHz to 50 MHz
	Conducted Susceptibility
CS01	Power Leads, 30 Hz to 50 kHz
CS02	Power Leads, 50 kHz to 400 MHz
CS03	Intermodulation, 15 kHz to 10 GHz
CS04	Rejection of Undesired Signal, 30 Hz to 20 GHz
CS05	Cross Modulation, 30 Hz to 20 GHz
CS06	Spikes, Power Leads
CS07	Squelch Circuits
CS09	Structure Currents, 60 Hz to 100 kHz
CS10	Damped Sinusoidal Transients, Pins and Terminals, 10 kHz to 100 MHz
CS11	Damped Sinusoidal Transients, Cables, 10 kHz to 100 MHz
	Radiated Emission
RE01	H-Field, 0.03 to 50 kHz
RE02	E-Field, 14 kHz to 10 GHZ
RE03	Spurious and Harmonics, Radiated Technique
UM03	E-Field, Tactical and Special-Purpose, 150 kHz to 1,000 MHz
UM04	E-Field, Engine Generators, Etc., 14 kHz to 1,000 MHz
UM05	E-Field, Commercial Eqpt./Critical Areas, 150 kHz to 400 MHz
	Radiated Susceptibility
RS01	H-Field, 0.03 to 50 kHz
RS02	H- and E-Fields, Spikes and Power Frequencies
RS03	E-Field, 14 kHz to 40 GHz
RS05	Electromagnetic Pulse Field Transients
UM04	E-Field, Engine Generators, Etc., 2 MHz to 10 GHz

Table 1.3—Volume 6 Sections Pertinent to MIL-STD-462 Test Methods

Column groups: **Conducted** — Emissions (CE: 01, 03, 06, 07; UM: 04, 05), Susceptibility (CS: 01–11). **Radiated** — Emissions (RE: 01, 02, 03; UM: 04, 05), Susceptibility (RS: 01, 02, 03, 05; UM: 04).

Section No.	Short Title	CE 01	CE 03	CE 06	CE 07	UM 04	UM 05	CS 01	CS 02	CS 03	CS 04	CS 05	CS 06	CS 07	CS 09	CS 10	CS 11	RE 01	RE 02	RE 03	UM 04	UM 05	RS 01	RS 02	RS 03	RS 05	UM 04
Chap. 2	Fundamentals of EMI Testing																										
2.2	Use of the dB	x	x	x		x	x							x	x			x	x	x	x	x	x				
2.3	NB/BB Determination		x	x	x	x	x												x	x	x	x					
2.4	Conducted Emissions Testing	x	x	x	x	x	x																				
2.5	Radiated Emissions Testing																	x	x	x	x	x					
2.6	Conducted Suscept. Testing							x	x	x	x	x	x	x	x	x											
2.7	Radiated Suscept. Testing							x	x	x	x	x	x	x	x	x	x						x	x	x	x	x
Chap. 3	Emissions Test Instrumentation																										
3.1	Basic EMI Analyzer	x	x	x		x	x							x				x	x	x	x	x	x	x	x		x
3.2	RF Preselection	x	x	x		x	x												x		x	x		x			
3.3	Bandwidth	x	x	x		x	x											x		x	x	x					
3.4	Sensitivity	x	x	x	x	x	x											x	x	x	x	x					
3.5	Impulsive Signals	x	x	x		x	x												x		x	x					
3.7	Use of Spectrum Analyzers	x	x	x		x	x								x			x	x	x	x	x	x	x	x		x
Chap. 4	Sensors for EMI Emissions Testing																										
4.1	Conducted Current Sensors	x	x			x	x		x							x	x										
4.2	Conducted Voltage Sensors									x							x										
4.3	Radiated Emissions Antennas																	x	x	x	x	x			x		
Chap. 5	Susceptibility Instrumentation & Transducers																										
5.1	Signal Sources	x	x					x	x	x	x	x	x	x	x	x		x	x	x	x	x	x	x	x		x
5.2.1	Conducted Injection Devices		x					x	x		x	x			x	x							x	x	x		x
5.2.2	Electric Field Producers												x	x	x								x		x	x	x

1.14

Table 1.3—page 2

Section No.	MIL-STD-462 Short Title	CE 01	CE 03	CE 06	CE 07	UM 04	UM 05	CS 01	CS 02	CS 03	CS 04	CS 05	CS 06	CS 07	CS 09	CS 10	CS 11	RE 01	RE 02	RE 03	UM 04	UM 05	RS 01	RS 02	RS 03	RS 05	UM 04
		Conducted Emissions						**Conducted Susceptibility**										**Radiated Emissions**					**Radiated Susceptibility**				
5.2.3	Magnetic Field Producers	x																					x				
5.2.4	Test Field Sensors																							x	x	x	x
Chap. 6	Automated EMI Testing																										
6.1.2	Emissions Scan Speed	x	x	x	x	x	x											x	x	x	x	x					
6.4	Suscep. Scan Speed														x								x	x	x		x
Chap. 7	Test Facilities and Enclosures																										
7.1	Open-Area Test Sites																	x	x	x	x	x	x	x	x	x	x
7.2	Shielded Enclosures	x	x	x	x	x	x	x	x	x	x	x	x	x	x	x	x	x	x	x	x	x	x	x	x	x	x
7.3	Anechoic Test Chambers																		x	x	x	x		x	x	x	x
7.4	Shielded Test Cells																			x	x	x			x	x	x
Chap. 8	Errors in EMI Testing																										
8.2	Instrumentation Errors	x	x	x	x	x	x	x	x	x	x	x	x	x	x	x	x	x	x	x	x	x	x	x	x	x	x
8.3	Calibration Errors	x	x	x	x	x	x	x	x	x	x	x	x	x	x	x	x	x	x	x	x	x	x	x	x	x	x
8.4	Setup & Procedure Errors	x	x	x	x	x	x	x	x	x	x	x	x	x	x	x	x	x	x	x	x	x	x	x	x	x	x
Sec. 9.1	Test Environment & EUT Deployment																										
9.1.1	Testing in Ambient Noise	x	x	x	x	x	x											x	x	x	x	x					
9.1.2	Test Eqpt-EUT Isolation	x	x	x	x	x	x	x	x	x	x	x	x	x	x	x	x	x	x	x	x	x	x	x	x	x	x
9.1.3	EUT Loading & Excitation	x	x	x	x	x	x	x	x	x	x	x	x	x	x	x	x	x	x	x	x	x	x	x	x	x	x
9.1.4	EUT Mounting & Grounding	x	x	x	x	x	x	x	x	x	x	x	x	x	x	x	x	x	x	x	x	x	x	x	x	x	x
9.1.5	Test Fixtures	x	x													x											
9.1.6	Susceptibility Criteria										x	x	x	x	x	x	x						x	x	x	x	x
9.1.7	Suscep. Signal Modulation									x	x		x	x	x	x								x	x		
9.1.8	Setup Intermod. & Spurious									x	x			x													

Table 1.3—page 3

Section No.	MIL-STD-462 Short Title	CE 01	CE 03	CE 06	CE 07	UM 04	UM 05	CS 01	CS 02	CS 03	CS 04	CS 05	CS 06	CS 07	CS 09	CS 10	CS 11	RE 01	RE 02	RE 03	UM 04	UM 05	RS 01	RS 02	RS 03	UM 04
		Conducted Emissions						Conducted Susceptibility										Radiated Emissions					Radiated Susceptibility			
Sec. 9.2	Test Environment & Layout for Military Testing																									
9.2.1.1	Ambient Levels	x	x	x		x	x											x								
9.2.1.2	Test Area Contents	x	x	x	x	x	x												x	x	x	x	x	x	x	x
9.2.1.3	Enclosure Wall Reflections																		x	x	x	x		x		x
9.2.1.4	Test Stand Characteristics																	x	x	x	x	x	x	x	x	x
9.2.2	EUT Layout & Operation	x	x	x	x	x	x	x	x	x	x	x	x	x	x	x	x	x	x	x	x	x	x	x	x	x
9.2.2.1	Height & Location of Leads	x	x	x	x	x	x	x	x	x	x	x	x	x	x	x	x	x	x	x	x	x	x	x	x	x
9.2.2.2	Power Lead Length	x	x	x	x	x	x	x	x	x	x	x	x	x	x	x	x	x	x	x	x	x	x	x	x	x
9.2.2.3	EUT Bonding	x	x	x	x	x	x	x	x	x	x	x	x	x	x	x	x	x	x	x	x	x	x	x	x	x
9.2.2.4	Impedance Matching		x					x	x	x	x	x	x	x	x	x	x	x	x	x	x	x	x	x	x	x
Sec. 9.4	Sampling Practices in EMI Testing																									
9.4.1	The Sampling Problem	x	x	x	x	x	x	x	x	x	x	x	x	x	x	x	x	x	x	x	x	x	x	x	x	x
9.4.2	EUT Modes of Operation	x	x	x	x	x	x	x	x	x	x	x	x	x	x	x	x	x	x	x	x	x	x	x	x	x
9.4.3	EUT Frequency Selection	x	x	x	x	x	x	x	x	x	x	x	x	x	x	x	x	x	x	x	x	x	x	x	x	x
9.4.4	Lead Sorting & Probe Position	x	x	x	x	x	x	x	x	x																
9.4.5	EUT Faces-Antenna Positions																	x	x	x	x	x	x	x	x	x
9.4.6	Susceptibility Scan Speeds													x												
9.5	Test Plans and Reports	x	x	x	x	x	x	x	x	x	x	x	x	x	x	x	x	x	x	x	x	x	x	x	x	x
9.6	Calibration	x	x	x	x	x	x	x	x	x	x	x	x	x	x	x	x	x	x	x	x	x	x	x	x	x
Chap. 10	Conducted Emissions Test Procedures																									
10.1	Current on AC/DC Power Leads	x	x			x																				
10.2	Current—Control/Signal Leads		x																							

Table 1.3—page 4

Section No.	Short Title	CE 01	CE 03	CE 06	CE 07	UM 04	UM 05	CS 01	CS 02	CS 03	CS 04	CS 05	CS 06	CS 07	CS 09	CS 10	CS 11	RE 01	RE 02	RE 03	UM 03	UM 04	UM 05	RS 01	RS 02	RS 03	RS 05	UM 04
		Conducted Emissions						Conducted Susceptibility										Radiated Emissions						Radiated Susceptibility				
10.3.1	Spikes on Power Leads			x																								
10.3.2	Testing Antenna Terminals		x																									
Chap. 11	Radiated EMI Emissions Test Procedures																											
11.1.1	Magnetic Fields at 7 cm.																	x										
11.1.2	Magnetic Fields at 1 m																											
11.2	E Fields in Shielded Encl.																		x		x	x	x					
11.3	Trans. Spurious & Harmonics																			x		x						
11.4	Vehicles and Engines																				x	x						
11.5	Overhead Power Lines																											
Chap. 12	Conducted Susceptibility Test Procedures																											
12.1.1	Power Leads, 30 Hz to 50 kHz							x																				
12.1.2	Power/C'trol Leads to 400 MHz								x																			
12.1.3	Spikes on Power Leads												x															
12.2.1	Receiver Intermodulation									x																		
12.2.2	Cross-Modulation											x																
12.2.3	Undesired-Signal Rejection										x																	
12.3	Squelch Circuit Suscptib'ty													x														
12.4	Common-Mode Structure Current														x													
12.5.1	Damped Sinusoids—Cables																x											
12.5.2	Damped Sinusoids—Pins/Trmnls															x												
Chap. 13	Radiated Susceptibility Test Procedures																											
13.1	Magnetic Fields, 0.03-50 kHz																							x				
13.1	Induced Power Freq's & Spikes																								x			
13.4	E Fields, 14 kHz - 40 GHz																									x		
13.5	EMP Field Transients																										x	x

1.3.1.3 MIL-STD-220, for Filter Tests

Captioned "Methods of Insertion Loss Measurement," MIL-STD-220 presents a method of measuring, in a 50 Ω system, the insertion loss of feedthrough EMI suppression capacitors and of radio-frequency (RF) filters, both single- and multiple-circuit, at frequencies up to 1 GHz.[9] (See Volume 4 of this series for detailed look at filters and power line conditioning.)

1.3.1.4 MIL-STD-285, Shielded Enclosure Tests

Entitled "Attenuation Measurements for Enclosures, Electromagnetic Shielding, for Electronic Test Purposes, Method of," MIL-STD-285 covers such measurements over the frequency range from 100 kHz to 10 GHz. The techniques used in this standard have also been applied to measurements down to power line frequencies and up to 26 GHz.[10]

Basically, MIL-STD-285 illustrates a few test setups for measuring transmission loss (attenuation vs. frequency) of low-impedance magnetic fields, high-impedance electric fields and intermediate-impedance electric and magnetic fields, including plane waves, through a barrier such as a shielded enclosure. The technique involves substitution measurements performed before and after the insertion of the barrier, in which the level of a signal source is changed to determine the amount required to give the same reading on the measuring detector or receiving system. By repeating the procedure at a number of test frequencies, a spectrum of attenuation at each of the sample points is obtained.

1.3.1.5 MIL-STD-704, for Airborne Electric Power

The purpose of MIL-STD-704, entitled "Electric Power Aircraft, Characteristics and Utilization of," is to foster EMC between either aircraft electric systems or ground-support electric systems and airborne-utilization equipment. It is intended to do this to the extent of confining the aircraft and ground-support electric power characteristics within definitive specification limits and by restricting the requirements imposed on the power source by the airborne power utilization.[11]

MIL-STD-704, which heavily emphasizes transient emissions and measurements, covers three utilization equipment categories as follow:

1. **Category A equipments** are those utilization equipments whose installation in aircraft will be controlled so that the power line voltage drop will be limited to 2 Vac or 1 Vdc, or both, as applicable. The power line drop is the voltage difference between the terminals of voltage regulation at the source and the power input terminals of the using equipment. Use of this category should be held to a minimum, and its use is subject to approval by the procuring activity.

2. **Category B equipments** are those utilization equipments destined for aircraft for which the power line voltage drop will be less than 4 Vac or 2 Vdc, or both, as applicable. When a detailed equipment specification does not designate a category, the equipment is considered to be Category B. This category includes the majority of aircraft electric equipment and is the preferred category.

3. **Category C equipments** are those equipments which are intermittently operated. During operation, voltage variations include a maximum of 8 Vac line drop, or 3 Vdc line drop, or both, as applicable.

The ac power system must be a three-phase, four-wire "Y" system having a nominal line voltage of 115/200 Vac and a nominal frequency of 400 Hz. The neutral terminal of the power source is connected to ground, and the ground plane is considered to be the fourth conductor. The dc power system must be a two-wire, grounded system having a nominal voltage of 28 Vdc. The negative terminal of the power source is connected to ground, and the ground plane is considered to be the second wire.

It is assumed that the smallest primary electric system to be tested to MIL-STD-704 is ac 1,500 VA or dc 50 A. Balance in the ac electric system is within 15 percent, i.e., the three phases are loaded so that not more than a 15 percent differential exists between one-third of the volt-amp system capacity and any single phase. Characteristics of the electric power sources covered by MIL-STD-704 are:

1. ac or dc generators driven by:
   a. constant-speed drives (speed control in hydraulic or mechanical torque converter)

      b. constant-speed turbines (speed control on air or gas turbine)

      c. narrow-range, variable-speed transmissions (turboprops, helicopter rotors, etc.)

  2. dc generators driven by wide-range, variable-speed transmissions (piston engines)

  3. inverters

  4. transformer-rectifiers

  5. batteries

MIL-STD-704 presents a number of definitions regarding aircraft grounds, transients, frequency modulations, frequency drift, phasing, ripple and other parameters germane to performing EMI tests on aircraft electric power systems. Specification limits are presented with regard to allowable transient surges and other parameters as criteria to meet indicated performance requirements. Tests peculiar to MIL-STD-704 are not covered in this handbook.

1.3.1.6 MIL-E-6051, for System and Vehicle EMI Testing

Captioned "Electromagnetic Compatibility Requirements," MIL-E-6051 is mandatory for use by all departments and agencies of the Department of Defense. This document outlines overall requirements for system EMC, including control of system electromagnetic emissions, lightning protection, static electricity, bonding and grounding. It is applicable to complete systems, including their associated subsystems and equipments. Its emphasis is on intrasystem compatibility, regardless of whether any equipment within the system conforms to other applicable specifications. The procedures given are general and require preparation and use of a detailed test plan by the testing organization.[12]

Several basic approaches may be followed, singly or collectively, as the basis for the test plan to demonstrate the intrasystem EMC, as discussed in Chapter 9. Choice of the approach used will depend on characteristics of the specific system to be tested.

The basic EMC requirements of MIL-E-6051 are that all elements of a system operate properly, individually and collectively, with a susceptibility level for each equipment at least 6 dB higher (20 dB for electro-explosive devices, or EEDs) than the electromagnetic noise environment existing at that equipment when the entire system is operating. This means that each and every element of the system must operate properly with twice the noise voltage level that actually exists at its location within the system. Because various elements of the system will be affected very differently by such noise characteristics as frequency, duration, modulation, waveform, repetition rate, duty cycle and sequence, each system element must be evaluated using instrumentation capable of determining all unique characteristics of its vulnerability.

1.3.1.7 MIL-STD-449, for Environmental EMI Testing

The title of MIL-STD-449 is "Radio Frequency Spectrum Characteristics, Measurement of." Its "C" revision was issued in March 1965, along with a supplement on formats for reporting radar and communication spectrum signatures. This issue was approved by the Department of Defense and is mandatory for use by tri-service agencies within DoD. Custodian for this standard is the Naval Ship Systems Command, Washington, D.C. 20360.[13]

MIL-STD-449 establishes uniform measurement techniques for determining the spectral characteristics of RF transmitters and receivers. The long-term goal is to provide a library of data for use during the design and development stages of systems which can be used to predict, and thus avoid, interference situations.

The general spectrum characteristic measurements specified in MIL-STD-449 are:

1. **RF characteristics at equipment terminals for a closed system.** These measurements are intended to disclose the radiation spectral characteristics at the antenna terminals of equipments designed either to transmit or receive RF energy.

2. **Antenna-radiated RF output in the open field.** These measurements are intended to disclose the RF spectral characteristics of a complete equipment, including the effects of the transmission line and the three-dimensional space distribution levels of the antenna pattern.

3. **Receiver susceptibility.** These measurements are designed to determine the susceptibility, i.e., the responsivity, of receiving equipment to radiation at other than the desired operating frequency. Such measurements are used to determine the spurious response characteristics of receivers and are referred

to in such terms as **unwanted response, receiver suscep- tibility, receiver vulnerability, image rejection, spurious-response rejection ratio, intermediate- frequency rejection ratio** and **off-frequency sensitivi- ty.** Knowledge of these effects is necessary to all communica- tions interference control activity.

Several of the EMI tests required under MIL-STD-449 are similar to those specified in MIL-STD-461/462. For example, type 1 tests as noted above are covered by Method CE06, antenna terminal tests; type 2 tests on transmitters having powers above 5 kW are covered in part (no antenna patterns) by Method RE03 tests; and type 3 tests are mostly covered by Methods CS03, CS04, and CS05. Tests peculiar to MIL-STD-449 are not covered in this handbook, but all of the above MIL-STD-462 test methods are covered in subsequent chapters.

1.3.2 ANSI, VDE, and Other CISPR-Based Standards

1.3.2.1 CISPR

In 1934, an **ad hoc** conference of interested international organizations met in Paris and decided to form the Comité Inter- nationale Special des Perturbations Radioelectriques (International Special Committee on Radio Interference, or CISPR). Radio broad- casting of audio was the only service in need of protection at that time, and the degree of annoyance to the listener was accepted as the proper measure of the respective degree of interference.[14]

Agreement on a quasipeak meter that provided readings cor- responding to the degree of listener annoyance had nearly been reached by 1939, when World War II intervened. It was not until 1953 that a specification for a CISPR meter covering 150 kHz to 30 MHz was finally adopted. Reference to Table 1.4 shows how the list of CISPR publications has expanded over the years to encom- pass most aspects of EMC. Note that the essential contents of earlier CISPR publications has been integrated into CISPR Publication 16.

Operating under the auspices of the International Electrotechnical Commission, the stated objective of the CISPR is to promote inter- national agreement on EMI limits and measurement techniques to facilitate international trade. Although the CISPR is a voluntary

Table 1.4—CISPR Publications

Publication	Description
CISPR 7, 7A, 7B	Recommendations of the CISPR with supplements
CISPR 8, 8A, 8B	Reports and study questions with supplements
CISPR 9	Limits of radio interference and report of national limits
CISPR 10	Organization, rules and procedures of the CISPR
CISPR 11	Limits and methods of measurement of radio interference characteristics of industrial, scientific, and medical (ISM) radio frequency equipment (excluding surgical diathermy apparatus)
CISPR 12	Limits and methods of measurement of radio interference characteristics of ignition systems of motor vehicles and other devices
CISPR 13	Limits and methods of measurement of radio interference characteristics of sound and television receivers
CISPR 14	Limits and methods of measurement of radio interference characteristics of household electrical appliances, portable tools and similar electrical apparatus
CISPR 15	Limits and methods of measurement of radio interference of fluorescent lamps and luminaires
CISPR 16	Specification for radio interference measuring apparatus and measurement methods
CISPR 17	Methods of measurement of the suppression characteristics of passive radio interference filters and suppression components
CISPR 18	Radio interference characteristics of overhead power lines and high-voltage equipment
CISPR 19	Guidance on the use of the substitution method for measurements of radiation from microwave ovens for frequencies above 1 GHz
CISPR 20	Measurement of the immunity of sound and television broadcast receivers and associated equipment in the frequency range of 1.5 to 30 MHz by the current-injection method; guidance on immunity requirements for the reduction of interference caused by radio transmitters in the frequency range of 26 to 30 MHz
CISPR 21	Interference to mobile radiocommunications in the presence of impulsive noise; methods of judging degradation and measures to improve performance
CISPR 22	Limits and methods of measurement of radio interference characteristics of information technology equipment

organization whose documents are not legally binding, many nations accept its measurement methods as the basis for their own national regulations. Such acceptance of CISPR EMC practices is a condition for membership in the European Economic Community.[15]

CISPR EMI testing methods differ from those of the U.S. military, as discussed above, primarily because the basic orientation is still the protection of entertainment broadcasting and voice communications against EMI. This single fact accounts for the primary differences of using quasipeak instead of peak detection to quantify interference and of performing radiated EMI testing in open-area test sites, as compared to the shielded enclosures used for military testing. These and many other less significant differences that will become apparent in later chapters all stem from the fundamental difference in mission of the equipment involved.

1.3.2.2 ANSI

The American National Standards Institute (ANSI) is an organization voluntarily sponsored by commercial companies in the United States to facilitate both national and international commerce by promulgating and maintaining standards for all facets of industrial activity. Standards for control and testing of EMI have assumed growing importance in recent years and are the concern of ANSI-Accredited Standards Committee C63 on EMC.

In recognition of the importance of international trade to the economic fortunes of both the sponsoring companies and the entire nation, in recent years the C63 Committee has exerted special efforts to facilitate such trade by bringing ANSI standards on EMC and those of the CISPR into close alignment. A further benefit of such commonality is that industrial companies in the U.S. do not have to maintain separate EMI testing facilities and procedures for domestic and export products.

ANSI Standard C63.2 covers characteristics of the instrumentation to be used for EMI testing. It includes a frequency-selective voltmeter with appropriate antennas and probes and detailed specifications for quasipeak, peak, rms and average detectors. Actual EMI measurement techniques are dealt with in ANSI C63.4 for low-voltage apparatus and C63.8 for high-voltage (600 V and above) apparatus, while ANSI C63.12 provides a rationale for determining limits and provides a suggested set for general application.

1.3.2.3 VDE

Der Verband Deutscher Elektrotechniker (VDE) is the Society of German Electrical Engineers. It is an important factor in EMI testing because it generates EMI specifications which become legal documents when they are accepted by the office of the German Postal Service, which is responsible for regulation of EMI. The VDE Testing and Certification Institute is the recognized testing agency of this office.[16]

VDE specifications are only advisory but become legal documents when they are referenced by German laws. Any product manufactured within or imported into West Germany must comply with these regulations and, correspondingly, must satisfy the respective VDE documents referenced by them. The specific regulations and VDE documents applicable to a specific product are determined by its function and the extent of its application. Some levels of regulation require testing by the VDE and certification by the German Postal Service, while others permit self-certification subject to sampling tests initiated by the Postal Service.

1.3.2.4 Other National CISPR-Based EMC Regulations

Nations which participate actively in CISPR or whose national regulations closely adhere to the CISPR documents include:

Australia	Austria	Belgium	Bulgaria
Canada	China	Czechoslovakia	Denmark
East Germany	Egypt	Finland	France
Italy	Japan	Netherlands	New Zealand
Norway	Poland	Portugal	South Africa
Sweden	Switzerland	Turkey	United Kingdom
United Kingdom	USSR	West Germany	Yugoslavia

Limits of radio interference (EMI) as shown in CISPR Publication 9 are adopted directly or in modified form by most of the above nations as their national limits. These nations also follow the CISPR recommendations on test instrumentation characteristics, including receiver bandwidths, use of synchronous tuning, overload protection, and primary use of quasipeak detection, as well as corresponding EMI test methods and procedures.

1.3.3 FCC and Other U.S. Government Standards

1.3.3.1 FCC Rules and Regulations

The Federal Communications Commission (FCC) is the U.S. government agency with jurisdiction over all civilian radio and wire communications. In addition to assigning operating frequencies and licensing transmitting stations and radio operators, the FCC, through its equipment authorization program, regulates electromagnetic interference to communications.

FCC control of EMI through equipment authorization is implemented through Parts 15 and 18 of its rules and regulations, which are published as Title 47 of the Code of Federal Regulations. Part 15 covers low-level RF devices whose use of RF is either incidental to their intended function or is severely restricted in output level. Part 18 covers industrial, scientific, and medical (ISM) devices, many of which use high levels of RF which must be restricted with regard to frequency and potentially interfering output.[17]

Part 2 of the rules and regulations covers the various categories of equipment authorization: verification, notification, certification, type acceptance and type approval, in addition to the marketing and importation regulations used for enforcement of the EMI limits.[18]

Part 15: RF Devices

Among the RF devices whose levels of EMI emission are restricted by Part 15 are broadcast and television receivers, low-level telemetry, garage door openers, radio-controlled toys, cordless telephones, field-disturbance/intrusion sensors, auditory training devices and devices such as VCRs and converters which conduct modulated signals to antenna terminals of television sets. Also covered are "computing devices," which include a wide variety of computers and other products employing digital techniques.

It is noteworthy that the EMI measurement instrumentation, EMI test methods and EMI limits prescribed by the FCC for compliance to Part 15J are closely parallel to ANSI, CISPR and VDE recommendations for similar equipment.

Part 18: ISM Equipment

Part 18 was revised drastically in August 1985 to accomplish a number of objectives, including simplification to facilitate its application. Nine subparts of the former version were reduced to only three, with the total text being shortened by 40 percent.[19]

Part 18 rules vest the FCC "with authority to regulate industrial, scientific, and medical equipment (ISM) that emits electromagnetic energy on frequencies within the radio frequency spectrum in order to prevent harmful interference to authorized radio communications services." Also included in revised Part 18 are the following definitions:

RF energy: Electromagnetic energy at any frequency in the radio spectrum from 9 kHz to 3 THz (3,000 GHz).

Harmful interference: Interference which endangers the functioning of a radio navigation service or of other safety services or seriously degrades, obstructs or repeatedly interrupts a radio communication service operating in accordance with this chapter.

ISM equipment: Equipment or appliances designed to generate and use locally RF energy for industrial, scientific, medical, domestic or similar purposes, excluding applications in the field of telecommunications. Typical ISM applications are the production of physical, biological or chemical effects such as heating, ionization of gases, mechanical vibrations, hair removal and acceleration of charged particles.

Industrial heating equipment: A category of ISM equipment used for or in connection with industrial heating operations utilized in a manufacturing or production process.

Medical diathermy equipment: A category of ISM equipment used for therapeutic purposes, not including surgical diathermy apparatus designed for intermittent operation with low power.

Ultrasonic equipment: A category of ISM equipment in which the RF energy is used to excite or drive an electromechanical transducer for the production of sonic or ultrasonic mechanical energy for industrial, scientific, medical or other noncommunication purposes.

Consumer ISM equipment: A category of ISM equipment used or intended to be used by the general public in a residential environment, notwithstanding use in other areas. Examples are domestic microwave ovens, jewelry cleaners for home use, ultrasonic humidifiers, etc.

ISM frequency: A frequency assigned by this part for the use of ISM equipment. A specified tolerance is associated with each ISM frequency.

Marketing: Marketing shall include sale or lease, offer for sale or lease, advertising for sale or lease, the import or shipment or other distribution for the purpose of sale or lease or offer for sale or lease.

Issue of MP-5, covering measurement methods at the same time as the major revision of Part 18, also brought recommended EMI test procedures and EMI measurement instrumentation for Part 18 into closer conformance with those of CISPR and ANSI.

1.3.3.2 Other U.S. Government Standards

1.3.3.2.1 FDA Standard for Medical Devices

Although MDS-201-0004 on EMC of medical devices was published by the Food and Drug Administration in 1979, it is not a mandatory requirement of any government agency. However, its existence attests to the critical importance of controlling EMI in hospital and other medical environments where it can be directly life threatening. EMI test methods of this standard are in close accord with those of MIL-STD-462. It is likely that use of this FDA publication will be superseded by ANSI C63.4, as revised to include medical devices.[20]

1.3.3.2.2 NACSIM 5100

NACSIM 5100 is a classified standard applicable to protection of information against possible compromise during its handling or processing by government agencies. Specialized measurements of

EMI emissions are required to ensure that conduction and radiation of possible information-bearing emissions are adequately suppressed.

1.3.4 IEEE, SAE and Other Voluntary EMI Standards

EMI standards written and supported voluntarily by industry and its professional employees constitute an important segment of the total activity toward standardization of EMI testing. Such standards are effective, despite the lack of any legal requirement for compliance. They help establish an industry-wide yardstick for the EMC aspect of product quality and frequently form the basis for federal, state and municipal standards which may then become legal mandates.[21]

1.3.4.1 IEEE EMC Standards Activity

The Institute of Electrical and Electronics Engineers (IEEE) is a professional organization devoted to technical advancement of its individual members through educational programs and information dissemination. Approximately half of its members participate in one or more of its 34 technical societies, one of which is devoted to EMC. A standards committee of the EMC Society operates in conjunction with seven specialized technical committees to generate and maintain a catalog of more than a dozen standards pertaining to EMI testing and other aspects of EMC. Other professional groups of the IEEE which develop and maintain standards pertinent to EMC are:

1. The Consumer Electronics Society, for standards on testing AM, FM and television receivers
2. The Industry Applications Society, for standards concerning EMI aspects of industrial controls and machinery
3. The Instrumentation and Measurement Society, for IEEE Std 248 on measuring CW field strength
4. The Power Systems Communications Committee, for IEEE Std 956, on "Recommendations to Users for Achieving EMC with Authorized Radio Services"
5. The Rotating Machinery Committee, for IEEE Std 792, on "Impulse Voltage Standards for Rotating Machinery"

6. The Power Engineering Society, for standards on EMI from overhead power lines
7. The Vehicular Technology Society, for IEEE Std 184 on testing FM mobile communication receivers

1.3.4.2 SAE EMC Standards Activity

The Society of Automotive Engineers (SAE) is dedicated to educational and scientific advancement of mobility technology. The SAE develops and publishes technical literature and formulates engineering standards, specifications and test procedures used in the design and manufacture of ground and aerospace vehicles.

Committee AE-4 on EMC operates through more than a dozen subcommittees to generate Aerospace Recommended Practices (ARPs), Aerospace Information Reports (AIRs) and various committee and subcommittee reports. Among the significant functions of AE-4 is that of recommending changes to the government on EMI standards; its Subcommittee AE-4A is the focus of activity on changes to MIL-STDs-461 and 462, while its Subcommittee AE-4D on Systems Compatibility recommends changes to MIL-E-6051.

While the orientation of the AE-4 committee clearly is toward aerospace, two separate subcommittees of the SAE Electronic System Committee are concerned with measuring EMI to, and generated by, electronic and electrical devices and subsystems on or within vehicles other than aircraft. The Electromagnetic Radiation (EMR) Subcommittee is responsible for the following standards:

1. SAE J55l: Electromagnetic Radiation from Vehicles and Devices (30 to 1,000 MHz)
2. SAE J1816: Performance Levels and Methods of Measurement of Electromagnetic Radiation from Vehicles and Devices, Narrowband, 10 kHz to 1,000 MHz

The EMI Standards and Test Methods (EMI) Subcommittee is responsible for the following standards:

1. SAE J1113: Electromagnetic Susceptibility Procedures for Vehicle Components (Except Aircraft)
2. SAE J1338: Whole-Vehicle Electromagnetic Susceptibility Tests in Open-Area Test Sites

3. SAE J1448: Electromagnetic Susceptibility Measurements of Vehicle Components Using TEM Cells, 14 kHz to 200 MHz
4. SAE J1507: Anechoic Test Facility for Testing of Whole Vehicles for Radiated Susceptibility 20 MHz to 18 GHz, Electromagnetic Field[22]
5. SAE J1547: Electromagnetic Susceptibility Procedure for Common Mode Injection (1 to 400 MHz), Module Testing
6. SAE J1595: Electrostatic Discharge Test for Vehicles
7. SAE J1812: Failure Mode Severity Classification

1.3.4.3 Other Voluntary Standards

In addition to organizations discussed above, EMC standards have been formulated by the following groups:

1. American Institute for Aeronautics and Astronautics (AIAA)
2. American Society for Testing Materials (ASTM)
3. Association for the Advancement of Medical Instrumentation (AAMI)
4. Computer and Business Equipment Manufacturers Association (CBEMA)
5. Electronic Industries Association (EIA)
6. National Electrical Manufacturers Association (NEMA)
7. National Fire Protection Association (NPFA)
8. Radio Technical Commission for Aeronautics (RTCA)
9. Underwriters Laboratories (UL)

1.3.4.4 Application of Voluntary Standards to EMI Testing

Some of the standards and other publications of the organizations listed above are particularly applicable to EMI testing.

Instrumentation calibration often utilizes the output of impulse generators, as described in SAE ARP 1267 and IEEE Std 376, or the noise temperature of noise generators, as measured in IEEE Std 298.

Frequently used for EMI measurements (less accurate but more convenient) are spectrum analyzers, as discussed in SAE AIR 1225 and IEEE Std 748.

Accessories for conducted EMI testing include the line impedance stabilization networks of IEEE Std 214 and the 10 μF capacitor of SAE ARP 936. For radiated measurements, SAE AIR 1209 covers antennas, and SAE ARP 958 specifically covers broadband antennas.

Some EMI testing techniques are discussed in EIA EMC-3, which is a designer's guide. IEEE Std 284 covers the factors affecting accuracy in measurement of steady-state field strengths.

Many standards are intended to handle EMI testing in specific products or applications. One category of standards pertains to EMI testing of various aspects of **electrical power distribution and control**. Procedures for measuring EMI emissions from overhead electric power lines are given in IEEE Std 430 for the frequency range 0.15 to 30 MHz, with guidance for higher frequencies. Somewhat different techniques are presented in IEEE Std 644 for measurement of electric and magnetic near fields close to ground level. IEEE Std 587 contains recommendations for protection and immunity against voltage or current surges on power lines. The special case of EMC problems with high-voltage dc power lines is dealt with by IEEE Std 368.

Measurement of EMI emissions from apparatus with dangerously high voltages is covered by NEMA 107. Voice-frequency EMI from electric power distribution transformers to paralleling communications circuits is tested using the practices recommended in IEEE Std 469, and EMI from lamp dimmers is covered by NEMA WD2.

Process control instrumentation must operate in industrial environments with many sources of high-level EMI. SAMA PMC 33.1 characterizes such environments and gives procedures for determining susceptibility to radiated EMI. Susceptibility to electrical disturbances on ac power lines can be determined by following procedures in SAMA 33.2.

Measurement of field strength above 300 MHz from **ISM equipment** is covered by IEEE Std 139.

EMI from **computers** is most appropriately measured using techniques given in CBEMA/ESC5, a report which provided important source material for ANSI C63.4 and FCC MP-4 test procedures.

EMI testing of **broadcast receivers** is covered by two IEEE standards: 186 for AM and 185 for FM types. IEEE Std 187 covers an open-field method of measuring spurious radiation, and EIA RS 378 covers the same subject using the EIA-Laurel broadband antenna. EMI conducted onto power lines from FM and TV receivers over the frequency range of 300 kHz to 25 MHz can be measured by methods given in IEEE Std 213. Test methods for AM broadcast and other receivers using ferrite core loop antennas are given in IEEE Std 189.

Five standards are particularly applicable to **land mobile communications**. EIA RS 152B provides definitions and methods of measurements for fixed or vehicular installations of FM or PM transmitters operating in the frequency range of 25 to 470 MHz. EIA RS 204B contains similar provisions for such receivers operating in the 25 to 947 MHz range. Both transmitter and receiver (and associated equipment) are to be measured under certain common test conditions which are detailed in EIA RS 388. For FM communications only, IEEE Std 184, which is coordinated with ANSI C16.39, details test conditions and methods for receivers over the range 25 MHz to 1 GHz. Similar information for spurious emissions from transmitters is given in IEEE Std 347.

FM or PM portable/personal radio transmitters, receivers or combinations of both, which can be hand carried or worn on the person and which are operated from their own portable power supply, are covered by EIA RS 316B for the frequency range from 25 MHz to 1 GHz.

EIA Telecommunications Systems Bulletin No. 10-D provides recommendations for mitigating EMI to **private radio services** operating in the microwave bands.

Although EMI testing of **automotive electronics** is well-covered by SAE documents discussed above, other standards provide useful information and techniques. Measurement of radiated EMI from ignition systems is the subject of ANSI C112.1 (20 to 100 MHz) and EIA report TR 8.10.

The shielding effectiveness of enclosures is covered by IEEE Std 299.

1.4 References

1. Schulz, R.B., *EMC Standards Handbook, Revision 4* (Annapolis, Md: IIT Research Institute under contract to DoD, ECAC, November 1982).
2. O'Neil, J.J. and Cofield, D.W., "Fifty Years of EMC in the Dept. of Army," *IEEE International EMC Symposium Record* (New York: IEEE), Tokyo, Japan, October 16-18, 1984, Vol. 2, 84-CH2097-4.

3. Pearlston, C.B., Jr., "Historical Analysis of Electromagnetic Interference Limits," TR-1001(2307)-12, Aerospace Corp., El Segundo, CA: April 1967.

4. MIL-STD-462, "Electromagnetic Interference Characteristics, Measurement of," 31 July 1967.

5. MIL-STD-463A, "Definitions and System of Units, Electromagnetic Interference Technology," 1 June 1977.

6. MIL-STD-469, "Radar Engineering Design Requirements, Electromagnetic Compatibility," 1 December 1966.

7. MIL-STD-461B, "Electromagnetic Emission and Susceptibility Requirements For The Control of Electromagnetic Interference," 1 April 1980.

8. MIL-STD-461C, "Electromagnetic Emission and Susceptibility Requirements For The Control of Electromagnetic Interference," 4 August 1986.

9. MIL-STD-220A, "Method of Insertion Loss Measurement," 15 December 1959.

10. MIL-STD-285, "Method of Attenuation Measurements for Enclosures, Electromagnetic Shielding for Electronic Test Purposes," 25 June 1956.

11. MIL-STD-704D, "Aircraft Electric Power Characteristics," 30 September 1980.

12. MIL-E-6051D, "Electromagnetic Compatibility Requirements, Systems," 7 September 1967.

13. MIL-STD-449D, "Measurement of Radio Frequency Spectrum Characteristics," 22 February 1973.

14. Stumpers, F.L.H.M., "The Activities of CISPR During Recent Years and Their Impact on Society," *IEEE International EMC Symposium Record* (New York: IEEE), June 20-22, 1973.

15. Mertel, H.K., "National and International Radio Interference Regulations for Consumer Products," *IEEE International EMC Symposium Record* (New York: IEEE), Washington, D.C., July 13-15, 1976.

16. Mertel, H.K., "VDE/FTZ Interference Regulations - West Germany," *Interference Technology Engineers' Master* (West Conshohocken, PA: R&B Enterprises, 1986).

17. FCC Rules and Regulations, Volume II, August 1976, consisting of Part 2: Frequency Allocations and Treaty Matters, Part 5: Experimental Radio Services (other than broadcast), Part 15: Radio Frequency Devices, and Part 18: Industrial, Scientific, and Medical Equipment. Available by subscription from Superintendent of Documents, U.S. Government Printing Office, Washington, D.C. 20402.

18. Wall, L.A., "Overview of FCC Equipment Authorization and Sampling Programs," *IEEE 1986 Regional Conference and Exhibition on EMC Record* (New York: IEEE), Anaheim, CA, 6 February 1986.
19. "In the Matter of Overall Revision of the Rules Regarding Industrial, Scientific, and Medical (ISM) Equipment under Parts 0, 2, and 18, General Docket No. 20718, Third Report and Order adopted August 5, 1985," Federal Communications Commission, Washington, D.C. 20554.
20. MDS-201-0004, "Electromagnetic Compatibility Standard for Medical Devices," The Food and Drug Administration (FDA) of the Department of Health and Human Services (HHS), 1 October 1979.
21. Bronaugh, E.L. and Schulz, R.B., "U.S. National Voluntary EMC Standards," *Proceedings of IEEE Regicon* (New York: IEEE), 1984, San Diego, CA, January 18, 1984.
22. Bronaugh, E.L., "Highlights of Forthcoming SAE J1507 and a Practical Realization of its Procedures for Radiated Susceptibility Testing of Automotive Systems," *IEEE International EMC Symposium Record* (New York: IEEE), Wakefield, MA, August 20-22, 1985.

Chapter 2

Fundamentals of EMI Testing

The purpose of this chapter is to present the fundamental considerations involved in EMI testing. Generic procedures will be outlined which are applicable to all testing of EMI emissions or susceptibility, both conducted and radiated. The basic parameters used to characterize and quantify EMI will be introduced and defined in the context of this generic information. All units are selected to conform to ANSI/IEEE Std 268-1982, "Metric Practice."

2.1 Measuring EMI Emissions and Susceptibility

As defined in Chapter 1, the basic task of EMI testing is to measure, and then compare to appropriate limits, electromagnetic energy which is (a) undesirably coupled out of an emitter or into a receptor via any of its connecting wires or cables (conducted EMI) or (b) undesirably coupled out of an emitter or into a receptor by means other than conduction (radiated EMI).

Figure 2.1 diagrams the basic context in which EMI testing of EMI emissions is performed, while Fig. 2.2 shows the basic elements used in testing EMI susceptibility. For emissions testing, the EMI being emitted from the EUT is intercepted by calibrated transducers and applied to an EMI analyzer to ascertain its amplitude, frequency and other pertinent characteristics. Converse-

2.1

ly, for susceptibility testing, it must be determined whether the functioning of the EUT is affected when it is subjected to specific generated levels of EMI, as measured at the EUT by transducers and appropriate instrumentation.

Since some basic properties of the EMI analyzer are implicit to many discussions in this chapter, it is important to note them before proceeding further. A more detailed treatment of the EMI analyzer is given in Section 3.1.

The EMI analyzer is a sophisticated, tunable RF voltmeter with defined bandwidths whose purpose is to provide accurate measurement of voltage levels and other pertinent characteristics of EMI signals applied to its input. As with the simplest of voltmeters, it has an input port with two terminals which are connected across a network or circuit element to measure the voltage between the points of connection. The basic EMI measurement thus is a measurement of the voltage between two terminals of a circuit within a defined bandwidth.

Typically, as shown in Fig. 2.1, the two terminals of the EMI analyzer input are connected to the output port of a transducer such as an antenna or line probe. Since the impedance at these output terminals is usually not known accurately at each frequency of measurement, it is important to realize that what is being measured is only the **voltage** across the parallel combination of the im-

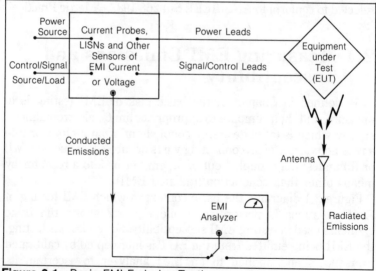

Figure 2.1—Basic EMI Emission Testing

pedances of the voltmeter and the circuit under test, and not the **power**, which would require knowledge of the vector impedance of the combination of the voltmeter and circuit under test.

As stated above, an important characteristic of the EMI analyzer is that its measurement bandwidths are well defined. Typically, modern EMI analyzers offer a switchable selection of at least two bandwidths at each tuned frequency, with the wider three or ten times the narrower. Although bandwidths are usually defined as the difference between frequencies at which the response is down from the maximum by specific amounts, an important characterization for EMI testing is that of **impulse bandwidth**. Although its precise definition must be deferred until Section 3.5 of Chapter 3, following the introduction of some pertinent elements of the definition later in this chapter, it may be stated at this point that the impulse bandwidth of an EMI analyzer is a calibrated measure of its degree of response, or sensitivity, to impulsive signals.

The other special feature of EMI analyzers to be mentioned at this point is the multiplicity of detector functions that they incorporate, the various types of which are covered in Section 3.6. The operator typically is able to choose a measurement reading of the level of EMI based on a choice of average, direct peak, slideback peak, quasipeak, or rms detection. Other detection processes, needed only for specialized measurements, involve statistical analysis

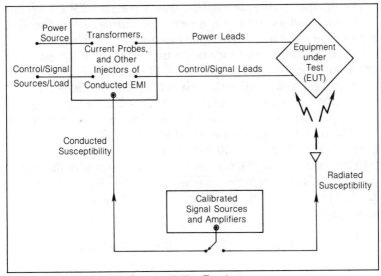

Figue 2.2—Basic EMI Susceptibility Testing

of EMI and include, among others, **amplitude probability distribution (APD)**, which shows the percentage of time that the noise levels exceeds various amplitudes, and **noise amplitude distribution (NAD)**, which shows how often each amplitude is exceeded.[1]

2.2 Use of the Decibel in EMI Measurements

Because of the extremely wide dynamic ranges involved in EMI testing, it would usually be very inconvenient to express measurement quantities in straight arithmetic terms; the use of so many digits would be unwieldy and potentially confusing. For this reason, use of the decibel (dB), which expresses ratios logarithmically, is very convenient and widely accepted. Throughout this volume, although the same basic symbols will be used for arithmetic and dB quantities, it will always be indicated clearly which units are being used. Unless subscripted to a different base, the logarithmic notation, **log**, will always be assumed to have a base of 10.

2.2.1 Defining the Decibel

The **decibel**, abbreviated **dB**, is widely used in EMI testing but is often misunderstood and misused. The purpose of this section is to define the dB and give guidance to its proper application.

To recognize the need for such a unit, consider a hypothetical amplifier which accepts a 1 μV rms CW signal at its 50 Ω purely resistive input and amplifies it such as to make it available at a level of 1 V rms into a purely resistive load of 50 Ω at its output. Since the output voltage level of the CW signal is one million times its input level, it is appropriate to say that the amplifier has a voltage gain of one million = 1,000,000 = 10^6.

Before introducing the dB into this context, consider the power gain of the same amplifier; namely, $P_2 = E_2{}^2/R_2$ at the output divided by $P_1 = E_1{}^2/R_1$ at its input. Since $R_1 = R_2 = 50 \Omega$, the power gain is:

$$(1^2)/(10^{-12}) = 10^{12} = 1,000,000,000,000$$

Rather than use 6 or 12 zeros to express this gain, it is apparent from the above equivalences that it is much more convenient to express these quantities as 10 to some power; namely, 10^6 and 10^{12}, respectively. This convenience led to introduction of the **bel**, which was defined simply as the expression of a power ratio as its logarithm to the base 10:

$$\text{Power ratio, } (P_2/P_1), \text{ in bels } = \log (P_2/P_1) \qquad (2.1)$$

In the example of the amplifier above, the power ratio is 10^{12}, and the logarithm to the base 10 is 12, making the gain of the amplifier 12 bels.

The bel did not gain widespread use in electronics because there are too many instances in which power ratios are less than 10, making their logarithms and their expression in bels fractional. Instead of the bel, there was defined the **decibel (dB)** which expresses a power ratio as **ten times** its logarithm to the base 10 of that power ratio:

$$\text{Power ratio, } (P_2/P_1), \text{ in decibels } = 10 \log (P_2/P_1) \qquad (2.2)$$

Expressed in dB, the gain of the above amplifier thus becomes:

$$10 \log (P_2/P_1) = 10 \log (10^{12}) = 10 (12) = 120 \text{ dB}$$

2.2.2 Proper Application of Decibel to Voltage Ratios

From the definitions above, it is clear that the dB is defined and valid only as a **power** ratio. However, with proper attention to circuit impedances at the points of reference, the dB ratio can be stated in many instances in terms of corresponding voltages. As was true in the amplifier example in Section 2.2.1, a power ratio is the same as the square of the ratio of the corresponding voltages, **provided both are developed across the same level of impedance**. When $Z_2 = Z_1$:

$$P_2/P_1 = (E_2^2/Z_2)/(E_1^2/Z_1) = E_2^2/E_1^2 = (E_2/E_1)^2$$

and the dB expression for the power ratio becomes:

$$dB = 10 \log (P_2/P_1) = 10 \log (E_2/E_1)^2 = 20 \log (E_2/E_1) \qquad (2.3)$$

Thus, $20 \log E_2/E_1$ becomes an equally valid expression for the power ratio, but only when the two voltages are developed across equal impedances.

2.2.3 Another Application of the Decibel to Voltage Ratios

In EMI testing, as well as in many other endeavors in electronics, it is convenient to apply the decibel to express a ratio of two voltages which are not developed across equal impedances. In the amplifier example of Section 2.2.1, if the output were designed to operate into 10 kΩ instead of 50 Ω, it would be common practice still to express its gain in dB as 20 times the log of the ratio of output voltage to input voltage, or 120 dB. However, since the output power is now only $1^2/10^4 = 10^{-4}$, the power gain is:

$$P_2/P_1 = 10^{-4}/(10^{-12}/50) = 5 \times 10^9$$

Expressed in dB, this becomes:

$$10 \log (5 \times 10^9) = 97 \text{ dB}$$

Thus, simply converting to decibels without taking impedance into account produced a dB level too high by 23 dB. Although direct application of the dB to express voltage ratios despite unequal impedances is a great convenience, it is done at the cost of an increased chance of errors. Also, this practice has fostered the erroneous belief that there are two kinds of dB, one for power and another for voltage.

Despite the foregoing caveat, it should be emphasized that most applications of the dB to voltage ratios in EMI measurements are completely legitimate. For example, all readings by EMI analyzers are in terms of dBμV, based on the ratio of the measured voltage to 1 μV. Since all such readings are referred to the same input terminals of the EMI analyzer and calibrated to be accurate relative to a 1 μV level at those terminals, all readings can be expressed accurately in dB, relative both to one microvolt and to each other.

For application of the dB to measurements of conducted EMI, see Section 2.4.1.

2.2.4 Other EMI Applications of Logarithmic Ratios

In most EMI test reporting, it is typical to include graphical plots of EMI amplitude as the Y-axis plotted against the **logarithm** of frequency as the X-axis. This is a convenient convention because on such a graph each frequency segment which is defined as a ratio (e.g., an octave or a decade) occupies the same space as every other octave or decade, respectively. In addition, it is common for the agencies which govern EMI testing to request that EMI levels be recorded at a specific number of frequencies per octave or per decade.

The following are some useful relationships involving octaves and decades:

1. Number of decades, N_{10}, between two frequencies:

$$N_{10} = \log_{10}(f_U/f_L) = \log_{10} f_U - \log_{10} f_L,$$

where,

f_U = upper frequency

f_L = lower frequency

2. Number of octaves, N_8, between two frequencies:

$$N_8 = \log_2(f_U/f_L) = \log_2 f_U - \log_2 f_L$$
$$= (\log_{10} f_U - \log_{10} f_L)/\log_{10} 2$$

3. Number of octaves per decade:

$$N_{8/10} = \log_2 10 = 1/\log_{10} 2 \approx 3.321$$

4. Number of decades per octave:

$$N_{10/8} = \log_{10} 2 = 1/\log_2 10 \approx 0.3010$$

5. One-half of an octave is:

$$f_L \sqrt{2} \text{ or } f_U/\sqrt{2}$$

To determine the specific frequencies in compliance with a requirement for a given number of frequencies per octave or decade, use the following:

Frequencies per octave:

$$f_n = f_0\, 2^{n/m}$$

where,

> n = the frequency number: 0, 1, 2,...,u
> m = number of frequencies per interval: 1, 2, 3,...
> f_n = frequency number (n + 1)
> f_0 = initial frequency (n = 0)

and,

> u = (maximum value of n) = 1 + [$\log_2 (f_U/f_0)$]3
> (use the nearest integer)

Thus, for three frequencies per octave, which is a typical MIL-STD-462 requirement, the frequencies may be found by solving the following for the family n = 0, 1, 2,.... This is usually done for only one decade of the spectrum: for n = 0 through 9; these frequencies are then determined for the required spectrum by multiplying them by 10 raised to the appropriate power.

$$f_n = f_0\, 2^{n/3:}$$

n	f_n	n	f_n	n	f_n
0	f_0	3	$2\,f_0$	6	$4\,f_0$
1	$1.26\,f_0$	4	$2.52\,f_0$	7	$5.04\,f_0$
2	$1.59\,f_0$	5	$3.17\,f_0$	8	$6.35\,f_0$
				9	$8\,f_0$

Frequencies per decade:

$$f_n = f_0\, 10^{n/m} \quad \text{(where the variables are as given above)}$$

2.8

For ten frequencies per decade, the analysis is as above for three frequencies per octave:

$$f_n = f_0\, 10^{n/10:}$$

n	f_n	n	f_n	n	f_n
0	f_0	3	$2\,f_0$	6	$3.98\,f_0$
1	$1.26\,f_0$	4	$2.51\,f_0$	7	$5.01\,f_0$
2	$1.58\,f_0$	5	$3.16\,f_0$	8	$6.31\,f_0$
				9	$7.94\,f_0$

2.3 Characterizing Types of EMI

This section analyzes and characterizes the various forms of electromagnetic energy which can constitute EMI.

2.3.1 Narrowband and Broadband EMI

The terms **narrowband** and **broadband** are widely used in various disciplines of electronic engineering, with widely different meanings in different contexts. For use in EMI measurements and testing, these terms have unique meanings and must be precisely defined.

Both terms imply a frame of reference against which some unknown bandpass characteristic can be compared. For EMI testing purposes, that reference ideally is the bandwidth of the receptor potentially threatened by the EMI being measured. This, in turn, implies that the EMI analyzer or measuring receiver being used for the EMI testing should have a bandpass characteristic equivalent to that of a potential victim.

To illustrate the narrowband/broadband concept, consider the single pulsed CW emission in Fig. 2.3 of amplitude A and pulse width τ at a carrier frequency of f_c. The resulting Fourier-

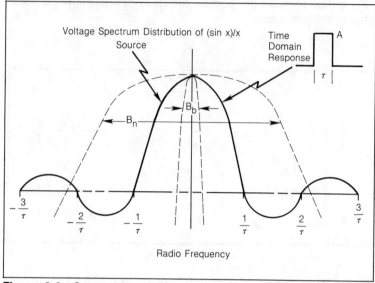

Figure 2.3—Comparison of EMI Analyzer Bandwidths to Pulsed RF Spectrum

transformed (sin x)/x frequency-domain distribution is centered at f_c with X-axis crossings on both sides of this center frequency at intervals of $1/\tau$, $2/\tau$, etc.

If measurements are made with an EMI analyzer having a bandwidth B_b (shown by the innermost dashed line), which is less than that of the emission being considered in Fig. 2.3, the emission will appear to be **broadband**. However, if an EMI analyzer is used which has a bandwidth wider than that of the emission, such as B_n (shown by the outermost dashed line in Figure 2.3), the emission will appear to be **narrowband**. The following sections consider this narrowband/broadband determination more quantitatively.

2.3.2 Tests to Differentiate EMI as Narrowband or Broadband

Although, as discussed in Section 3.3.3, the trend in EMI

2.10

specifications is away from separate limits for narrowband and broadband EMI and toward the use of a single EMI analyzer bandwidth and detector function, analysis of EMI to determine whether its spectral occupancy is narrowband or broadband will always be fundamental to its control. Four categories of tests are used to differentiate narrowband from broadband EMI:

1. Change in amplitude with RF tuning
2. Comparison of pulse repetition rate to impulse bandwidth
3. Amplitude change with change in detector function
4. Amplitude change versus bandwidth change

Before considering these tests in detail, it is important to note that many EMI signals are not clearly either narrowband or broadband, making the results of the tests ambiguous. When this happens, additional test procedures should be applied until the scale is tipped toward either narrowband or broadband. A CRT IF monitor, or panoramic adapter, as required by some EMI specifications, can be very helpful in determining the nature of an EMI signal.

2.3.2.1 RF Tuning Test

For the RF tuning test, the EMI analyzer is carefully tuned for maximum response to an EMI signal and then deliberately detuned higher and lower in frequency by an amount equal to two of its impulse bandwidths. If the decrease in its indicated response to the signal, ΔV, is greater than 3 dB at both tuning extremes, the EMI signal is said to be **narrowband**. If its indicated response to the signal decreases by only 3 dB or less at both extremes, then the signal is said to be **broadband**. The extent to which the change in EMI analyzer indication either exceeds or falls short of the 3 dB criterion as it is tuned two impulse bandwidths on either side of the maximum response shows the extent to which the signal is narrowband or broadband relative to the bandwidth of the EMI analyzer.

In summary, for detuning equal to plus and minus two impulse bandwidths of the EMI analyzer, the EMI signal is:

1. Narrowband if $|\Delta V| > 3$ dB at both tuning extremes
2. Broadband if $|\Delta V| \leqslant 3$ dB at both extremes

2.3.2.2 Repetition Rate vs. Impulse Bandwidth Test

This test consists of comparing the repetition rate of the EMI pulses to the impulse bandwidth of the EMI analyzer being used, with the bandwidth assumed to be appropriate for the EMI being tested. The EMI is defined as narrowband interference when its repetition rate equals or exceeds the impulse bandwidth, and as broadband interference when its pulse rate is less than the impulse bandwidth. Repetition rate of EMI pulses can be determined by feeding the IF of the EMI analyzer to either a time-domain oscilloscope or a frequency counter, while impulsive bandwidth can be determined by the methods outlined in Section 3.5 of Chapter 3.

2.3.2.3 Detector Function Test

In this test, the amplitude indication for the EMI signal is monitored while switching the detector function of the EMI analyzer from **peak** to **average**. Absence of any decrease in indicated amplitude shows that the signal is narrowband, while presence of any decrease shows that the signal is broadband. Table 3.2 in Chapter 3 illustrates the rationale for this criterion, in the context of response of various types of detectors to three types of signals.

2.3.2.4 Bandwidth Change Test

The bandwidth change test may be used when the EMI analyzer has a second bandwidth with a known and calibrated response characteristic. This test is less desirable than the preceding three methods because results depend on characteristics of this second bandwidth, which may not be the same among various EMI analyzers. More importantly, this method requires that the signal be defined as of the same type when either bandwidth is primary, as defined below.

As stated above in Section 2.1.1, defining a signal as narrowband or broadband implies some reference bandwidth to which the "narrowness" or "broadness" can be related. That reference bandwidth is logically that of the EMI analyzer in use for the particular test. This fact points to the wisdom of the ongoing trend in EMI measurements to specify the EMI analyzer bandwidth to be used for each EMI test.

For the purposes of performing this bandwidth change test for determining whether a signal is narrowband or broadband, it will be assumed that the proper bandwidth is being used, and it will be referred to as the **primary bandwidth**.

2.3.2.4.1 Narrowband Test

Determining that an unknown signal is narrowband requires that the EMI analyzer have a second bandwidth which is at least twice that of the primary bandwidth. The test then consists simply of tuning for maximum response to the signal and switching from the primary bandwidth to the wider bandwidth, noting the extent of any increase in indicated level of the signal. If the increase is less than 3 dB the signal is narrowband.

2.3.2.4.2 Broadband Test

Determining that an unknown signal is broadband requires the presence of a second bandwidth which is no wider than one-half the primary bandwidth. The test consists of tuning for maximum signal response, then switching to the narrower bandwidth, retuning for maximum response and noting any decrease in indicated level of the signal. If the decrease exceeds 3 dB, the signal is broadband.

2.3.2.5 Summary of Tests for Narrow/ Broadband Determination

The four test methods for determining whether an EMI signal

is narrowband or broadband are summarized by the following matrix, shown as Table 2.1:

Table 2.1—Summary of Criteria for Narrowband and Broadband EMI Identification

Test Type	EMI Type		Notes
	NB	BB	
RF Tuning: $|\Delta E|$ for ± 2 Impulse Bandwidths	> 3 dB	≤ 3 dB	At <u>Both</u> Detunings
PRF to Impulse Bandwidth Comparison Subtract B_i from f_r	≥ 0 dB	< 0 dB	
Detector Function: $|\Delta E|$ for Switching from Peak to Average Detection	0 dB	> 0 dB	
Bandwidth Change: $|\Delta E|$ for BW Switch. NB Test: Switch from Narrow to Wide. WB Test: Switch from Wide to Narrow.	< 3 dB ----	---- > 3 dB	

2.3.3 Transients, Impulses and Other Pulsed Broadband EMI

An analysis of transients and various forms of pulsed energy is important to any survey of EMI testing because both are common sources of broadband EMI. Whenever operation of an emitter or a receptor involves a relatively wide band of frequencies, it is likely that it develops and/or responds to EMI from transients and various forms of pulsed energy. Since impulses are a representative form of such energy, impulse generators, as discussed in Section 3.5, are convenient sources for simulating and calibrating response to pulsed broadband EMI. Both transients and impulses can produce EMI which is broadband to most potential victims.

The IEEE Dictionary defines a **transient** as "a change in the steady-state condition of voltage or current, or both."[2] For this handbook, it is posited that transients, by definition, occur at irregular intervals and are sufficiently separated in time of occurrence that the response of the potential receptor to each transient is an independent event unaffected by earlier or later transient events.

2.3.4 Spectrum Amplitude and Occupancy

The full potential EMI impact of transients and various forms of pulsed energy can be conveyed only by analyzing their respective frequency spectrum occupancies and amplitude distributions. Both the Fourier and Laplace transforms are very useful for characterizing in the frequency domain various waveforms which were originally defined in the time domain. It is only through use of such frequency-domain characterizations that the broadband nature of various transients and pulsed waveforms can be fully appreciated.

2.3.4.1 Expressing Spectrum Amplitude

Fundamental to any consideration of broadband EMI is the concept of **spectrum amplitude**.[3] Spectrum amplitude, S(f), is defined as twice the absolute magnitude of the Fourier transform, V(f), of a time-domain signal function, v(t), i.e.:

$$S(f) = 2|V(f)| \qquad (2.4)$$

where,

$$V(f) = \int_{-\infty}^{\infty} v(t)e^{-j2\pi ft}\, dt \qquad (2.5)$$

The dimensional units of spectrum amplitude are volts per hertz (V/Hz) or its mathematical equivalent, volt-seconds (Vs). The unit most commonly used is microvolts per megahertz (μV/MHz) and its logarithmic equivalent relative to one microvolt per megahertz:

$$S(f) = 20 \log [S(\mu V/MHz)/(1\ \mu V/MHz)] \qquad (2.6)$$

for,

$$S(f) \text{ in } dB\mu V/MHz$$

Every physical signal can be described in both the time and frequency domains. The following widely used pair of Fourier transform equations is one mathematical expression for this time/frequency duality:

Fourier transform:

$$V(f) = \int_{-\infty}^{\infty} v(t)e^{-j2\pi ft}\, dt \qquad (2.7)$$

Inverse Fourier Transform:

$$v(t) = \int_{-\infty}^{\infty} V(f)e^{j2\pi ft}\, df \qquad (2.8)$$

$V(f)$ and $v(t)$ represent the same signal as mathematically represented in the frequency and time domains, respectively; these two equations are used to transform between the two domains. Graphic plots of any given signal as represented in the two domains will differ from each other because the algebraic equations for the two domains are different; the only exception to this rule is a single Gaussian pulse, for which the equations and their plots take the same form in both domains. To be transformable, the algebraic time-domain function, $v(t)$, must satisfy the three Dirichlet conditions; fortunately, however, all physical signals of interest in EMI work do satisfy these conditions.[3]

Similarly, the Laplace transform also is used for transforming representations of various waveforms between the time and frequency domains. Either the Fourier or Laplace Transform can be used to derive frequency-domain representations of the time-domain waveforms discussed in the following paragraphs.[4]

2.3.4.2 Frequency-Domain Occupancy of the Step Function

Figure 2.4a illustrates the basic step function which characterizes the sudden change in voltage or current amplitude typical of most EMI-producing transients, while Fig. 2.4b shows the frequency-domain representation of this important waveform.

As plotted in Fig. 2.4b, it is apparent that the first null in amplitude occurs at a frequency of $1/\tau_r$, which is the rise time of the step function, and that successive nulls occur at integral multiples of this frequency. This plot also shows that, for a finite rise time, at frequencies above that of this first null, the envelope of the amplitude falls off inversely as the square of the frequency, or at the rate of 40 dB/decade. It can also be shown that if the tran-

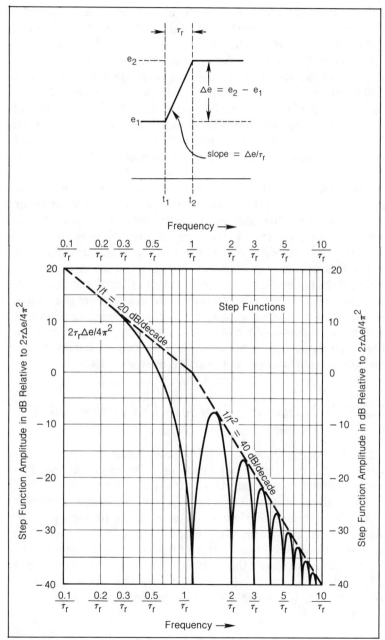

Figure 2.4—Time- and Frequency-Domain Representations of Basic Step Waveform

sition is a smooth function rather than an abrupt one, the slope of the envelope for frequencies above that of the first null falls off at a rate of at least 60 dB/decade.[3]

It is clear from this frequency-domain plot that the longer the rise time of the step function, the lower the frequency at which each null occurs and the more confined the frequency spectrum occupied by the energy of the step-function event. Conversely, when the rise time becomes so fast that the first null is moved well beyond the frequency range of interest, the spectrum amplitude over the range of interest falls off inversely with frequency at the rate of 20 dB/decade.

Interpretation of the meaning of Fig. 2.4b as frequency approaches zero must be done with care. The available voltage never exceeds the dc ($f = 0$) value except for ringing and overshoot, which are functions of the circuit RLC components—not of the available voltage. However, Fig. 2.4b implies that the spectrum amplitude at $f = 0$ is infinite. The highest value of the spectrum amplitude is that of the derivative of the step. For practical steps, this derivative does not have infinite height because the rise time of the step is not zero. For critically damped circuits the spectrum amplitude of a step approaches $4.4\Delta e$ as a limit as frequency approaches zero. For under-damped RLC circuits which have ringing and overshoot, the amount of the overshoot is convoluted with $4.4\Delta e$.

2.3.4.3 Frequency-Domain Occupancy of Pulses

A pulse having finite rise and fall times can be analyzed by constructing it as made up of step functions as shown in Fig. 2.5a. The pulse waveform is essentially two back-to-back step functions. When rise and fall times are equal, i.e., $\tau_r = \tau_f$, the frequency-domain plot of this waveform is as shown in Fig. 2.5b. As frequency, f, approaches zero, the spectrum amplitude, S(f), approaches $2\tau\Delta e$ V s or V/Hz. The dashed line in Fig. 2.5b represents the envelope of the function and shows that between $1/\pi\tau$ and $1/\pi\tau_r$ the slope is 20 dB/decade, and above $f = 1/\pi\tau_r$, the slope becomes 40 dB/decade. When rise and fall times are arbitrarily fast, $\tau_r = \tau_f = 0$:

$$S(f) = 2\tau\Delta e \ (\sin \pi f\tau)/\pi f\tau \qquad (2.9)$$

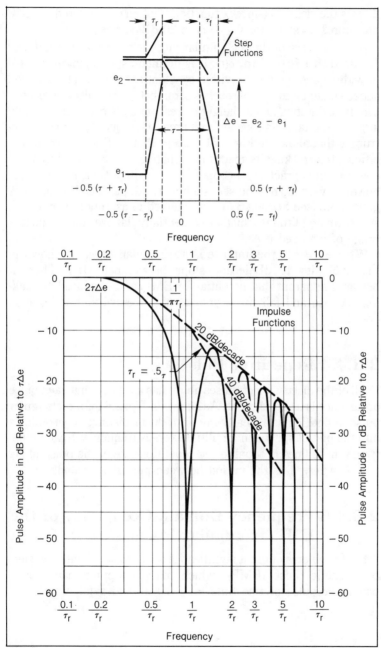

Figure 2.5—Time and Frequency Domain Representation of Pulse Waveform

This is the classical (sin x)/x function so often encountered in EMC literature. Its slope for $f > 1/\pi\tau$ is 20 dB/decade.

A special case of the rectangular pulse is the **true impulse**, or **Dirac delta function**, $\delta(t)$. It is defined as a rectangular pulse of width τ and height $1/\tau$ with a constant area of one (1), with the added condition that τ approaches zero; that is, the pulse approaches zero time duration and its height correspondingly becomes infinitely large, as it retains its constant unit area. Its frequency-domain spectrum is that shown in Fig. 2.5b, except that its first null occurs at infinity, thus making its spectrum amplitude constant at all frequencies. In actual practice, of course, this true impulse is not realized; however, very narrow pulses, such as those produced by impulse generators (see Section 3.5), are referred to as impulses and have spectrum amplitudes which are essentially flat over the frequency range of intended use.

When $\tau_r = \tau/2$, the impulse is a triangular wave. As shown in Fig. 2.5b, its 40 dB/decade slope breaks near $1/\tau_r$. Thus, it becomes apparent that potential for EMI can be reduced by making the rise and fall times approximately equal and as large as possible.

2.3.4.4 Repetitive Pulses

All of the discussion of pulses above has assumed that each pulse occurrence is a single event. As shown in Fig. 2.6 for a rectangular pulse, repetition at a steady rate introduces distinct spectral lines into the plot of spectrum amplitude versus frequency. Spacing between these lines is equal to the repetition rate of the pulse in Hz = 1/T, where T is the period between pulses in seconds.

2.3.4.5 Frequency-Domain Occupancy of the EMP Triangular Pulse

EMI problems of great significance are associated with the electromagnetic pulse (EMP), which may be approximated by a triangular pulse of rise time $\tau_r = 10$ ns and a fall time, $\tau_f =$

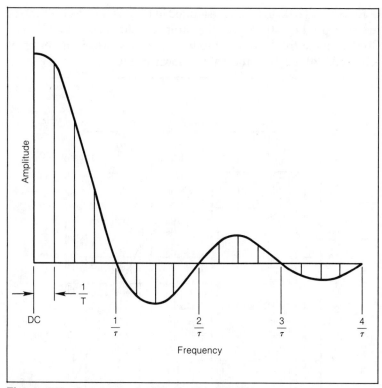

Figure 2.6—Spectrum of a Rectangular Pulse

500 ns. Thus, the pulse width, $\tau = (\tau_r + \tau_f)/2 = 255$ ns, or approximately one-half of the fall time τ_f.

The spectrum amplitude of this special pulse versus frequency is:

$$S(f) = 2\tau\Delta e = \tau_f\Delta e \qquad \text{for } 0 \leqslant f \leqslant 1/\pi\tau_f \qquad (2.10)$$

$$= \Delta e/\pi f \qquad \text{for } 1/\pi\tau_f \leqslant f \leqslant 1/\pi\tau_r \qquad (2.11)$$

$$= \Delta e/\pi^2 f^2 \tau_r \qquad \text{for } f \geqslant 1/\pi\tau_r \qquad (2.12)$$

Equations (2.10) to (2.12) are plotted in Fig. 2.7, in which all values are increased by 10^3 so that the ordinate reference is now V/kHz. To determine the EMI amplitude in a bandwidth, B, in terms of kHz, add 20 log B to the value shown in Fig. 2.7.

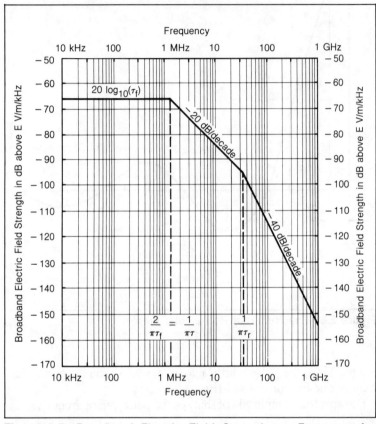

Figure 2.7—Broadband Electric Field Strength vs. Frequency for Simulated EMP

2.22

Illustrative Example 2.1

Assume that the electric field strength arriving at a measurement site from an EMP source is E = 10 kV/m and that we wish to determine the equivalent field strength at a frequency of 10 MHz for a measuring impulse bandwidth of 10 kHz (see Section 3.5). Figure 2.7 shows the spectrum amplitude (defined per kHz) field strength (per meter) resulting from an EMP field strength of E V/m. At 10 MHz, the resulting field strength spectrum amplitude per meter is −84 dB(E/kHz). Since E is 10 kV/m, or 20 dB(kV/m), the spectrum amplitude field strength in dB(kV/m/kHz) is:

−84 dB(E/kHz) + 20 dB(kV/m) = −64 dB(kV/m/kHz)

For a 10 kHz bandwidth, which is +20 dB(kHz), the field strength becomes:

−64 dB(kV/m/kHz) + 20 dB(kHz) = −44 dB(kV/m) = 6.31 V/m

2.3.4.6 Lightning Stroke Pulse

Lightning strokes, which also can cause severe EMI problems, can be simulated by a pulse width, τ, of about 50 μs and a 10 to 90 percent rise time, τ_r, of about 500 ns. The average stroke amplitude is about 30 kA, making the rate of rise about 60 kA/μs. The spectral intensity is $2\tau A \approx$ 3 A/Hz = 3 kA/kHz = 190 dBA/kHz, and the first notch frequency, $1/\pi\tau$, is 6.3 kHz. The second notch frequency is 637 kHz. Figure 2.8 shows the current spectral density of the stroke in the left ordinate and the magnetic flux density at a distance of 100 m in the right ordinate. To calculate the magnetic flux density at other distances in meters, R, add 20 log (R/100) dB.

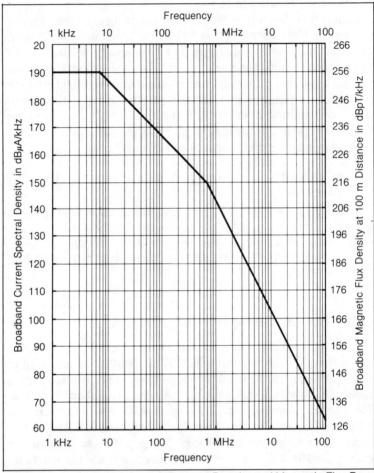

Figure 2.8—Broadband Current Spectral Density and Magnetic Flux Density from a Lightning Stroke

2.3.4.7 RF-Modulated Pulses

The spectrum of a rectangular RF pulse is simply that of the rectangular pulses discussed in Sections 2.3.4.3 and 2.3.4.4, transposed in frequency by the RF carrier frequency f_c. As shown in Fig. 2.9, the (sin x)/x spectrum distribution about zero frequency is translated to a (sin x)/x distribution centered at f_c. For regularly repetitive bursts of RF pulses, spacing of the spectral lines is equal to 1/T, the repetition rate of the pulses.

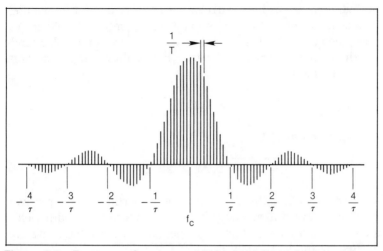

Figure 2.9—Frequency Spectrum of Pulse-Modulated Carrier

2.3.4.8 Coherent and Noncoherent Broadband Emissions

A signal is said to be **coherent** when neighboring frequency components within it are related to each other or well defined in both **amplitude** and **phase**. For broadband signals, the neighboring components are both equal and in phase. Examples of sources of coherent broadband emissions are pulsed sources such as computer clocks, radar and pulse-code modulation (PCM) telemetry, provided that the narrowband/broadband test criteria of Section 2.3.2 confirm them as broadband.

Conversely, when neighboring frequency components are random, or unrelated, both in amplitude and phase or in phase alone, a signal is said to be **noncoherent**. Examples of noncoherent broadband signals are high-voltage corona noise, internal receiver noise and emissions from noise diodes and dc-energized gas lamps.

Coherent Broadband Emissions

Referring to the frequency-domain representation for a rectangular pulse, it can be seen from Eq. (2.9) and Fig. 2.5b that the amplitude is flat within 1.3 dB for $0 \leqslant f \leqslant 1/\pi\tau$. Thus, this qualifies as a coherent broadband emission. Consequently, the voltage, V_i, developed under the (sin x)/x curve within a receiver impulse bandwidth B_i for $f < 1/\pi\tau$ (as shown in Fig. 2.5b) is simply the area under the curve:

$$V_i = 2\tau\Delta e B_i \qquad (2.13)$$

or, expressed in dBV:

$$V_i = 20 \log 2\tau\Delta e + 20 \log B_i \qquad (2.14)$$

All coherent broadband voltages are proportional to the receiver impulse bandwidth, and any change in impulse bandwidth yields a corresponding proportional change, ΔV_i, in the voltage level indicated by the EMI analyzer:

$$\Delta V_i = 20 \log (\text{new } B_i/\text{old } B_i) \qquad (2.15)$$

Noncoherent Broadband Emissions

When phase is random among neighboring frequency components of a signal, such as for thermal noise, the incremental voltages combine on an rms basis rather than directly, and the signal is said to be **noncoherent**. The voltage of such a signal within a bandwidth B_n is:

$$V_n = [(2\tau\Delta e)^2 (B_n)]^{1/2} = 2\tau\Delta e \sqrt{B_n} \qquad (2.16)$$

or, expressed in dBV:

$$V_n = 20 \log 2\tau\Delta e + 10 \log B_n \qquad (2.17)$$

As can be seen from Eq. (2.16), all noncoherent voltages are proportional to the square root of their respective bandwidths. For a change in bandwidth, the change in indicated output voltage, ΔV_n, is:

$$\Delta V_n = 10 \log (\text{new } B_n/\text{old } B_n) \qquad (2.18)$$

This voltage-versus-bandwidth relationship for noncoherent signals is further illustrated by the expression for internal receiver noise discussed in the next chapter. The receiver noise power, N, in watts is:

$$N = \underline{F}kTB_n \qquad\qquad (2.19)$$

where,

$\underline{F}$ = noise factor

k = Boltzmann's constant

T = absolute temperature

B_n = random noise bandwidth of receiver

Since voltage is proportional to the square root of power, noise voltage is proportional to the square root of this expression and thus is proportional to $\sqrt{B_n}$.

Illustrative Example 2.2

An EMI receiver operating at its narrowest bandwidth develops the same output readings, 30 dBμV, when measuring two input signals, from (1) an impulse generator and (2) a noise-diode generator. What would the two output readings be if the receiver bandwidth were changed to its widest position which is 100 times that of the narrowest, when measured both as a random noise bandwidth and an impulse bandwidth? From Eqs. (2.15) and (2.18):

Impulse Generator:

$$V_i = 30 \text{ dB}\mu\text{V} + 20 \log 100 = 70 \text{ dB}\mu\text{V}$$

Noise-Diode Generator:

$$V_n = 30 \text{ dB}\mu\text{V} + 10 \log 100 = 50 \text{ dB}\mu\text{V}$$

2.3.5 Sources of Transients and Other Broadband EMI

The duty factor, δ, of an emitting source is defined as:

$$\delta = \tau \times f_r$$

where,

τ = equivalent pulse or impulse width at the 50 percent height
f_r = pulse repetition rate or, for random occurrences, the average number of pulses or impulses per second

Most pulsed forms of EMI from incidental emitting sources have duty factors less than 10^{-5}. Table 2.2 lists approximate duty factors for some sources of pulsed EMI identified to the nearest order of magnitude. Also included in this table are approximate average rates of occurrence for transients, which occur at irregular intervals.

As a practical matter, the direction of technological development in the U.S. over the past two decades has been such as to introduce into the electromagnetic environment both more sources of pulsed broadband EMI and more devices susceptible to it.

Table 2.2—Some Sources of Pulsed Broadband EMI

Pulsed EMI Source	Repetition Rate in Hz	Impulse Width in s	Duty Factor
Fluorescent Lamps	100	10^{-7}	10^{-5}
Ignition Systems:			
Idle Speed	100	10^{-8}	10^{-6}
Fast Speed	10^3	10^{-8}	10^{-5}
Relays and Solenoids:			
Casual use	10^{-3}	—	—
Pinball Machine	1	10^{-7}	10^{-7}
Teletype	10	10^{-7}	10^{-6}
Brush-Comutator Motor	10^3	10^{-8}	10^{-5}
On-Off Switches:			
Wall Switch	10^{-4}	—	—
Lathe	10^{-3}	—	—
Copy Machine	10^{-3}	—	—

2.4 Conducted EMI Emissions Testing

Conducted EMI has been identified as electromagnetic energy which is undesirably coupled out of an emitter or into a receptor via any of its connecting wires or cables. The basic task of testing conducted EMI emissions thus becomes that of measuring accurately the EMI escaping from an emitter via its connecting wires or cables and of comparing the results against allowable limits.

Several EMI specifications state their limits on conducted EMI in terms of the magnitude of EMI **current** flowing out of the EUT through each conductor or cable, while most EMI specifications state their limits in terms of the **two-terminal voltage** appearing at that point where the cable or conductor leading out of the EUT interfaces with the outside world.

Two widely used standards, CISPR Publications 14 and 16, specify use of a special absorbing clamp calibrated to measure the "power" of the EMI conducted out of small appliances via their respective ac line cords.[5,6] This absorbing clamp test is used in lieu of radiated EMI testing of the respective appliances, based on the premise that the ac line cord would be the source of most EMI radiation. (Refer to Section 4.4.1 for more details on this device.)

2.4.1 Conducted EMI Units of Measurement

Before proceeding any further with a discussion of conducted EMI testing, it is appropriate to consider the measurement units utilized. A fundamental unit of reference is one watt (W) of power, which is equal to one joule per second (J/s). Because of the relatively low power levels involved in much EMI emissions testing, a more convenient level of power reference is the milliwatt (mW), which is simply 10^{-3} W. This commonly used reference level of power is usually referred to as 0 dBm, or 0 dB referenced to 1 mW. Thus:

$$1 \text{ mW} = 10^{-3} \text{ W} \tag{2.20}$$

or,

$$1 \text{ mW} = 0 \text{ dBm} = -30 \text{ dBW} \tag{2.21}$$

Thus,

$$1 \text{ W} = 0 \text{ dBW} = 10 \log (10^3 \text{ mW}) = +30 \text{ dBm} \tag{2.22}$$

Power levels in dBm are 30 dB higher than corresponding levels in dBW.

EMI specification limits and measurements rarely use power as the reference. Among the reasons for this are that a power measurement cannot identify whether EMI is coherent or noncoherent (see Section 2.3.4.8), and power is not readily measured (see Section 2.1). The EMI community uses voltage, V, or current, A, as the basic unit for conducted measurements.

As emphasized in the discussions of the dB (Section 2.2), voltage ratios can be properly used in lieu of power ratios only when the two voltages in a given ratio are developed across equal impedances.

In EMI testing, the microvolt, μV, is used as the basic unit of voltage reference:

$$1 \ \mu V \ = \ 10^{-6} \ V \ = \ 0 \ dB\mu V \qquad (2.23)$$

To express V in units of dBμV:

$$1 \ V \ = \ 20 \ \log \ (1 \ V/10^{-6} \ V) \ = \ 20 \ \log \ 10^6 \ = \ 120 \ dB\mu V \quad (2.24)$$

Thus, since 1 V is 120 dBμV, 120 dB must be added to any dB level expressed relative to 1 V to refer that level down to 1 μV.

The relationship between voltage and power is:

$$P \ = \ V^2/R \qquad (2.25)$$

where,

V = circuit voltage in volts
R = circuit resistance in ohms across which V is measured

Expressed in dB relative to one watt, this becomes:

$$P \ = \ 10 \ \log \ (V^2/R) \qquad (2.26)$$

Since 1 mW is 30 dB below 1 W, expressed as dBm this becomes:

$$P \ = \ 10 \ \log \ (V^2/R) \ + \ 30 \ dB \qquad (2.27)$$

However, since:

$$10 \log (V^2/R) = 10 \log V^2 - 10 \log R = 20 \log V - 10 \log R$$

then,

$$P = 20 \log V - 10 \log R + 30 \text{ dB} \qquad (2.28)$$

Since $20 \log V$ is the expression for dBV, it can be replaced in the last equation by $dB\mu V - 120$ dB. This yields an equivalency for power in dBm in terms of voltage in $dB\mu V$, namely:

$$\text{Power in dBm} = \text{Voltage in } dB\mu V - 90 \text{ dB} - 10 \log R \quad (2.29)$$

When $R = 50 \ \Omega$:

$$10 \log 50 = 17 \text{ dB}$$

and,

$$\text{Power in dBm} = \text{Voltage in } dB\mu V - 107 \text{ dB} \qquad (2.30)$$

or,

$$\text{Voltage in } dB\mu V = \text{Power in dBm} + 107 \text{ dB} \qquad (2.31)$$

The following tabulation shows the dB levels in this equivalency for some other common impedances.

When Impedance Level (Resistive) in Ω is:	To Convert dBm to $dB\mu V$, add:
10	100.0 dB
50	107.0
150	111.8
300	114.8
600	117.8
1,000	120.0
10,000	130.0

Table A.1 of the Appendix tabulates this equivalency at 50 Ω for a wide range of narrowband and broadband levels.

2.4.2 Measuring Conducted EMI Current

A possible way of determining the EMI current flow in a conductor would be to measure the EMI voltage drop across a resistor of known small value which is inserted in series with the conductor. One then may calculate the EMI current by using Ohm's Law. This method is seldom used in actual practice because it disturbs the EUT and is too cumbersome where multiple-conductor cables are involved.

2.4.2.1 Using a Clamp-On Current Probe to Measure EMI Current

Clamp-on current probes are convenient to use since they are simply closed around one or more wires and then clamped shut to make them functional. Such a probe works on the principle of treating the conductor under test as the primary winding of a transformer, with the current probe acting as its toroidal-wound secondary winding. Physical implementation of this principle into actual hardware is discussed in Chapter 4, along with accessory devices used to make current probe measurements more consistent and reliable.

It should be noted that clamping the toroidal current probe as the transformer secondary around a wire which itself is the transformer primary effectively transforms the load impedance on the probe down to a small value of impedance inserted in the probed wire. Thus, the clamp-on current probe is equivalent to measuring the voltage drop across a small resistance inserted in series with the current being measured, as mentioned above in Section 2.4.2. Typically, the impedance inserted is in the order of 0.5 Ω.

2.4.2.2 Transfer Impedance

As shown in Fig. 2.1, the current probe is used as a pickup or sensor of the EMI current, and its output is fed to the EMI analyzer. Since the EMI analyzer is always calibrated to read the **voltage** appearing at its input terminals, determining the EMI current in the conductor producing such a voltage level requires knowledge of the **transfer impedance, Z_T**, of the current probe, which is the ratio of output voltage to current flow. It is defined as:

$$Z_T = V_{out}/I_{in} \qquad (2.32)$$

where,

V_{out} = output voltage across the current probe when terminated in 50 Ω (input impedance of the EMI analyzer)

I_{in} = unknown input current flow in the conductor(s) around which the probe is clamped

In units of dB relative to 1 Ω, Z_T becomes:

$$Z_T = V_{out} - I_{in}$$

for, V_{out} in dBμV and I_{in} in dBμA

An unknown EMI current in dBμA is:

$$I_{in} = V_{out} - Z_T$$

for, V_{out} in dBμV and Z_T in dBΩ

Typically, the current probe manufacturer furnishes a plot of the transfer impedance over the frequency range for which the probe is usable. The measurement of EMI current (in dB relative to 1 μA) is then obtained by reading the two-terminal indication of the EMI analyzer (in dB relative to 1 μV) and then subtracting from it the transfer impedance of the current probe (in dB relative to 1 Ω). Some manufacturers give the **transfer admittance** in terms of dB relative to one siemens, the inverse of ohm, which necessitates that this dB quantity be **added to**, rather than subtracted from, the two-terminal voltage reading.

2.4.3 Measuring Conducted EMI Voltage

2.4.3.1 Line Impedance Stabilization Networks

The primary function of the **line impedance stabilization network (LISN)** is to couple to an EMI analyzer the level of EMI voltage being fed by the EUT onto the leads connected to furnish its operating power, while rejecting any EMI signals coming from the power mains supply to these leads. Figure 4.12 (Chapter 4) shows the schematic diagram of a typical LISN. Other names for a LISN include **artificial mains network, power line impedance stabilization network (PLISN)** or simply **line stabilization network (LSN)**. These devices are analyzed and discussed further in Chapter 4.

2.4.3.2 Voltage Probes

Situations exist in which it is not feasible to use LISNs to measure EMI voltages on conductors, either because the LISN is unable to handle the high level of intended current flowing in the conductor or because the impedance of the LISN is too low for the high-impedance conductor being tested. In such cases, a **line probe** or **voltage probe** is very useful, provided that some voltage division loss of the EMI level to be measured can be tolerated. Figure 4.14 (Chapter 4) is the schematic of a line probe recommended by the FCC for measuring EMI emissions from computing devices when a LISN with adequate current-handling capacity is not available and the calibration factor implied by the attenuation through the 1,500 Ω resistor into the 50 Ω impedance of the EMI analyzer is allowable.[7]

Another implementation of the voltage probe is exemplified by a series of coupling blocks still specified by the U.S. Army for reprocurements, covering measurements in accordance with Method CE07 of Notice 3 to MIL-STD-462. These coupling blocks utilize a series capacitor as a high-pass filter to block the dc or power-mains ac and to couple the higher-frequency EMI to the EMI analyzer. They are treated further in Chapters 4 and 10.

A third type of voltage probe discussed in Chapter 4 as applicable to EMI testing and analysis is represented by the **passive** and **active probes** provided by manufacturers of oscilloscopes.

2.5 Radiated EMI Emissions Testing

2.5.1 Basic Procedure for Measuring Radiated EMI Emissions

Radiated EMI was defined in Chapter 1 as electromagnetic energy which is undesirably coupled out of an emitter or into a receptor by means other than conduction. The basic task of testing radiated EMI becomes that of measuring accurately, and then comparing to appropriate limits, any undesired electromagnetic fields emanating from an emitter.

The basic procedure for testing radiated EMI requires the use of a calibrated antenna or transducer feeding into a calibrated EMI analyzer. The calibrated antenna is immersed at an appropriate or specified position in the field to be measured; the voltage resulting at the end of its connecting cable, which is the point of interface with the interference analyzer, is measured and then converted into units of the immersed field using a conversion factor. The following paragraphs discuss characteristics of radiated fields and considerations affecting their accurate measurement using such conversions, or **antenna factors.**

2.5.2 Near and Far Fields

Any testing or analysis of radiated emissions must take into account the characteristics of the electromagnetic field, specifically whether it is a **near** or **far** field. Radiated energy in the far-field region is sometimes referred to as **plane waves** or a **plane-wave field**. In this region, the power-flux flow, or power density, P_D, in units of watts per square meter (W/m^2) is:

$$P_D = E_\theta \times H_\phi \qquad (2.34)$$

where,

E_θ = electric field strength in V/m
H_ϕ = magnetic field strength in A/m

In this **far-field region** only, electric and magnetic fields are related by a constant wave impedance, Z_0:

$$Z_0 = E_\theta/H_\phi = 377 \ \Omega \qquad (2.35)$$

Thus, for plane waves, the electric and magnetic fields are uniquely related by 377 Ω.

Generally, however, E and H are vector quantities possessing both magnitude and direction; this will be assumed in all following discussions. The orthogonal spatial and in-phase time relationships between E and H exist only in the far field. In the near field, it will be shown that the impedance Z, also a vector quantity which continues to be the quotient of the electric field divided by the magnetic field, may assume very small values when the magnetic field dominates (low-impedance fields) and very high values when the electric field is dominant (high-impedance field).

The relationship $2\pi/\lambda$ ($= \omega/c$) occurs so often in any analysis of electromagnetic fields that, for convenience, it is termed the **wave number** and designated simply as β. This convention will be applied in all following discussions.

The degree to which the type of field is near or far is characterized by the interface distance, r, from the field-producing element, and depends on D, the size or aperture dimension of the field-producing element in terms of λ, the wavelength of the emitted energy. When D is much smaller than a full wavelength, λ, the interface distance is:

$$r = \lambda/2\pi = 1/\beta \qquad \text{for } D \ll \lambda \qquad (2.36)$$

When D is greater than or equal to one-half a wavelength, $\lambda/2$, the interface distance is:

$$r = D^2/2\lambda \qquad \text{for } D \geqslant \lambda/2 \qquad (2.37)$$

Note that when $D = \lambda/2$, Eq. (2.37) becomes $r = \lambda/8$ which is close in value to Eq. (2.36). The two situations, of D much smaller than a wavelength and of D greater than or equal to one-half wavelength, will now be discussed separately.

2.5.2.1 Near/Far Fields for Radiating Element Size, $D \ll \lambda$

To consider the near/far-field results for small dimensions of radiating elements, it is necessary to state a few concise pertinent relations developed from Maxwell's equations, only a few aspects of which are presented here.

The electric ($E_\ominus$, E_r) and magnetic (H_ϕ) fields existing about an infinitesimally short wire are obtained from applying Maxwell's equations:

$$E_0 = \frac{Z_0 \, ID\beta \, \sin \ominus}{2\lambda} \left[-\left(\frac{1}{\beta r}\right)^3 \cos\psi - \left(\frac{1}{\beta r}\right)^2 \right.$$

$$\left. \sin\psi + \left(\frac{1}{\beta r}\right) \cos\psi \right] \tag{2.38}$$

$$E_r = \frac{Z_0 ID\beta \, \cos \ominus}{\lambda} \left[\left(\frac{1}{\beta r}\right)^3 \cos\psi + \left(\frac{1}{\beta r}\right)^2 \sin\psi \right] \tag{2.39}$$

$$H\phi = \frac{ID\beta \, \sin \ominus}{2\lambda} \left[\left(\frac{1}{\beta r}\right)^2 \sin\psi + \left(\frac{1}{\beta r}\right) \cos\psi \right] \tag{2.40}$$

where,

Z_0 = free space impedance (for $r \gg 1/\beta$) = 377 Ω

I = current in short wire

D = length of short wire

$\ominus$ = zenith angle to r

λ = wavelength corresponding to frequency, f

ω = angular velocity = $2\pi f$

β = wave number = $2\pi/\lambda$ = ω/c

r = distance from short wire doublet to measuring point

ψ = $\beta r - \omega t$

t = time

Several observations can be made about the near and far fields from an analysis of Eqs. (2.38) and (2.40):

1. When $r = 1/\beta$ (about one-sixth wavelength), all coefficients of sine and cosine terms are unity and equal. This distance corresponds to the transition-field condition or boundary between the near field (first term of equations) and far field (last term).
2. When $r \gg 1/\beta$ (far-field conditions), only the last term of Eqs. (2.38) and (2.40) is significant. For this condition, the wave impedance, $Z_0 = E_\theta/H_\phi = 377\ \Omega$. This is called the **radiation field** (plane waves), and both E_θ and H_ϕ are in time phase ($\cos \psi$) although in directional quadrature.
3. When $r \ll 1/\beta$ (near-field conditions), only the first term of each equation is significant. For this condition, the wave impedance $E_\theta/H_\phi = Z_0\lambda/2\pi r$. Note that the wave impedance is now $\gg Z_0$ since $1/\beta r \gg 1$. This is sometimes called simply an electric field or a **high-impedance field**; i.e., high relative to plane wave impedance of 377 Ω. It is also the induction field, and E_θ and H_ϕ are in both phase and directional quadrature.

Figure 2.10 illustrates these three observations in terms of the amplitudes of each of the three terms in the electric field equation, Eq. (2.38). Note that in the near-field region the term for the quasi-stationary field term is the largest, and the induction field term is the second largest. In the far-field region the radiation term is the largest. All three terms are equal for $r = 1/\beta$.

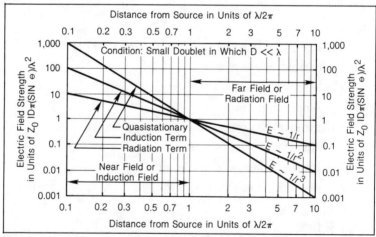

Figure 2.10—Electric Field Intensity vs. Source Distance

Figure 2.11a illustrates the third observation above for near-field conditions. Shown in the figure is a monopole or straight wire in which the RF current is low and the source or circuit impedance V/I is high. The wave impedance close to the radiating element also is high, as the electric field dominates. As is evident from Eqs. (2.38) and (2.40), in this induction region the electric field attenuates more rapidly with an increase in distance from the source ($1/r^3$) than does the magnetic field ($1/r^2$). Thus, the wave impedance decreases with an increase in distance and asymptotically approaches $Z_0 = 377 \ \Omega$ in the far- or radiation-field region ($r \gg 1/\beta$).

If the radiating source were a small wire loop exhibiting low circuit impedance, as shown in Fig. 2.11b, rather than a short wire or doublet exhibiting high circuit impedance, as shown in Fig. 2.11a, the first term appearing in Eqs. (2.38) and (2.39) would vanish, but a similar first term would appear in Eq. (2.40). For this condition, the wave impedance in the near field, $E_\theta/H_\phi = Z_0\beta r$, is now $\ll Z_0$. This is sometimes called a **magnetic** or a **low-impedance field**, i.e., low relative to Z_0, the plane-wave (radiation) impedance. In contrast to the situation for the straight wire or doublet situation discussed above, this impedance increases with distance, asymptotically approaching 377 Ω in the far-field region. Figure 2.12 illustrates the variation of both impedance as a function of distance, r, from the radiating source.

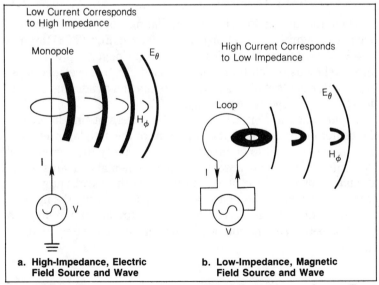

Figure 2.11—Conceptual Illustration of Field Intensities vs. Source Type and Distance

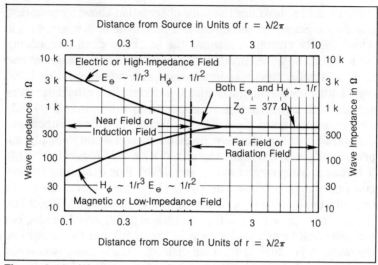

Figure 2.12—Wave Impedance as a Function of Source Distance

2.5.2.2 Near/Far Fields for Radiating Element Size, $D \geqslant \lambda/2$

When the dimension, D, of a radiating source (an antenna) becomes a significant fraction of a wavelength, Eqs. (2.38) through (2.40), derived from Maxwell's equations, no longer apply. The different relations which then must be used can be developed most easily in the context of a receiving antenna and a radiating source, using the principle of reciprocity.

As illustrated in Fig. 2.13, where the wavefront first intercepts the center of the antenna, the curvature of the arriving wavefront no longer permits it to be intercepted in phase by the incremental elements of a receiving antenna. The incremental elements of the antenna away from its center point intercept the wavefront with increasing time delay and phase lag. Thus, determining the net vector amplitude of energy received by the entire antenna requires a phase-sensitive summation of the portions intercepted by all of its elements.

The result is approximated by numerical summation, as illustrated in Fig. 2.13, in which $k\lambda$ = $\lambda/8$, $\lambda/4$, $\lambda/2$, $3\lambda/4$, λ, and $3\lambda/2$. The results of this summation are shown in Fig. 2.14 in which relative gain of the antenna is plotted as a function of distance from it. Note the oscillatory performance in the near field with a decreasing amplitude of envelope as distance from the antenna is decreased and contributions of antenna elements toward its extremes are increasingly out of phase.

Determining the value for distance, R, which yields the point of near-far field interface first requires decision as to tolerable amount of error from the asymptotically-approached far-field maximum. Antenna and propagation disciplines often use $k\lambda$ = $\lambda/16$, which corresponds to an error of about 0.1 dB in antenna gain. The EMC

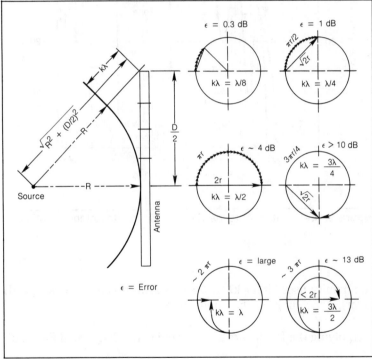

Figure 2.13—Conceptual Illustration of Phase Error Caused by Curvature of Wave Front

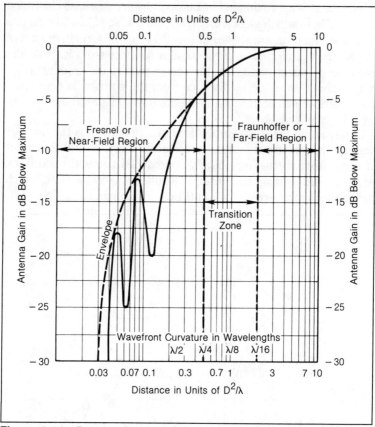

Figure 2.14—Relative Antenna Gain vs. Source-to-Antenna Distance

community uses either $k\lambda = \lambda/8$ (0.3 dB error) or $k\lambda = \lambda/4$ (1 dB error), depending on the application.

Applying the Pythagorean Theorem to the diagram in Fig. 2.13:

$$(R + k\lambda)^2 = R^2 + (D/2)^2 \qquad (2.41)$$

$$2 Rk\lambda + (k\lambda)^2 = (D/2)^2$$

Thus, since $2Rk\lambda \gg (k\lambda)^2$,

$$2Rk\lambda \approx (D/2)$$

or,

$$R \approx D^2/8k\lambda \qquad (2.42)$$

When $k\lambda = \lambda/4$ is chosen (i.e., 1 dB error in gain), Eq. (2.42) becomes:

Near-Far Field Interface $= R = D^2/2\lambda$ for 1 dB error $\qquad (2.43)$

An important special case of radiating structures which are an appreciable fraction of a wavelength long is the monopole over perfect ground (or dipole in free space) which is **electrically** one-quarter wavelength or longer. The base-loaded monopole or whip antenna tuned to quarter-wavelength resonance is an example of an intentional form of this structure. This case is important to the measurement of EMI because many EUTs with their associated wires and cables inadvertently form such a radiating structure![8]

Brown,[9] Carter,[10] and King[11] have shown that the near fields of linear antennas whose **electrical** length is one-quarter wavelength or more have characteristics which differ from those of elementary dipole theory. For these antennas, the near field exists from the antenna out to a distance somewhat less than $1/\beta$, where the phase angle between the tangential electric field component becomes less than 30 degrees out of phase with the annular magnetic field component. The transition zone exists between this distance and the distance where the tangential electric field and the annular magnetic field are in phase and their magnitudes have reached a fixed ratio. This fixed ratio is commonly called the **wave impedance**, and in the far field in free space is approximately $120\pi = 377 \ \Omega$.

The general field equations for a vertical linear antenna on a perfectly conducting ground plane given by Brown are listed below. The coordinates are rectangular, as shown in Fig. 2.15.

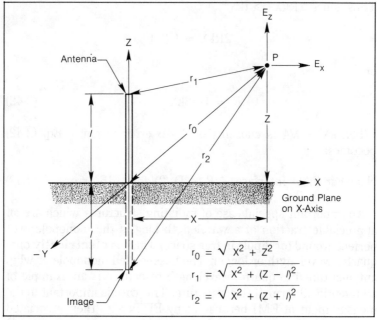

Figure 2.15—Rectangular Coordinate System for Brown Analysis

$$E_z = -\frac{30\,I}{\sin\beta l}\left[\left(\frac{\sin\beta r_1}{r_1} + \frac{\sin\beta r_2}{r_2} - 2\cos\beta l\,\frac{\sin\beta r_0}{r_0}\right)\right.$$

$$\left. + j\left(\frac{\cos\beta r_1}{r_1} + \frac{\cos\beta r_2}{r_2} - 2\cos\beta l\,\frac{\sin\beta r_0}{r_0}\right)\right]$$

$$(2.44)$$

$$E_x = \frac{30\,I}{x\,\sin\beta l}\left[\left(\frac{Z-l}{r_1}\sin\beta r_1 + \frac{Z+l}{r_2}\sin\beta r_2 - \right.\right.$$

$$\left. 2z\cos\beta l\,\frac{\sin\beta r_0}{r_0}\right)$$

$$\left. + j\left(\frac{Z-l}{r_1}\cos\beta r_1 + \frac{Z+l}{r_2}\cos\beta r_2 - 2z\cos\beta l\,\frac{\cos\beta r_0}{r_0}\right)\right]$$

$$(2.45)$$

$$H_\phi = \frac{I}{4\pi \times \sin \beta l} \left[\left(\sin \beta r_1 + \sin \beta r_2 - 2 \cos \beta l \sin \beta r_0 \right) \right.$$

$$\left. + j \left(\cos \beta r_1 + \cos \beta r_2 - 2 \cos \beta l \cos \beta r_0 \right) \right] \quad (2.46)$$

The magnetic field vector points into and out of the paper in Fig. 2.15, since it is annular to the antenna, i.e. circles around it. These equations, which were derived rigorously by both Brown and King, show that the only near-field term is E_x, which is proportional to $1/r^2$. The E_z and H_ϕ components that eventually form the far field are orthogonal in space and are approximately invariant with distance into the transition zone. After the transition zone, their ratio is fixed and they are proportional to $1/r$. This is shown graphically in Fig. 2.16, where E_z is the vertical E-field and E_x is the horizontal (radial) E-field. Note that the curves for E_z and E_x cross each other at a distance of $1/\beta$. These considerations are important in measuring EMI from sources that approximate electrically large linear antennas.

Another important feature of the relationship between E_z and E_x is the variation in their relative strengths versus height above the ground plane. E_x is zero at the ground plane and becomes stronger with increasing height until reaching a maximum at a point more than half the length of the antenna above the ground plane. This is illustrated in Fig. 2.17 which shows the electric field strength versus height above ground for a quarter-wavelength monopole at a distance of $1/\beta$. The elevation for the maximum value of E_x

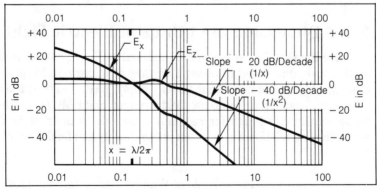

Figure 2.16—Relative Electric Fields from Vertical λ/4 Antennas over Perfectly Conducting Ground

varies with the length of the antenna and the distance from it relative to the wavelength.

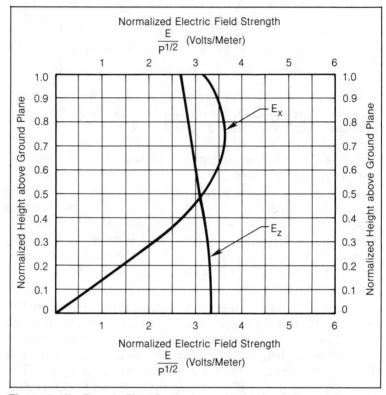

Figure 2.17—Electric Field Strength vs. Height above Ground Plane for a Quarter-Wave Monopole at $1/\beta$

2.5.3 Dimensions and Units of Electric Fields

Power density, P_D, as previously defined in Eq. (2.34), is used as the basic dimension of power flux flow at microwave frequencies, where far-field conditions usually apply. EMC and broadcast engineers, however, prefer to use field strength, and EMC specifications usually cite limits for radiated emissions in units of field strength. The relationship between power density and field strength is:

$$P_D = E^2/Z \quad \text{W/m} \tag{2.47}$$

where,

E = electric field strength in volts per meter (V/m)
Z = wave impedance which, for far-field conditions only,
$= Z_0 = 120\pi = 377 \; \Omega$

Expressing P_D in dB relative to one watt per square meter (dBW/m^2):

$$P_D = 20 \log E - 10 \log Z \qquad (2.48)$$

Expressed in dB relative to one milliwatt per square meter (dBm/m^2):

$$P_D = 20 \log E - 10 \log Z + 30 \; dB \qquad (2.49)$$

When E is expressed in units of dB relative to one microvolt per meter (dBμV/m), this becomes:

$$P_D = E - 90 \; dB - 10 \log Z \qquad (2.50)$$

For $Z = 377 \; \Omega$,

$$P_D = E - 116 \; dB \qquad (2.51)$$

or, expressing E in units of dB relative to 1 μV/m and in terms of P_D in units of dB relative to 1 mW/m^2, for $Z = 377 \; \Omega$:

$$E = P_D + 116 \; dB \qquad (2.52)$$

This last equation is tabulated for various units in Table A.2 of the Appendix.

In work involving hazardous levels of EMI, a commonly-used unit is milliwatts per square **centimeter**. Any expression for power density above in dB relative to a square **meter** can be translated relative to a square **centimeter** by subtracting 40 dB:

$$P_D \text{ in dBm/cm}^2 = P_D \text{ in dBm/m}^2 - 40 \; dB \qquad (2.53)$$

2.5.4 Dimensions and Units of Magnetic Fields

Power density, P_D, expressed in terms of magnetic field strength is:

$$P_D = H^2 Z \quad W/m^2 \tag{2.54}$$

where,

H = magnetic field strength in A/m
Z = Wave impedance, which for far-field conditions only
   = Z_0 = 120π = 377 Ω

Expressing P_D in terms of dB relative to 1 W/m^2.

$$P_D = 20 \log H + 10 \log Z \tag{2.55}$$

Equating this to the expression for P_D in terms of E (Eq. 2.48 above):

$$20 \log H + 10 \log Z = 20 \log E - 10 \log Z \tag{2.56}$$

or,

$$20 \log H = 20 \log E - 20 \log Z \tag{2.57}$$

This states that the magnetic field H, in units of dB relative to one ampere per meter, equals the electric field E, in dB relative to one volt per meter, minus the wave impedance in dB relative to one ohm. When far-field conditions apply, Z = Z_0 = 377 Ω. Thus, since log 377 = 2.58, the relationship in dB between H and E becomes:

$$H = E - 51.6 \text{ dB, for \textbf{far-field} conditions} \tag{2.58}$$

Stated in arithmetic terms, Eq. (2.55) becomes:

$$H = E/Z \tag{2.59}$$

or, for far-field conditions:

$$H = E/377 \tag{2.60}$$

Having stated this basic relationship, it is now necessary to define the units actually used by the EMC community for magnetic field EMI measurements. MIL-STD-461 and other EMI documents specify limits in terms of **flux density**, B, in tesla (T) rather than magnetic field strength, H, in A/m:

$$B = \mu H \quad \text{tesla} \tag{2.61}$$

where,

μ = absolute permeability of the medium in henries/m

Taking μ as the permeability of a vacuum, $4\pi \times 10^{-7}$ henries/m:

$$B = 4\pi \times 10^{-7} \quad H \tag{2.62}$$

Expressing B in dBT and H in dBA/m, this becomes:

$$B = H - 118 \text{ dB(henries per meter)} \tag{2.63}$$

If H is in dB relative to 1 μA/m:

$$B = H - 120 \text{ dB(A/}\mu\text{A)} - 118 \text{ dB (henries per meter)} \tag{2.64}$$

As a convenience, simply subtract 238 dB from H in dBμA/m:

$$B = H - 238 \text{ dB} \tag{2.65}$$

Since the tesla, or dBT is such a large unit, the basic unit used in EMI testing is the picotesla, which is 10^{-12} T. Accordingly, 240 dB must be added to dBT levels to express them as dBpT. Thus, Eq. (2.63), converting H in dBA/m and Eq.(2.65), converting H in dBμA/m to B in dBT become:

$$B = H + 122 \tag{2.66}$$

For B in dBpT and H in dBμA/m,

$$B = H + 2 \tag{2.67}$$

2.49

Combining Eqs. (2.59) and (2.60):

$$B = \mu E/Z \tag{2.68}$$

Combining Eqs. (2.58) and (2.66), for B in dBpT and E in dBV/m:

$$B = E + 70.4 \tag{2.69}$$

If E is in units of dBμV/m:

$$B = E + 190 \tag{2.70}$$

Finally, it is useful to identify a few other relationships involving magnetic field and flux terms which are no longer to be used but might be encountered in older specifications used for reprocurement:

$$1 \text{ Wb/m}^2 = 1 \text{ T} = 10^4 \text{ } gauss \tag{2.71}$$

$$1 \text{ } gamma = 10^{-9} \text{ tesla} \tag{2.72}$$

$$B \text{ in dBpT} = B \text{ in dB} gauss + 160 \text{ dB} \tag{2.73}$$

$$B \text{ in dBpT} = B \text{ in dB} gamma + 60 \text{ dB} \tag{2.74}$$

2.5.5 Antenna Factor for EMI Emissions Testing

Antenna factor is the term applied in radiated EMI emissions testing to convert a voltage level fed by a transducer to the input terminals of an EMI analyzer into the field-strength units of the electromagnetic field producing that voltage. Thus, as illustrated in Fig. 2.18, for an electric-field antenna, the antenna factor, AF, is:

$$AF = E/V_L \tag{2.75}$$

where,

E = unknown electric field being measured in V/m
V_L = voltage at antenna terminals delivered into a specified load, e.g., 50 Ω, in volts

2.50

From Eq. (2.75), it can be seen that units of antenna factor are 1/m. Expressed in units of dB(1/m), for E in dBμV/m and V in dBμV:

$$AF = E - V_L \qquad (2.76)$$

or,

$$E = V_L + AF \qquad (2.77)$$

Thus, to determine an unknown electric field in units of dBμV/m, simply add to V_L, which is the output voltage into the antenna cable in dBμV, the antenna factor AF in dB(1/m). Be sure to use as V_L the voltage referred to the antenna terminals after correcting for loss between the antenna terminals and the input to the EMI analyzer.

Although manufacturers of EMI test antennas sometimes omit the dimensions of 1/m and express antenna factor simply in units of dB, this omission should always be recognized and corrected.

Antenna factor can also be viewed as a figure of merit for the "sensitivity" of antennas. It is apparent from Eq. (2.75) that the larger the voltage, V, produced by an electric field, E, the smaller the antenna factor. Conversely, a large antenna factor indicates a small voltage output from a relatively insensitive antenna. Typical

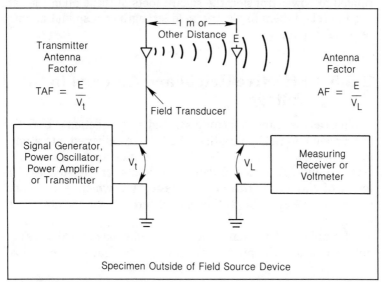

Figure 2.18—Antenna Factors for Emission and Susceptibility Testing

antenna factors, which range from 0 to 60 dB for some antennas, are listed in Table 4.1 (Chapter 4).

Although its concept and usage are deceptively simple, antenna factor actually comprises multiple constituent factors, or coefficients which imply how a specific antenna functions with its interfacing connections. Two coefficients always included are a **conversion factor** which relates values of field strength in which the antenna is immersed to values of open-circuit voltage resulting at the antenna output terminals, and a **load correction factor** which relates that open-circuit voltage to the voltage actually produced across the load circuit connected at those output terminals. Additional coefficients are included in the antenna factor to account for impedance mismatches, impedance transformations and any losses effective up to the point of interface at which the antenna factor is defined.

At the heart of the antenna factor is the conversion factor because it encompasses the **effective height**, length or area of the antenna, including antenna gain and pattern characteristics. The antenna factor is usually given for the maximum of the antenna gain pattern, since that is how the antenna is typically used in EMI testing. For dipole and monopole antennas, the conversion factor is the reciprocal of the effective height or length; for loop antennas it is proportional to the reciprocal of the square root of the effective area. For complex antennas, since the gain and effective area are always related to power transfer, the square roots of these quantities are used to relate them to electric field strength or resultant antenna terminal voltage.

2.5.5.1 Effective Height and Antenna Induced Voltage

Whereas the antenna factor discussed in this section is based on conversion into field strength of the voltage delivered into a finite load impedance, some earlier EMI specifications such as MIL-I-6181D and MIL-I-26600 delineated limits for radiated EMI in terms of **antenna-induced voltage, V_0,** which is the open-circuit voltage available at the antenna terminals in the absence of any load.

A formulation for antenna factor of an antenna defined at its output terminals is the product of its conversion factor and its load correction factor which, for dipole and monopole antennas, is:

$$AF = (1/h_e) (V_0/V_L) \qquad (2.78)$$

where,

h_e = antenna effective height in meters

V_0 = antenna-induced voltage (the unloaded antenna terminal voltage)

V_L = antenna voltage deliverable into a specific load, e.g., the 50 Ω input to the EMI analyzer

Expressing AF in dB(1/m) and h_e in dB(meter):

$$AF = 20 \log (V_0/V_L) - h_e \qquad (2.79)$$

The term **effective height** means the electrical height (or length) of the antenna in coupling to an electric field and does **not** mean the height of the antenna above the earth.

The effective height of a rod or whip antenna with a ground plane is equal to one-half of its mechanical or physical height because the induced voltage increment is zero at the base and increases linearly to the incremented voltage per unit length, ΔV, at the top. When integrated over the mechanical height of a rod the voltage induced by the electric field is only $V/2 \times h = V \times h/2$, rather than $V \times h$. Thus, a 1 m (41-inch) rod has an effective height, h_e = 0.5 m.

Equating the above equation for AF in linear units to the expression for AF in Eq. (2.75) yields:

$$V_0/h_e V_L = E/V_L$$

or,

$$V_0 = E \times h_e \qquad (2.80)$$

Thus, antenna induced voltage, V_0, is obtained by multiplying field strength, E, by the effective height of the antenna, h_e. Or, expressing V in units of dBμV, E in dBμV/m and h in dB(meter):

$$V_0 = E + h_e \tag{2.81}$$

The above discussion may be generalized for dipole antennas which are no longer than one-half wavelength. For such antennas the effective height (length) is given by equation (a) from Ref. 12:

$$h_e = (2/\beta)\tan (\beta l/2) \tag{2.82}$$

where,

β = the wave number = $2\pi/\lambda$ = ω/c
l = the half-length of the antenna

For a half-wavelength resonant dipole, the longest for which Eq. (2.82) holds, $\beta l/2$ = $\pi/4$ and h_e = $2/\beta$ = λ/π.

It is important to note that the field must be uniform (plane wave) over the length of the antenna for any of the above relationships to be correct, since their derivations are based on this assumption!

2.5.5.2 Far-Field Antenna Factor vs. Antenna Gain

For many large, highly efficient antennas, performance can be predicted only under far-field conditions. Building on Eq. (2.80), a general expression for antenna factor can be developed which applies in the far field both for half-wavelength dipoles and other, more complex antennas. From Eq. (2.80):

$$h_e = V_0/E \tag{2.83}$$

However, from Eq. (2.47):

$$E = \sqrt{P_D Z_0} \tag{2.84}$$

Since:

$$P_0 = P_D A_e = [(V_0/R_a + R_L)^2 R_L) \tag{2.85}$$

where,

A_e = the effective area of the antenna, or the ratio P_0/P_D
P_0 = the power available out of the antenna into the load
R_L = the load impedance connected to the antenna

and,

R_a
= the radiation resistance of the antenna, or the real part of the antenna input impedance

and since,

$$A_e \text{ also } = g\lambda^2/4\pi \text{ (see Ref. 12)}$$

where,

g = the antenna gain at its pattern maximum relative to isotropic

Therefore, Eq. (2.83) can be rewritten as:

$$h_e = \cfrac{V_0}{\sqrt{\left(\dfrac{V_0}{R_a + R_L}\right)^2 R_L \left(\dfrac{4\pi}{\lambda^2 g}\right) 120\,\pi}}$$

(2.86)

Equation (2.86) can be rearranged and simplified into:

$$h_e = \frac{1}{\beta} \sqrt{\left(\frac{R_a + R_L}{R_L}\right)^2 \left(\frac{g}{120}\right)}$$

(2.87)

When $R_L = R_a$,

$$h_e = \frac{1}{\beta} \sqrt{\frac{4R_a g}{120}} = \frac{2}{\beta} \sqrt{\frac{gR_a}{120}} \qquad (2.88)$$

For an infinitely thin $\lambda/2$ dipole antenna, $R_a = 73.2\ \Omega$ and $g = 1.64$ so that:

$$h_e = 2/\beta$$

This is the same result found earlier using Eq. (2.82).

Now a generalized equation for antenna factor may be written. Recalling the earlier Eq. (2.78), $AF = (1/h_e)(V_0/V_L)$, and taking into account that $R_a = R_L$, making $V_0/V_L = 2$:

$$AF = 2/h_e \qquad (2.89)$$

Using h_e from Eq. (2.88):

$$AF = \beta \sqrt{\frac{120}{g\ R_a}} \qquad (2.90)$$

If $R_a \neq R_L$, Eq. (2.90) must be adjusted by including a factor to account for either the mismatch or the impedance transformation. If there is a mismatch, the factor would be $1 + R_a/R_L$, but if the impedances are matched through a balun or other transformer, the factor will be:

$$N = \sqrt{R_a/R_L} \qquad (2.91)$$

An expanded factor which accounts for both situations is:

$$(R_a + N^2 R_L)/(2NR_L) \qquad (2.92)$$

and Eq. (2.90) becomes:

$$AF = \beta \sqrt{\frac{120}{gR_a}} \left(\frac{R_a + N^2 R_L}{2NR_L} \right) \qquad (2.93)$$

If there is a mismatch ($R_a \neq R_L$) and there is no impedance transformation, $N = 1$. The expanded factor then degenerates to $1 + (R_a/R_L)$. If $R_a \neq R_L$ but they are matched through an impedance transformation wherein:

$$N = \sqrt{R_a/R_L}$$

the expanded factor degenerates to N. If there is no mismatch ($R_a = R_L$) and no impedance transformation, the expanded factor becomes unity. If there are other losses in the antenna, such as ohmic loss in a transformer an efficiency η factor must be included, changing Eq. (2.93) to:

$$AF = \beta \sqrt{\frac{120}{gR_a}} \left(\frac{R_a + N^2 R_L}{2NR_L} \right) \eta \qquad (2.94)$$

where,
   η = the ohmic loss in the antenna stated as a ratio to an ideal lossless antenna, i.e., = $\eta = \sqrt{P_{out}/P_{in}}$

This is now a complete general equation for antenna factor in the direction of antenna pattern maximum.

If the antenna is a lossless 50 Ω antenna used in a 50 Ω system, Eq. (2.94) becomes:

$$AF = \frac{9.73}{\lambda\sqrt{g}} \qquad (2.95)$$

which is the relationship given by SAE ARP 958.

Equation (2.95) is plotted in Fig. 2.19 for various levels of antenna gain, with AF in dB as a function of frequency. Note the prohibited region of the plot, where the indicated antenna gains are not realizable at the 1 m spacing.

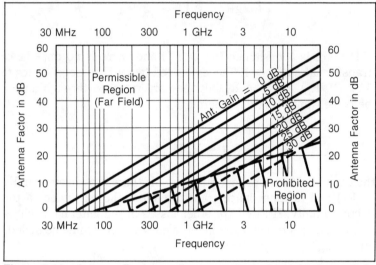

Figure 2.19—Antenna Factor vs. Frequency for Indicated Antenna Gain

An experimental technique for determining antenna factor at a distance of one meter from the test sample is given in SAE report ARP958. It is valid only at frequencies above about 50 MHz, since it also is based on free-space conditions which are difficult to achieve at lower frequencies.

2.6 Conducted EMI Susceptibility Testing

The basic task of testing **susceptibility to conducted EMI**, as it was defined in Chapter 1, becomes that of injecting specified levels of such EMI onto the wires or cables connected to a receptor and of then noting any deterioration in performance of the receptor in response to such EMI injection (see Fig. 2.2). Chapter 12 covers these procedures in detail.

2.6.1 Coupling Devices for Testing EMI Susceptibility

2.6.1.1 Injection Transformer

The use of a transformer for injecting EMI onto power leads is recommended by MIL-STD-462 and covered in detail in Chapter 12. The basic technique is to couple to each power lead (by means of the transformer secondary inserted in series with it) the specified signal level over the entire appropriate frequency range, noting any deterioration in performance of the EUT.

2.6.1.2 Injection Current Probe

The current probe used for this susceptibility test is quite similar to that described above in conjunction with testing emissions of conducted EMI current (Section 2.4.2.1). For military EMI susceptibility testing, MIL-STD-462 specifies levels and pulses of current to be injected onto all interconnecting cables of the EUT, including its power leads.

2.7 Radiated EMI Susceptibility Testing

The basic task of testing **susceptibility to radiated EMI**, as it was defined in Chapter 1, becomes that of immersing the receptor in specified levels of electromagnetic fields and of then noting any deterioration in performance of the receptor in response to such immersion.

2.7.1 Field-Producing Devices

Many of the same antennas used to intercept and measure radiated EMI emissions can be used to radiate specified levels of fields for testing susceptibility, provided they are designed to handle the required levels of power. Specific antennas appropriate to various frequency ranges as transducers for susceptibility testing are discussed in Chapter 5.

2.7.1.1 Antenna Factor for Susceptibility Testing

All discussions of antenna factor thus far in this section have dealt with antenna factors of receiving antennas; our concern has been the efficiency with which the antenna being characterized could convert the field in which it is immersed into voltage for measurement by an EMI analyzer. An analogous term, the **transmitter antenna factor (TAF)**, will now be defined. The TAF rates how effectively an antenna develops levels of field strength at specified distances. The higher the TAF, the lower the input power required into the antenna or test chamber to produce a specified level of field strength.

Referring to Fig. 2.18, the TAF is defined as follows:

$$TAF = E/V_t \qquad (2.96)$$

In this equation, units of TAF are V/m per V, or 1/m, the same as the AF for receiving antennas. Expressed in dB(1/m):

$$TAF = 20 \log (E/V_t) \qquad (2.97)$$

where,

E = field strength in V/m at the EUT distance from the developing transducer (typically 1 m)

V_t = voltage at the antenna or test chamber input terminals in volts (being fed from source of RF power)

From Fig. 2.18 it is apparent that the TAF for a transmitting antenna can readily be determined, provided that the AF of the receiving antenna is known for the measuring distance in question. Note that the AF of the receiving antenna must be valid for its distance from the transmitting source; for example, at a test frequency of 10 MHz, this would be true at 1 m spacing for a 1 m (41-inch) rod antenna, but not for a dipole-fed, parabolic reflector antenna which would not have its pattern established at such a short distance from the source. Equating E in the formula for TAF, Eq. (2.96), with E in the formula for AF, Eq. (2.75), there results:

$$TAF = AF \times (V_L/V_t) \qquad (2.98)$$

With both TAF and AF in dB(1/m):

$$TAF = AF + 20 \log (V_L/V_t) \qquad (2.99)$$

Thus, the transmitter antenna input voltage, V_t, is measured and compared to the resulting voltage, V_L, fed by the receiving antenna into the cable connecting it to the EMI analyzer. The dB ratio of V_L/V_t is then calculated and added to the receiving antenna factor, AF, in dB(1/m), to produce the TAF of the respective transmitting antenna. Note that both V_L and V_t are voltages at the terminals of the respective antennas.

It is possible to develop a general equation for the TAF of an antenna in terms of the AF of that same antenna, based on the following equation from Friis:[13]

$$E = \frac{\sqrt{30 \, P_t \, g_t}}{d} \qquad (2.100)$$

where,

E = the electric field strength produced by the antenna in V/m
g_t = the gain of the antenna relative to isotropic
P_t = the power actually transmitted
d = the distance from the antenna at which the E-Field is produced

Assuming that the antenna is lossless, the power actually transmitted, $P_t = V_t^2/R_a$, where V_t is the voltage fed to the antenna terminal and R_a is the radiation resistance of the antenna, both as defined in Section 2.5.5.2. Substituting this for P_t in Eq. (2.100) and substituting the resulting expression for E into Eq. (2.96):

$$TAF = \frac{1}{d} \sqrt{\frac{30 \, g_t}{R_a}} \qquad (2.101)$$

Using the relationship between g_t and AF for receiving as given by Eq. (2.90) in Section 2.5.5.2 and solving for g_t:

$$g_t = \frac{120 \, \beta^2}{R_a \, (AF)^2} \qquad (2.102)$$

Substituting Eq. (2.102) into Eq. (2.101) results in:

$$TAF = \frac{60\ \beta}{R_a(AF)d} \qquad (2.103)$$

If the antenna is not lossless, an efficiency factor, η, as defined in Section 2.5.5.2, must be inserted, making the generalized expression for TAF in terms of AF for the same antenna:

$$TAF = \frac{60\ \beta\eta}{R_a(AF)d} \qquad (2.104)$$

2.7.1.2 TAF as Figure of Merit for Field-Producing Transducers

The TAF is a convenient figure of merit for indicating the relative efficiency of various types of antennas in producing electromagnetic fields. TAF values in the order of 0 dB indicate highly efficient antennas. They imply relatively low RF power requirements (e.g., about 2 W) to produce field strengths of 10 V/m. Antennas with TAF values in the order of −10 dB should be avoided since they require power output levels in the order of 20 W to produce that same field strength: 10 V/m. TAF for passive rod antennas range in the order of −5 to −25 dB and should be avoided.

2.8 References

1. ANSI C63.12-1984, "Recommended Practice on Procedures for Control of System Electromagnetic Compatibility."
2. *IEEE Standard Dictionary of Electrical and Electronics Terms*, ANSI/IEEE Std 100-1984.
3. Andrews, J.R. and Arthur, M.G., "Spectrum Amplitude—Definition, Generation and Measurement," NBS Technical Note 699, National Bureau of Standards, October 1977.
4. *Howard W. Sam's Reference Data for Engineers, Radio, Electronics, Computer and Communications*, 7th Edition, Edward C. Jordan, editor in chief (Indianapolis: Howard W. Sams, Inc., 1985).

5. CISPR Publication 14, "Limits and Methods of Measurement of Radio Interference Characteristics of Household Electrical Appliances, Portable Tools, and Similar Apparatus."

6. CISPR Publication 16, "Specification for Radio Interference Measuring Apparatus and Measurement Methods," second edition, 1987.

7. FCC MP-4, "FCC Methods of Measurement of Radio Noise Emissions from Computing Devices."

8. Bronaugh, E.L. and Kerns, D.R., "Electromagnetic Emissions Measurement Techniques and Problems," *Electro 77 Symposium Record*, Session 9 (New York, April 1977).

9. Brown, G.H., "Directional Antennas," *Proceedings of the IRE*, Vol. 25, January 1937, p. 78.

10. Carter, P.S., "Circuit Relations in Radiating Systems," *Proceedings of the IRE*, Vol. 20, June 1932, p. 1004.

11. King, R.W.P., *The Theory of Linear Antennas*, (Cambridge, MA: Harvard University Press, 1956).

12. F.M. Greene, "NBS Field-Strength Standards and Measurements (30 Hz to 1000 MHz)," *Proceedings of the IEEE*, Vol. 55, No. 6, pp. 970-981, June 1967.

13. Friis, H.T., "A Note on a Simple Transmission Formula," *Proceedings of the IRE*, Vol. 34, pp. 254-256, May 1946.

Chapter 3

Instrumentation for EMI Emission Testing

Understanding of and respect for the capabilities and limitations of EMI instrumentation are essential to obtaining accurate EMI measurements. As analyzed in Chapter 8, improper use of instrumentation is a major source of errors in EMI testing.

This chapter covers the basic instrumentation used for testing EMI emissions; transducers for emission testing are covered in the next chapter, while both transducers and instrumentation for susceptibility testing are the subjects of Chapter 5. Automated systems for both emission and susceptibility testing are discussed in Chapter 6, while test sites and enclosures for all types of EMI testing are covered in Chapter 7.

3.1 Basic EMI Analyzer

As shown in Fig. 2.1 of the preceding chapter, the basic role of the EMI analyzer is to accept some unknown EMI voltage and then to produce from it a meter reading or other indication which permits the user to determine its level and other characteristics.

3.1.1 Instrument Characteristics

The basic EMI analyzer is a tunable, selective RF voltmeter with a number of features appropriate to its unique role in measuring and characterizing EMI, including:

1. Continuous tuning of some relatively wide segment of the electromagnetic spectrum, beginning at frequencies as low as a fraction of a hertz and extending to as high as 100 GHz
2. Front-end, or RF, sensitivity and overall gain which allow it to provide accurate readings of the lowest levels of EMI it must measure, as determined by pertinent specification limits and transducer conversion factors
3. Wide dynamic range, achieved in part by front-end selectivity and appropriately distributed, built-in attenuation, which allows it to measure high levels of EMI without saturating or producing spurious responses from overload
4. Carefully tailored bandpass characteristic which permits accurate measurement and characterization of impulsive EMI
5. Multiple detector functions which provide EMI demodulation as specified by diverse regulatory requirements
6. Post-detector video and audio circuits which accurately convey detected waveforms for monitoring and analysis
7. Built-in signal source for accurate amplitude calibration to read both narrowband and broadband EMI
8. RF-shielded housing to mitigate susceptibility to radiated EMI, which otherwise could result in spurious readings

Although there has been relatively little standardization in EMI instrumentation in the past, it will be seen in Section 3.3.3 that a growing trend toward standardization of bandwidths is being encouraged via the evolving requirements of some regulatory bodies.

3.1.2 Applications for EMI Analyzers

Instrumentation with characteristics defined above is suited for measuring EMI emissions in various applications. Such applications include:

1. **Specification testing,** which is performed to determine whether a test sample complies with specified limits for levels of conducted or radiated emissions

2. **Electromagnetic ambient surveys,** which search and record electromagnetic emissions at one or more sites to:
   a. determine radiation profiles for emission control, such as at test ranges
   b. determine radiation profiles at intended installation sites, to ascertain ambient levels that must be tolerated
   c. assist in selecting an electromagnetically quiet site from among several candidate pieces of real estate
   d. assist in identifying relatively quiet segments of the frequency spectrum for co-locating proposed new equipment or for reassigning frequencies of existing equipment
3. **Spectrum signatures,** which require measuring transmissions at their fundamentals, harmonics, emission sidebands and other spurious radiations. This type of data is needed for procurement compliance to specifications and for EMI prediction and analysis.
4. **Identification of culprit emitters** to localize sources of EMI, such as would develop from items 1 and 2 above, with the object of determining the source and nature of emissions. Examples of culprits include interfering or illegal radiators; RF-leaky cabinet joints; "hot" cables or wires; noisy power line insulators; and interfering industrial, scientific or medical equipment.
5. **Peripheral applications**, which include propagation studies, discrete antenna pattern measurements, spectrum attenuation tests on filters and shielding enclosures, circuit crosstalk measurements and establishing EMC performance of shields and grounds.

3.1.3 Functional Description of the EMI Analyzer

The typical modern EMI analyzer is basically a superheterodyne receiver with one to three stages of frequency conversion. Figure 3.1 is a functional block diagram of a typical instrument. Signal flow in the figure is from the input at the upper left (no. 1) through the receiver operations in the center to the processing circuits at the lower right. Among sensors typically available for connection to its input are current probes and line impedance stabilization networks (for conducted measurements) and antennas (for picking up radiated emissions). These sensors were introduced in Chapter 2 and are discussed further in the next two chapters. Also selectable as a source of input signal is an internal generator (no. 2) which can be selected to provide a known level of continuous wave (CW) or broadband signal for amplitude calibration.

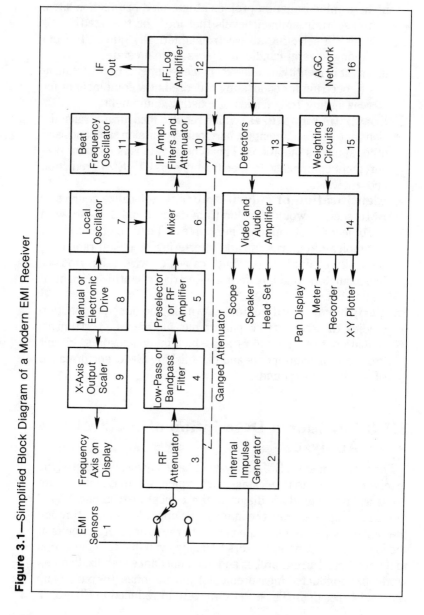

Figure 3.1—Simplified Block Diagram of a Modern EMI Receiver

The selected input signal is passed through an RF attenuator (no. 3) with at least three or four decades of attenuation which is broadband and accurate over the entire frequency range of the EMI analyzer. In some older EMI analyzer models which are still in use, the first decade of attenuation is inserted at the intermediate frequency (IF) amplifier, thus reducing the level of noise indication. However, this practice is avoided in more recent designs because insertion of attenuation reduces the useful dynamic range of any preceding stages of amplification or mixing.

Either before insertion of RF attenuation or after it, as shown, the signal is subjected to a low-pass or bandpass filter (no. 4), to eliminate out-of-band signals which might induce spurious responses within the instrument. Next, as discussed further in Section 3.2, nearly all EMI analyzers have either preselectors or tunable RF amplifiers (no. 5) to mitigate signals outside the band of immediate interest and thus further reduce vulnerability to intermodulation and spurious responses.

The output from the preselector or RF amplifier drives the first stage of frequency conversion, consisting of a mixer (no. 6) and local oscillator (LO, no. 7). With the exception of low-frequency receivers and EMI analyzers, which usually up-convert, this first conversion stage is generally one of down-conversion. In older instruments, the local oscillator is tuned manually by a variable capacitor, while more modern instruments use either analog voltage-tuned or digitally synthesized LO designs. The tuning voltage can be developed either by a front-panel potentiometer or generated internally or externally as a voltage ramp (no. 8) which can be scaled (no. 9) and then used simultaneously to drive the X-axis of a plotter or oscilloscope. This facilitates a display of signal amplitude versus frequency. Although the synthesized designs facilitate high degrees of accuracy in the tuned frequency of the EMI analyzer, this feature is typically not of great importance in EMI testing. However, a distinct advantage of the synthesized design is that it permits direct control of frequency via digital instructions from a controlling computer.

The mixed output from the converter drives an IF amplifier and attenuator (no. 10), including passband filters (usually of Gaussian, Bessel or similar design) to avoid overshoot and facilitate calibration from impulse generators (IGs). Data on the actual bandpass characteristics of an instrument is important since it directly affects its response to impulsive noise. IF stages must also be designed to handle the greatest possible signal amplitude to preserve the maximum possible dynamic range.

A beat-frequency oscillator (BFO, no. 11) generally is provided to facilitate identification of noise-embedded CW signals. An audible tone is produced at the audio output jack as a result of the BFO beating with the IF signal.

Most modern EMI analyzers incorporate some sort of circuitry whose purpose is to compress the amplitude of excursions at their outputs without compromising overall dynamic range. Methods of implementing this feature in existing EMI analyzer designs include application to IF stages of an automatic gain control (AGC) voltage (no. 16) or imposition of a logarithmic characteristic onto IF stages (no. 12) by means of voltages developed by successively detecting their outputs. Alternatively, the logging can be imposed onto the video signal (no. 14) after linear IF amplification, detection (no. 13) and application of appropriate weighting (no. 15) such as for quasipeak detection. Although each of these methods has limitations and is difficult to implement without compromising the response to impulsive signals, most modern instruments avoid the use of AGC because of errors which can be introduced by AGC sensitivity to duty factor and the pulse width of the signal being processed. Design constraints also arise because quasipeak detection as specified for FCC, VDE and other testing in accordance with ANSI standards or CISPR publications requires linear IF signals. Section 3.6 discusses such detector requirements in more detail.

The IF is applied to any one of a number of selectable detector functions (no. 13). Either or both of the AM or FM detector outputs is applied to drive video and audio amplifiers (no. 14) whose outputs may then be presented on a high-impedance oscilloscope or a low-impedance speaker or headset. After processing by selected detectors and their respective weighting circuits, the signal is also applied to circuits whose outputs are used to drive the front-panel meter or various external indicators or processors.

The typical modern EMI analyzer includes a number of output connectors which expand its versatility:

1. Oscilloscope outputs for both amplitude and frequency analogs permit display of signals in either the time or frequency domain.
2. Outputs for connection to both axes of X-Y plotters permit plotting of permanent records of amplitude versus frequency.

3. An IF output allows connection of the signal to a panoramic display or high-frequency oscilloscope for analysis, or to an additional receiver tuned to the IF, for additional selectivity.
4. Various connectors provide control and monitoring from a remote location. The most recent modern EMI analyzers incorporate capability for full computer-controlled operation via the IEEE-488 general purpose interface bus (GPIB) as discussed in Chapter 6.

3.2 The Role of RF Preselection

An important point made in the foregoing discussion of the EMI analyzers and in the discussion of spectrum analyzers (see Section 3.7) is that EMI analyzers generally have front-end preselection while spectrum analyzers do not. The presence or absence of such preselection is important because it is the chief determinant of two vital aspects of instrument performance: broadband dynamic range and vulnerability to producing spurious readings in response to out-of-band signals.

Reference to functional block diagrams for the EMI analyzer and the spectrum analyzer (Figs. 3.1 and 3.17, respectively) shows that both have a stage of mixing, or conversion, functionally close to their input connectors. Inherent in any heterodyning process is the generation of many harmonics of the LO; thus, any signal reaching the signal input port of the mixer that is removed from any harmonic of the LO frequency by the IF difference can result in a mixer output which subsequent circuits will treat as if it were a legitimate signal. Any degree of preselection or filtering ahead of the mixer reduces the number of signals capable of producing spurious responses out of the mixer and thus reduces vulnerability of the receiver to spurious responses from out-of-band signals.

The significance of front-end preselection in enhancing the ability of a receiver to handle wide dynamic ranges of coherent broadband signals, as discussed in Section 2.3.4.8 of Chapter 2, is perhaps best illustrated by a simplistic example comparing two hypothetical amplitude-calibrated receivers, only one of which has front-end preselection. As noted above, the receiver with preselection is representative of most EMI analyzers, while the one without preselection is more representative of most spectrum analyzers. Hypothetical specifications are:

Specification	Receiver No. 1	Receiver No. 2
RF tuning range:	100-1,100 MHz	100-1,100 MHz
Impulse BW into first mixer		
@ RF = 150 MHz:	10 MHz	1,000 MHz
Impulse BW into detector		
@ RF = 150 MHz:	1.0 MHz	1.0 MHz

For purposes of this example, the two receivers are identical in design except as specified above.

Consider the results if both receivers are tuned to a center frequency of 150 MHz and both have connected to their inputs identical broadband impulsive signals at a level of 80 dBμV/MHz. For purposes of this example, it will be assumed that the coherent broadband signal is equivalent to that from an impulse generator, the output spectrum amplitude of which is uniform over the entire 100 to 1,100 MHz tuning range of the receivers. Both calibrated receivers should register readings of +80 dBμV since both are specified as having impulse bandwidths of 1 MHz. However, assuming that no front-end attenuation has been inserted and that the signal paths from the input connector to the mixer input in both receivers are lossless, the mixer in receiver no. 1 is subjected to the +80 dBμV/MHz spectrum amplitude as seen through a window of 1,000 MHz, which is a voltage of:

$$80 \text{ dB}\mu\text{V/MHz} + 20 \log (1{,}000 \text{ MHz}/1 \text{ MHz}) = 140 \text{ dB}\mu\text{V} = 10 \text{ V}$$

By contrast, the corresponding level into the mixer of receiver no. 2 is only:

$$80 \text{ dB}\mu\text{V/MHz} + 20 \log (10 \text{ MHz}/1 \text{ MHz}) = 100 \text{ dB}\mu\text{V} = 0.1 \text{ V}$$

It is apparent that Receiver no. 1 would probably respond nonlinearly to such high levels and that its input levels and dynamic range of operation for such signals would have to be severely restricted to maintain linear operation.

This example, although simplistic, illustrates the importance of incorporating RF preselection to restrict unwanted broadband signal energy from reaching the first mixer of a superheterodyne receiver. Together with the concomitant effect of also reducing or eliminating access to the mixer of strong out-of-band CW signals, these advantages make RF preselection an essential element of any receiver or spectrum analyzer to be used for EMI measurements.

3.3 Bandwidths for EMI Signals

Since essentially all EMI analyzers are of the superheterodyne type, they employ amplification at the IF stage. Thus, the selectivity characteristic into the detector is usually determined almost entirely in the IF amplifier. Where double- or triple-conversion schemes are utilized, it is usually the final IF which determines the selectivity window. The resulting signal into the detector, V_{if}, is therefore the convolution, or product, of the RF signal, as applied to the input terminals, and the transfer function of all predetection circuitry:

$$V_{if} = \int_0^\infty S(f)G(f) \, df \qquad (3.1)$$

where,

$S(f)$ = frequency-domain characterization (Fourier or Laplace transform) of the RF signal

$G(f)$ = frequency-domain characterization of the EMI analyzer gain from its RF input to its detector input

Although the mathematical execution of Eq. (3.1) will not be further pursued here, it should be noted that appropriately tuned and coupled IF stages are used to obtain the Gaussian, Bessel or similar response mentioned in Section 3.1 as required to avoid overshoot and keep responses to pulsed signals separated in the time domain. This also simplifies amplitude measurements using different detector types, as discussed in Section 3.6.

3.3.1 Bandwidth Comparisons

Figure 3.2, taken from the NAVSHIPS publication, "The Radio Frequency Interference Meter," shows the relationship among the bandwidth definitions most commonly used in EMI testing.[1] B_n is the random noise bandwidth, and B_i is the impulse bandwidth which is discussed in detail in Section 3.5.

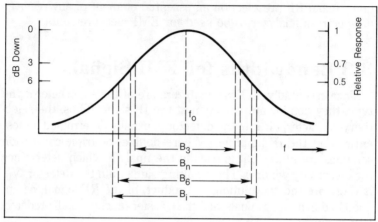

Figure 3.2—Bandwidth Comparisons in a Typical Bandpass Amplifier

3.3.2 Random Noise Bandwidth

Random noise is noise such as that resulting from the thermal heating of natural sources and falls into the category of noncoherent broadband signals discussed in Section 2.3.4.8. Thus, since its spectrum is essentially flat over any range of practical interest in EMI testing, the random noise power reaching the detector of an EMI analyzer is directly proportional to its predetector random noise bandwidth, B_n.

For an EMI analyzer with predetection voltage gain G(f), as shown in Fig. 3.3, the random noise bandwidth, B_n, is the width, in hertz, of a rectangle which has an area equal to that of the predetector amplitude-squared-versus-frequency response curve and a height equal to the maximum value of that curve. Note that B_n is not the same quantity as the 3 dB bandwidth, B_3, unless the shape of the response curve is such that the rectangle and curve intersect at an ordinate of 0.5; generally, B_n will be found to lie between 1.0 and 1.15 × B_3, as shown in Fig. 3.4, which gives the factor needed to convert B_3 to B_n for various shape factors of the response curve.

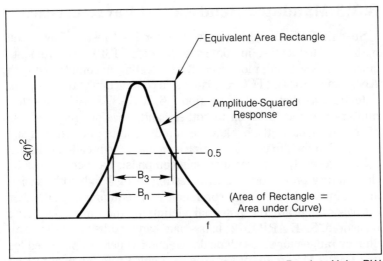

Figure 3.3—Rectangular Area Method for Determining Random Noise BW

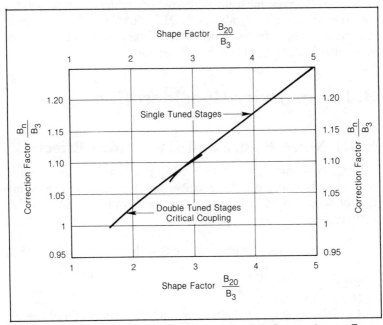

Figure 3.4—Three Decibel to Random Noise BW Conversion as Function of Shape Factor

3.3.3 Mandated Bandwidth Characteristics

Specific EMI analyzer bandwidths for EMI testing have been mandated for testing in conformance with CISPR requirements since the 1930s and, more recently, for testing in compliance with ANSI standards and FCC regulations, in conjunction with quasipeak detection, as discussed in Section 3.6. MIL-STD-461 and other military specifications, on the other hand, have not required use of specific bandwidths but have required accurate calibration of any impulse bandwidth used for testing compliance to broadband limits.

More recently, however, increasing emphasis has been placed by the military on performing EMI testing using bandwidths which approximate those of the communication equipment and other devices which are the potential victims of the emissions being measured. SAE ARP-1972[2] lists single bandwidths for various frequency ranges for use with peak detection which are proposed for use by the U.S. military services as a substitute for dual testing which requires distinction between narrowband and broadband interference. These same bandwidths and procedures are incorporated into the British military standard, DEF-STAN 59-41.[3] This trend toward use of specific bandwidths for military testing of EMI emissions has increasing strength and support.

3.4 Sensitivity Considerations

3.4.1 Noise Figure and Bandwidth Effects

Receiver sensitivity, S, is defined in terms of its internal noise power, N, as referred to the receiver input terminals. The definition of sensitivity which is most widely accepted in EMI testing activity is:

$$(S + N)/N = 2, \text{ or } S = N \qquad (3.2)$$

where,

$N = \underline{F}\,kTB$ watts

$\underline{F}$ = Noise factor of the receiver, which is the ratio of the actual noise power referred to its input terminal divided by the theoretical minimum noise power, kTB

k = Boltzmann's constant = 1.38×10^{-23} J/K (units also W/Hz/K since J = W/Hz)

3.12

T = thermal temperature of receiver front end in K
B_n = receiver random noise bandwidth in Hz

For a receiver front end at typical room temperature ($T \approx 70°F \approx 21°C = 293K$), Eq. (3.2) becomes:

$$N \approx 4 \times 10^{-21} \underline{F} B_n \text{ watts}$$

$$= 4 \times 10^{-18} \underline{F} B_n \text{ milliwatts} \qquad (3.4)$$

With N expressed in dBm, Eq. (3.4) becomes:

$$N = -174 \text{ dBm} + 10 \log (\underline{F} B_n) \qquad (3.5)$$

$$= -174 \text{ dBm} + F + 10 \log B_n,$$
$$\text{for } B_n \text{ in Hz} \qquad (3.6)$$

$$= -114 \text{ dBm} + F + 10 \log B_n,$$
$$\text{for } B_n \text{ in MHz} \qquad (3.7)$$

Note that $\underline{F}$ (as underlined) is being used to express the numerical ratio (noise factor), while F (not underlined) is used for **noise figure**, the equivalent ratio in dB, i.e., $F = 10 \log \underline{F}$.

As shown in Section 2.4.1, for a 50 Ω system the voltage in dBμV corresponding to a power level in dBm is obtained by adding 107 dB. Thus, noise in an idealized 50 Ω system with no excess noise is -174 dBm + 107 dB = -67 dBμV for each hertz of bandwidth. The general equation for sensitivity, V_n, in dBμV becomes:

$$V_n = F - 67 + 10 \log B_n, \quad \text{for } B_n \text{ in Hz} \qquad (3.8)$$

$$V_n = F - 7 + 10 \log B_n, \quad \text{for } B_n \text{ in MHz} \qquad (3.9)$$

Equations (3.6) and (3.8) are useful for quickly determining the receiver noise power in units of dBm for any specified receiver noise figure and bandwidth. They are plotted in Fig. 3.5. The right ordinate is receiver sensitivity in dBm, the X-axis is receiver 3 dB bandwidth, and the parameter is noise figure in dB. The left ordinate is in units of dBμV and corresponds to the right ordinate in dBm for a 50 Ω system.

The preceding definition of sensitivity is in terms of receiver thermal noise which is noncoherent (phase components of adjacent frequency increments are random) and holds for either narrowband signals or broadband noncoherent noise, as shown in Section 2.3.4.8. However, as shown in this same section, when the signal is developed from an impulse-like source and is broadband coherent, the spectrum becomes voltage responsive rather than power responsive, leading to a second definition of sensitivity. For coherent broadband signals **only**, the sensitivity in dBμV/MHz is:

$$V_i = F - 7 - 10 \log B_i \qquad (3.10)$$

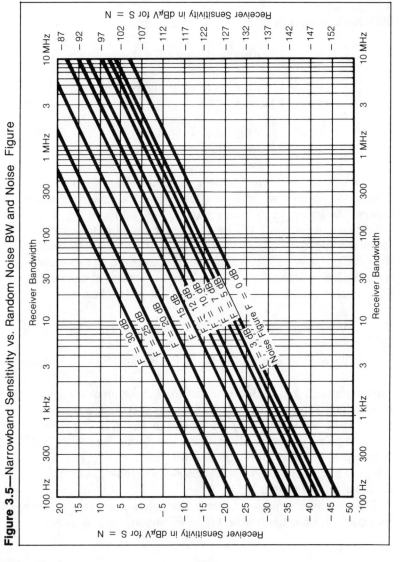

Figure 3.5—Narrowband Sensitivity vs. Random Noise BW and Noise Figure

where,

$$B_i = \text{impulse bandwidth in MHz}$$

Note that because the bandwidth factor in dB is **subtracted**, the equation illustrates that sensitivity to broadband coherent noise **improves** as bandwidth is increased, at the rate of 10 dB/decade. This is apparent in Fig. 3.6, where receiver sensitivity is plotted against bandwidth with noise figure as a parameter.

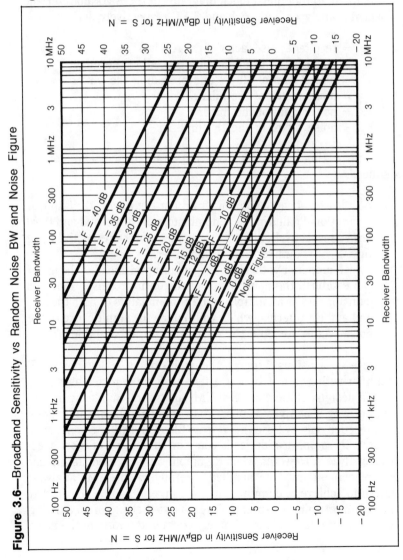

Figure 3.6—Broadband Sensitivity vs Random Noise BW and Noise Figure

3.15

3.4.2 Front-End Design and Sensitivity

A generalized formula for the resultant noise factor (a ratio) of three networks in series is:

$$\underline{F} = \underline{F}_1 + \frac{\underline{F}_2 - 1}{G_1} + \frac{\underline{F}_3 - 1}{G_1 G_2} \qquad (3.11)$$

Referring to functional block diagrams of the EMI analyzer and spectrum analyzer, Figs. 3.1 and 3.17, respectively, let:

$\underline{F}$ = resultant noise factor of the receiver
$\underline{F}_1$ = noise factor of all circuits preceding the mixer
G_1 = power gain of all circuits preceding the mixer
$\underline{F}_2$ = noise factor of the mixer
G_2 = power gain of the mixer
$\underline{F}_3$ = noise factor of the IF amplifier

By inspecting Eq. (3.11), two important conclusions can be deduced:

1. Any losses ahead of the mixer and in the mixer itself appear as fractional gains in the denominators of the second and third terms, respectively, and effectively magnify the respective noise figures of the mixer and IF amplifier.
2. An RF amplifier with adequate gain inserted ahead of the mixer can establish the noise factor of the entire receiver, since its gain appears as a multiple in the denominators of both the second and third terms, which will reduce the significance of the noise factors for both the mixer and the IF amplifier.

These conclusions support the inclusion of a low-noise RF amplifier with a gain of 10 or greater ahead of the mixer, as is common in designs of most modern EMI analyzers. Similarly, they illustrate why sensitivity is poor when wideband harmonic mixers are preceded only by losses in low-pass filters and other components, without RF amplification, as is common in designs of most spectrum analyzers. However, when RF amplification is used, its amount and placement must be handled carefully in the EMI analyzer design to achieve maximum dynamic range. It can be shown that the optimum gain for a preamplifier inserted ahead of an existing spectrum analyzer is approximately equal to the ratio of the noise factor of the spectrum analyzer to that of the preamplifier. This produces a noise factor for the combination which is twice (3 dB) more than that of the preamplifier alone and a dynamic range which is half (3 dB less than) that of the spectrum analyzer alone.[4]

3.5 Measurement and Calibration of Impulsive Signals

The repetition rate of impulsive emissions is generally low compared to the maximum IF bandwidth selectable in EMI analyzers. Some exceptions to this include high-data-rate digital signals such as computer clock pulses and simultaneous reception of EMI from numerous automobile ignition systems such as would be experienced along a crowded highway.

3.5.1 Impulse Response

When a train of short-duration pulses is applied to the receiver input, a synchronously-tuned IF amplifier produces an output response such as shown in Fig. 3.7. Both the width and delay time of the IF response are of the order of the reciprocal of the IF amplifier bandwidth. When the repetition rate of the pulses is significantly less than the impulse bandwidth of the receiver, which is essentially that of the IF amplifier, the responses are discrete and non-overlapping, as shown in the left section of Fig. 3.7.

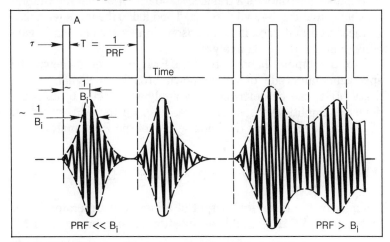

Figure 3.7—Impulse Response of a Linear IF Amplifier

When the pulse repetition frequency (PRF) of the input pulses approaches or exceeds the receiver bandwidth, as shown in the right section of Fig. 3.7, the responses merge and no longer produce the same peak output. If the LO of the receiver is stable over the observation interval, and if the pulse train exhibits no pulse-to-pulse jitter, then the merged IF response to the overlapping pulses corresponds to a coherent IF carrier. The phase relation of these IF carriers depends on the RF tuning and the interval between pulses. For certain unique relations between the two, the IF carriers are all in phase and add in amplitude to produce the familiar Fourier series spectral "lines" when the PRF is much greater than the impulse bandwidth.

3.5.2 Application and Measurement of Impulse BW and Spectrum Amplitude

Accurate knowledge of the impulse bandwidth of an EMI analyzer is a vital piece of information in EMI testing whenever EMI is to be compared to a limit expressed in terms of spectrum amplitude, such as, "40 dBμV/MHz." Accurate calibration of the predetection impulse bandwidth of the EMI analyzer is frequently done by noting its response to the output of a calibrated impulse generator (see Section 3.5.3); in this event, accurate calibration of that impulse generator becomes the limiting factor in determining the spectrum amplitude accurately. Many EMI analyzers incorporate internally an impulse generator as a transfer standard for amplitude calibration; its output can be switch selected and fed to the input terminals or measured and used in comparison circuits for automatic gain adjustment of the EMI analyzer.

Once the impulse bandwidth of the EMI analyzer is known, the spectrum amplitude of an unknown broadband signal, V_b, in dBμV/MHz, can be determined by applying a factor to its peak-detected amplitude, V_s, in dBμV, as read on the EMI analyzer. This is a factor relating the impulse BW of the EMI analyzer, B_i, to 1 MHz:

$$V_b = V_s - 20 \log B_i, \text{ for } B_i \text{ in MHz} \qquad (3.12)$$

Similarly, the calibrated output of an impulse generator, V_i, in units of dBμV/MHz, could be substituted to produce an EMI analyzer reading equal to that for an unknown narrowband signal, V_n, to determine its amplitude:

$$V_n = V_i + 20 \log B_i, \text{ for } B_i \text{ in MHz} \qquad (3.13)$$

The spectrum amplitude, $S(f)$, of an impulse generator can be calibrated in a number of ways, including:

1. Video pulse method
2. Pulse substitution method
3. Standard transmission line method
4. Harmonic method
5. Energy method

Additionally, a quick check of impulse generator performance can be made by one of the following methods:

1. Comparison to 7 dB bandwidth, for synchronous tuning only
2. Multiple IG comparisons
3. Direct-current voltage check

The remainder of this section discusses these techniques and methods.[5] IEEE Std 376 should be studied prior to implementing any of the following procedures.[6]

3.5.2.1 Video Pulse Method

The video pulse method is the one currently accepted by the U.S. military for the calibration of impulse generators.[7] The IEEE also recognizes it as a valid measurement technique.[6] It involves connecting the IG to an EMI analyzer or other selective filter and observing with an oscilloscope the output of the filter, i.e., the IF output of the EMI analyzer.

Spectrum amplitude of a pulse in units of volt-seconds (volts/Hz) is the area under the amplitude-versus-time representation of that pulse, whatever its shape. After processing through an amplifier-filter system such as a typical EMI analyzer, the Fourier time-domain expression for the resulting normalized spectrum amplitude in V/Hz is:

$$S(f) = (1/G_0) \int_{-\infty}^{\infty} V(t)dt \qquad (3.14)$$

$$= (1/G_0) \int_{t_1}^{t_1 + \delta t} V(t)dt$$

$$= \text{area under response curve divided by system gain} \qquad (3.15)$$

where,

$V(t)$ = envelope of the voltage response in the time domain of the amplifier-filter system

G_0 = maximum overall gain of the amplifier-filter system from impulse generator output to oscilloscope input

t_i = time corresponding to beginning

$t_i + \delta t$ = time corresponding to end of significant amplitude response, $V(t)$

Since the accepted convention is to calibrate impulse generators in terms of the **root-mean-square (rms) equivalent** rather than the peak spectrum amplitude, both S(f) and V(t) are measured and calibrated as 0.707 of the observed peak amplitudes.

Certain precautions should be observed in the test setup for measuring spectrum amplitude, as shown in Fig. 3.8:

1. The impulse and signal generators should be impedance matched to the narrowband filter (EMI analyzer) input impedance, and the oscilloscope connection should be made so as not to interfere with normal operation of the filter-amplifier (EMI analyzer).
2. The amplifier (if used), the oscilloscope and all active components in the setup should have flat gain versus frequency and linear response over the passband of the narrowband filter. Special care should be taken to avoid saturation of the impulsive signal; any AGC connections or influences should be eliminated.
3. The oscilloscope should have linear deflection systems and accurate calibration of scales in both horizontal and vertical axes.

Once these precautions are observed, the calibration procedure is as follows (see Fig. 3.8):

1. Initially, set switch S in the measure ("Meas.") position. Adjust the IG output, the amplifier or EMI analyzer gain and the oscilloscope controls to provide a stable, undistorted pulse response envelope on the oscilloscope screen, with minimal observable internal noise from the amplifier or EMI analyzer. Change settings of the IG attenuator to ensure that linear operation is measured.

2. Measure the area, in cm^2, of both positive and negative sections of the pulse response envelope by using either an oscilloscope camera or by tracing the pattern onto graph paper and then using a planimeter. Record the peak amplitude, h, in cm. Also record the corresponding indicated IG output, in $\mu V/MHz$.

3. Calibrate the height, h, in microvolts rms, by placing switch S in the calibrate ("Cal.") position and adjusting the CW generator in frequency for maximum response and in amplitude to equal the peak-to-peak excursion, h. Record the rms voltage, V in μV, being fed to the switch by the generator, after determining that it is accurately calibrated.

4. Calibrate the time axis of the oscilloscope, t, in $\mu s/cm$, by substituting an accurately-calibrated sweep generator at the horizontal input terminals.

5. Calculate the spectrum amplitude of the IG output in $\mu V/MHz$ as:

$$S(f) = AtV/h \qquad (3.16)$$

where,

A = the area, in cm^2, of the pulse envelope
t = the time dimension of the oscilloscope axis in $\mu s/cm$
V = the rms voltage equivalent to the height, h
h = the height of the pulse response, in cm

6. Finally, calculate the impulse bandwidth, B_i, in MHz as:

$$B_i = V/S(f) \qquad (3.17)$$

7. Repeat the above steps at each frequency of interest.

The performance of this procedure will produce a tabulation of IG output settings, measured output levels and B_i at the selected frequencies. For use in actual EMI testing, the indicated output levels of the IG must be corrected to their true values. If feasible, the IG output settings should be adjusted to their measured values. For use in determining compliance to MIL-STD-461 requirements, the amplitude accuracy should be within $\pm$ 2 dB.

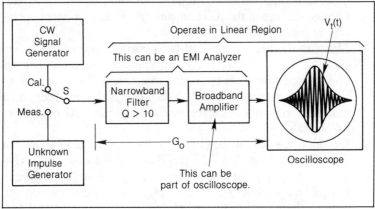

Figure 3.8—Test Setup for Measuring Impulse Bandwidth and Spectrum Amplitude

3.5.2.2 Pulse Substitution Method

Impulse generators can also be calibrated by generation and substitution of pulses having controlled characteristics which allow their spectrum amplitudes to be computed.

Solid-state switches make it possible to switch on a carrier sine wave for a precisely-measured time interval, τ, as diagrammed in Fig. 3.9. This permits measurement of spectrum amplitude at a particular frequency in terms of the "on-time" interval of the switch and of the rms voltage, V, of a continuous sine wave at that same frequency when not being switched. The rms voltage is measured using a power meter of impedance Z. If the impulse bandwidth of the narrowband filter is not greater than one-tenth the reciprocal of the on-time interval, τ, the spectrum amplitude in V/Hz is:

$$S(f) = (PZ)^{1/2} \, \tau = 2\tau V \qquad (3.18)$$

For this procedure to be valid, it must be determined that the sine wave amplitude is the same when modulated and that switching is "clean," so that no spurious products are generated by chatter, bounce, overshoot or ringing. This method, also known as the "Pulse-Modulated Sine Wave Technique," is described in detail in IEEE Std 376.[6]

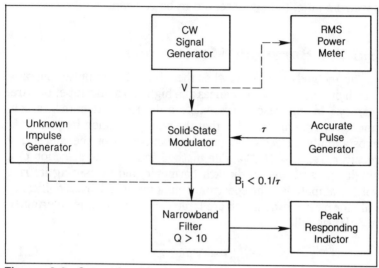

Figure 3.9—Setup for Measuring Spectrum Amplitude by Pulse Substitution

3.5.2.3 Standard Transmission Line Method

Another method of generating a substitute pulse for comparison with the output of an IG involves the use of a specific length of transmission line.[8]

A transmission line of length corresponding to a one-way propagation time, $\tau/2$, and charged to a voltage, V_c, is discharged into a load resistance equal to the characteristic impedance of the line. The transmission line is here considered to consist of the actual line as well as the charged section of the line contained in the switch housing. The line is charged to a Voltage, V_c, which is twice the amplitude of the desired pulse, V_o. The maximum spectrum amplitude S(f) of the resulting pulse equals twice its area in volt-seconds, or $2 \times V_o\tau$, peak (or $\sqrt{2}\ V_o\tau$ rms) in the low-frequency portion of the spectrum in which it is constant with frequency. The spectrum amplitude is independent of the existence of distributed or stray impedances between the line and the load resistance (i.e., inductance, capacitance or contact resistance) or of finite switching time. The value S(f) can be calculated directly from the measured values of V_c and τ in the frequency range in which the measured spectrum amplitude is observed to be constant.

3.5.2.4 Harmonic Measurement

This method can be used when there is available a pulse generator which produces pulse sequences at a high and stable repetition frequency.[8] In this case, there exists a discrete rather than a continuous spectrum, provided that the pulse repetition frequency, f_r, substantially exceeds the impulse bandwidth of the measuring receiver (i.e., $f_r \geqslant 10 \ B_i$). The method calls for the selection of a single spectral line as the kth harmonic and measuring its rms voltage amplitude. The spectrum amplitude, which has significance only for bandwidths which are large compared to f_r, is determined in V/Hz as follows:

$$S(f,k) = V_k/f_r \qquad (3.19)$$

In the event that the repetition rate is not sufficiently high so as to prevent more than a single spectrum component from contributing to the output, the effects of the additional components can be taken into consideration if the bandpass characteristics of the filter are sufficiently well known.[9]

The pulse generator then can be used to calibrate the pulse response characteristics of a network whose bandwidth is sufficiently wide to accept many harmonic components (approximately 10 or more within the impulse bandwidth).

3.5.2.5 Energy Method

This method of measuring spectrum amplitude is based on a measurement of spectrum intensity, SI, which is defined as follows:[5, 10]

$$SI = \lim_{\Delta f \to 0} \left(\frac{P}{\Delta f} \right)$$

where,

P = power content of frequency range Δf

The output of the IG is fed through a bandpass filter and amplifier (or an EMI analyzer) into a power meter. In addition, to accurately measure the amplified IG output power, this technique also requires accurate measurements of the gain and **power bandwidth** of the filter-amplifier, which is defined as:

$$B_p = \frac{1}{G_o} \int_0^\infty |G(f)|^2 \, df \qquad (3.20)$$

where,
$G(f)$ = voltage gain at any frequency, f
G_o = voltage gain at the reference frequency corresponding to maximum filter response

The spectrum amplitude in V/Hz rms is then given by:

$$S(f) = \frac{1}{G_o} \left(\frac{P_{av} R_o}{f_r B_p} \right)^{1/2} \qquad (3.21)$$

where,
P_{av} = average power measured into the power meter
R_o = input resistance into which IG feeds in ohms
f_r = repetition rate of applied impulses in Hz

This technique has the advantage that it permits the measurement to be made using ordinary metrology lab equipment to measure average power and pulse repetition rate. Its accuracy is affected by the following:

1. The input impedance of the network, or EMI analyzer, should be purely resistive at the frequency of measurement.
2. The power meter must be able to respond accurately to waveforms having a high peak-to-average ratio.
3. Background noise from the EMI analyzer between pulses may introduce errors in power measurement unless a suitable gating technique is used.
4. The impulse generator may not be capable of producing uniform output pulses at a sufficiently high repetition rate to avoid errors from factors 2 and 3 above.

3.5.2.6 Quick Checks of IG Performance

As mentioned at the beginning of Section 3.5.2, three methods are available for quick checks of IG calibration:

1. The 7 dB Bandwidth Method

a. The 7 dB bandwidth of a synchronously tuned, linearly operating EMI analyzer or bandpass filter is measured, using conventional CW signal-generator methods. The result approximates the impulse bandwidth (B_i) for synchronous (undercoupled) tuning.

b. The IG to be measured is connected to the EMI analyzer or filter, and the output of the IF amplifier or filter is connected to the vertical axis input of an oscilloscope. Controls are set for a convenient pulse pattern, corresponding to the IG level being measured, and it is confirmed that no saturation exists.

c. Next, the output of a CW signal generator is substituted to furnish the input to the EMI analyzer or filter, in place of the IG, and tuned for maximum response on the CRT face. Its output is adjusted to that level, V_s, which duplicates the pattern height established in step b.

d. The IG output level in dBμV/MHz is calculated, using Eq. (3.12):

$$IG\ level = V_s - B_i \qquad (3.22)$$

In Eq. (3.22) V_s is in dBμV and B_i is expressed in dBMHz.

2. Multiple IG Comparisons

This method is simply the comparison of the output of an IG with suspect calibration to that of an IG which is known to be calibrated. When both produce the same output, within ± 1 dB, from an EMI analyzer or filter at various frequencies over their ranges of coverage, it can reasonably be assumed that the suspect IG is usable. Similarly, two IGs with output levels in disagreement by more than ± 1 dB can be compared to a third unit which is calibrated.

3. DC Voltage Level

Improper charging voltage is most frequently involved in improper IG operation. Check to determine that it is within the manufacturer's specifications, to within ±5 percent. The next most common element of failure is the mercury-wetted switching relay. However, since a faulty relay probably will not affect the charging voltage, measuring a correct charging voltage does not imply a properly functioning relay.

3.5.2.7 Measuring Impulse Bandwidth

Incorporated in the video pulse method for measuring spectrum amplitude (see Section 3.5.2.1) is the amplitude-time area method of determining impulse bandwidth, B_i, as given in MIL-STD-462.[7]

Whenever both a calibrated IG and a calibrated CW signal generator are available, B_i can readily be determined by substitution testing. The steps are:

1. The IG is connected to an EMI analyzer without AGC, and its IF amplifier output is connected to the vertical signal input terminals of an oscilloscope. Controls are set for a convenient pulse response pattern deflection corresponding to an IG level, V_b, in dBμV/MHz, which does not overload.
2. Next, a CW signal generator is substituted to furnish the input signal and tuned for maximum response. Its output level is adjusted to that level of rms voltage, V_s in dBμV, which produces the same height as in step 1.
3. B_i is then calculated in dBMHz as:

$$B_i = V_s - V_b \qquad (3.23)$$

Since modern EMI analyzers typically offer many octaves of frequency coverage, departures from perfect tracking of the front-end preselector and other factors can result in variations in B_i with frequency. However, this effect is corrected in most modern instruments by using the output of a built-in IG as a calibrated substitution signal.

When 3 dB, 6 dB, and 20 dB bandwidths are known or can be more easily determined, impulse bandwidth can be closely approximated by use of Fig. 3.10.[1]

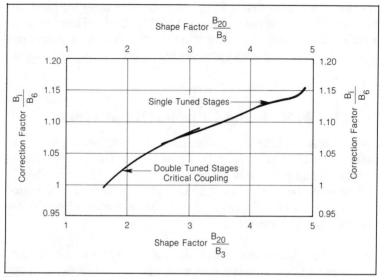

Figure 3.10—Six Decibel to Impulse Bandwidth Conversion as Function of Shape Factor

3.5.3 Impulse Generator Design Factors

This section discusses impulse generators, which are instruments designed to produce the calibrated levels of spectrum amplitude discussed above for calibration of EMI analyzers and other purposes over the frequency spectrum from about 200 Hz to over 18 GHz. Impulse generators intended for receiver calibration and other relatively low-level applications typically have broad spectrum coverage, with spectrum amplitude outputs in the order of 100 dBμV/MHz. Similar instruments intended to produce higher-level outputs for susceptibility testing are covered in Chapter 5.

The design of the typical impulse generator for emissions testing charges a pulse-forming transmission line with a one-way propagation delay of $\tau/2 = 0.05$ ns to a voltage, V_c, of about 200 V. It then rapidly discharges it into a 50 Ω resistive load which matches the characteristic impedance of the line. Figure 3.11 illustrates this design in simplified form. This process results in a pulse which is twice the propagation delay of the line, $2 \times \tau/2 = \tau$ s, in width and one-half of the charging voltage, $V_c/2 = V_o$, in amplitude. For a charging voltage V_c = 200 V and a line $\tau/2$ = 0.05 ns in length, the result is a pulse with an amplitude V_0 = 100 V and a pulse width τ = 0.1 ns. The resulting maximum rms-equivalent spectrum amplitude at frequencies << $1/\tau$ is $\sqrt{2}$ $V_0\tau$ = $\sqrt{2}$ × 100 × 10^{-10} volt-seconds (volts per hertz) = 83 dBμV/MHz rms.

The discharging switch shown in Fig. 3.11 is usually a coaxial reed relay with contacts which are mercury-wetted to avoid pitting and to prolong their life. Switching of the relay can be activated manually for single-shot operation, synchronized to the ac line for 60 Hz operation, or controlled by a simple built-in, variable-frequency oscillator to provide a variable repetition rate.

The output of the IG is calibrated in spectrum amplitude units of dBμV/MHz as discussed above. As shown at the top of Fig. 3.12, the time-domain waveform actually delivered into a matched load (usually 50 Ω), has an amplitude $V_0 = V_c/2$, or half of the dc charging voltage, and a duration, τ, which is twice the effective propagation time of the transmission line as modified by the input parameters of the switch.

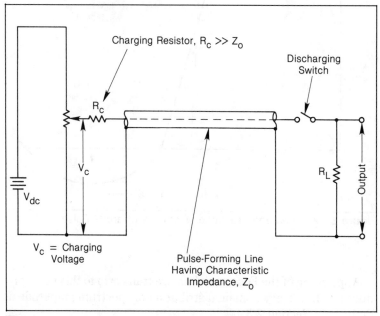

Figure 3.11—Simplified Schematic of Impulse Generator

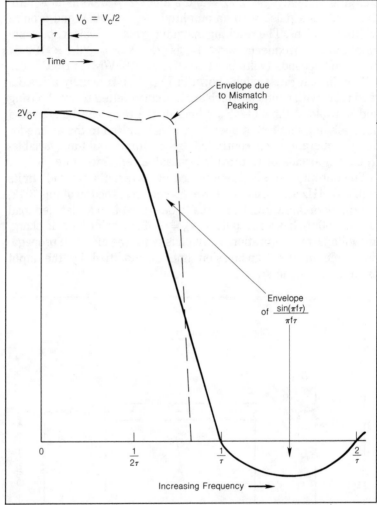

Figure 3.12—Time and Frequency Domains of an IG Pulse

Application of the Fourier or Laplace transform to this pulse produces its frequency-domain distribution of spectrum amplitude as defined in Section 2.3.4.3:

$$S(f) = 2\, V_o \tau\ \frac{\sin \pi f \tau}{\pi f \tau} \qquad (3.24)$$

where,

> $S(f)$ = spectrum amplitude in V/Hz (pk)
> V_0 = one-half the charging voltage = $V_c/2$ (V dc)
> f = frequency in Hz
> τ = pulse duration in seconds

The term $\pi f \tau$ is often referred to as x, resulting in the familiar (sin x) /x distribution shown in Fig. 3.12. The first null is at $1/\tau$ Hz, and for τ = 0.1 ns (10^{-10} s), $1/\tau$ = 10 GHz. Perhaps of more practical significance is the "corner" frequency of the distribution, f_c = $1/\pi\tau$, out to which the response is nearly flat.

At lower frequencies, for which f $\ll 1/\tau$ and (sin $\pi f \tau$)/$\pi f \tau \approx$ 1, Eq. (3.24) becomes:

$$S(f) = 2V_0\tau \qquad (3.25)$$

Existence of this significant range of frequencies for which the spectrum amplitude of the IG is essentially flat is the basis for its use as a broadband calibrator.

To expand further the range over which the spectrum amplitude of an IG is essentially flat, spectral rolloff can be reduced by deliberate mismatch of the pulse-forming line and the load. As suggested by Fig. 3.12, a flatness of 1 dB can be achieved out to 5 GHz for a pulse width of 0.1 ns.

Another type of IG design is all electronic, rather than electromechanical, and utilizes a step-recovery diode to generate the required fractional-nanosecond pulse. This type of design has the advantage that it is not limited by relay switching and thus can generate pulses at much higher repetition rates. Its principal disadvantage is that its operating voltage limitations restrict the pulse amplitude which can be generated.

Various methods for calibrating impulse generators are outlined in Section 3.5.2.

3.6 Detector Functions for EMI Measurements

Selectability of multiple detector functions is a distinguishing characteristic of interference analyzers. Selection of the appropriate detector function is essential in order to obtain readings of EMI levels for comparison to appropriate limits in the governing specifications that are valid only for that specific type of detection. After the following summary, which identifies the most widely used types of detection, each is then discussed in more detail.

All of the detector types being discussed appear as the final stage of demodulation in superheterodyne receivers and perform the basic function of filtering out the IF components to recover the envelope of the input or baseband signal. In this process, each type of detector affects the baseband signal at least slightly. For subsequent viewing of the signal in video form on an oscilloscope CRT, the degree of such modification should be minimized. However, to produce readings which are valid for comparison to established specification limits, the baseband signal must be subjected to deliberate and controlled weighting and modification as determined by the particular detector function applied.

1. **Peak** detection is required for all testing of EMI emissions to U.S. military standards and is essential to obtaining correct readings for levels of impulsive interference, as discussed in Section 3.5. Stretching and other modifications of the signal in the detection process are performed primarily to facilitate accurate reading and recording of its level.

2. **Slideback Peak** detection is an indirect process employing an adjustable bias voltage and is used primarily to obtain accurate peak readings of signals which are not suited to detection by the direct-peak method.

3. **Quasi-peak** detection employs controlled charge and discharge time constants which function together with controlled predetection bandwidths and other circuit constraints to produce readings which are weighted to correspond to the degrading effects of the EMI signal.

4. **Average** detection employs equal charge and discharge time constants to produce readings of the average voltage level of the EMI signal.

5. **RMS** detection produces readings equivalent to the **power** developed by the EMI signal at the detector input.

6. **Amplitude Probability Distribution (APD)**, while not a detector function per se, is one of a number of processes which treat the IF carrier or detected envelope of the EMI signal statistically to derive analytical presentations of its characteristics. For example, APD presents the percentage of

time that the envelope of the EMI signal exceeds various amplitudes of voltage.

3.6.1 Peak Detection

Obtaining a measure of the peak level of an EMI signal is a vital requirement in much EMI testing. As noted in Section 3.5, the accurate measurement of the spectrum amplitude of impulsive EMI depends on accurate peak detection; in addition, the proliferation of computers and other devices which are generous producers of short digital pulses makes measurements using peak detection essential to protect pulse-sensitive, electronically-controlled systems against their inadvertent emanation. MIL-STD-461 specifies its limits in terms of peak detection, in recognition of the vulnerability of military equipment to such pulsed EMI, as well as to achieve proper response to EMI signals when using automatic frequency scanning. As was the case with the measurement of spectrum amplitude, peak detectors as used in EMI analyzers respond to the peak amplitude of the measured signal. However, they are calibrated in terms of the rms value of a sine wave signal of the same peak amplitude.

As implemented by circuitry such as that shown in Fig. 3.13, peak detection is characterized by rapid charge time and slow discharge time. The charge time must be short compared to the rise time of the fastest IF pulse produced by the preceding stages in response to an impulsive signal, while the discharge time must be sufficiently long to permit devices such as front-panel meters and X-Y plotters to respond fully to the detected peak amplitude.

For an EMI analyzer using a circuit such as that shown in Fig. 3.13, some specific design rules and precautions applicable to accurate peak detection are:

1. Active devices and circuitry should be selected to be independent of the duty cycle of signals to be handled. Specifically, AGC should be avoided.
2. The time constant consisting of the impedance of the charging source plus that of the forward resistance of the detector diode, R_c, together with capacitor, C, should be the lesser of:
   a. one-tenth the reciprocal of the largest predetector bandwidth

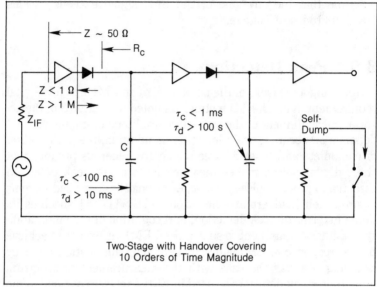

Figure 3.13—Basic Schematic of Modern Peak Detector

    b. the reciprocal of the predetector IF carrier frequency, in the event that the ratio of that frequency to the widest IF bandwidth is five or less, i.e., only a few cycles of IF occupy the narrowest IF pulse

3. The discharge, or decay, time constant should be on the order of 100 s to assure time for the Y-axis of a plotter to move the pen up to full response.

4. Dump circuitry should be included to clear the detector for response to another signal following closely upon the previous one. Design of such a circuit must take into account a number of factors. It must allow sufficient time for the plotter to register full response to a relatively large signal without truncating it, but must accomplish the discharge, or dumping, as soon as possible so as not to obscure a small signal following in the wake of a large one.

3.6.2 Slideback Peak Detection

    Although developed originally as the primary method of peak detection because suitable direct-peak detector circuits were not available, the slideback detector continues to be useful in spite of the interim development of high-performance, direct-peak circuits.

An example of the slideback detector is shown in Fig. 3.14. A back-bias voltage is increased until the unknown pulsed EMI signal, as being heard in headphones or viewed on an oscilloscope, is extinguished. At this point, the diode is just cut off, and the voltage producing that condition is equal to the positive-going peak of the unknown signal. The bias voltage can then be read and taken as the signal amplitude, or a calibrated IG can be substituted and increased in output to determine the level at which the threshold is just exceeded.

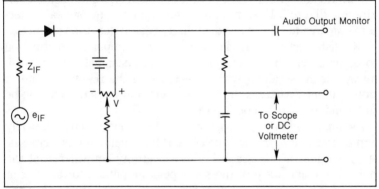

Figure 3.14—Basic Schematic of Slideback Detector

The slideback peak detector still is usually employed only when the capability of the available direct-peak detector is not equal to the task. Its limitations are apparent; the need to hear or view the unknown signal implies that it be repetitive. Thus, it is not suitable for single-shot pulses or transients or in tests where the test sample must be re-stimulated to produce a single output. However, it remains a useful tool for some specialized applications.

3.6.3 Quasi-peak Detection

Although the quasi-peak detector originally was developed in the 1930s to give a reading proportional to the annoyance effect of interference on listeners to broadcast radio, its usage has been perpetuated and modernized under sponsorship of CISPR (see Chapter 1, Section 1.3.2). Its continuing use also has been reinforced through harmonization of American National Standards with CISPR recommendations by the American National Standards Institute (ANSI) and their subsequent adoption by the FCC. These recommendations for quasi-peak detection are summarized in Table 3.1.

As is apparent from an inspection of Table 3.1, the specified quasi-peak detection involves not only the charge and discharge time constants of the detector itself, but also the predetector bandwidth, the electromechanical characteristics of the indicating meter and the overload capabilities of both the predetector and postdetector circuits. Figure 3.15 shows how the output of a quasi-peak detector compares to that of an ideal direct-peak detector as a function of the listed parameters. Perhaps the most important distinction to be noted is that the output of a given quasipeak detector will always decrease along with a decrease in the repetition rate of pulsed inputs, whereas the peak detector output is designed to be independent of the repetition rate.

As illustrated in Fig. 3.16, the quasi-peak output asymptotically approaches that of the peak detector as the repetition rate increases. Also implicit in this graph is the converging equivalence of the pulses to a sine wave of the same peak amplitude for all four of the detector types shown as their repetition rate approaches the 120 kHz predetection bandwidth.

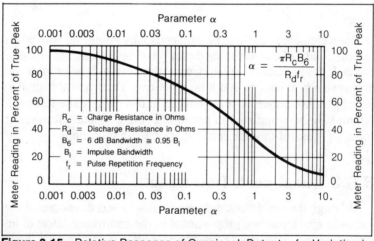

Figure 3.15—Relative Response of Quasipeak Detector for Variation in Repetition Rate and Receiver Design Parameters

Table 3.1—CISPR Quasipeak Detector Characteristics

Characteristic	0.01 to 20 kHz	9 to 150 kHz	0.15 to 30 MHz	25 to 1,000 MHz
Bandwidth @ − 6 dB	9 kHz*	200 Hz	9 kHz	120 kHz
Charge Time Constant of Detector	1 ms	45 ms	1 ms	1 ms
Discharge Time Constant of Detector	160 ms	500 ms	160 ms	550 ms
Mechanical Time Constant of Critically-Damped meter	160 ms	160 ms	160 ms	100 ms
Predetection Overload Factor (Minimum)	30 dB	24 dB	30 dB	43.5 dB
Postdetection Overload Factor (Minimum)	12 dB	6 dB	12 dB	6 dB

*9 kHz = Resultant Nontunable Bandwidth of Psophometric Network for "C-Message" and Wideband Voltmeter[13]

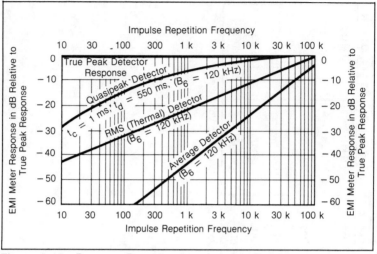

Figure 3.16—Detector Responses vs. Impulse Rate

3.6.4 Average Detection

Availability of average detection is a valuable feature in most EMI analyzers, both because of the significance of the average level in any EMI analysis of unknown signals and because many potential victims are more vulnerable to the average level of a signal than they are to its peak or quasipeak value. Examples are those which have long integration time constants (in the order of 1 s) for their output displays, such as the status indicators in aircraft, ships and mobile vehicles.

The average detector, sometimes called the **field intensity (FI)** detector, consists of an envelope detector followed by a series-resistor, shunt-capacitor averaging network which produces the average of the detected envelope. For example, an unmodulated CW signal will produce an average reading proportional to its peak value and give the same reading as an rms-equivalent calibrated peak detector. When the same signal is 100 percent modulated with a sine wave, increasing its peak detector reading by 6 dB, the average reading will remain unchanged. For pulsed signals, the average detector will produce readings proportional to the duty factor of the signal; the average reading for a pulsed train having a duty factor of 0.001 will be 60 dB less than the peak reading. Figure 3.16 shows the relationship between the average value of a signal and its pulse repetition rate for a CISPR receiver with the indicated characteristics. This relation is the duty factor of the pulses:

$$\delta = \tau \times f_r = f_r/B_i \qquad (3.26)$$

where,

δ = the duty factor
τ = pulse width from the IF amplifier
f_r = pulse repetition rate
B_i = impulse bandwidth of the IF amplifier

Thus, when $f_r = B_i$, $\delta = 1$ and the peak and average detectors produce the same reading.

3.6.5 RMS Detection

Although not incorporated in all EMI analyzers, the root-mean-square (rms) detector is valuable for analyzing EMI in that it provides readings proportional to signal power. As shown in Fig. 3.16 and verified in Table 3.2, the response of the rms detector to repetitive impulses is proportional to the square root of their repetition rate.

EMI analyzers are usually calibrated to read the rms value of a sine wave of equivalent peak value (usually called the "rms equivalent" sinewave), at the input, regardless of which detector is used. Table 3.2 compares the responses of the types of detectors just discussed to three types of input signals: sine wave, impulsive noise and random noise.

Table 3.2—Comparison of Detector Responses when Calibrated to Read RMS of Equivalent Sine Wave

Emission Input	Detector Type			
	Peak	Envelope Average	Quasipeak $t_c = 1$ ms $t_d = 600$ ms	RMS
Sine Wave RMS Value $= V_o$	V_o	V_o	V_o	V_o
Impulse Spectrum Amplitude $= S(f)$	$\sqrt{2}\ SB_i$	$\sqrt{2}\ Sf_r$	$\sqrt{2}\ SP(\alpha)\ B_i$	$S\sqrt{2B_i f_r}$
Random Noise; Power Spectral Density $= P_n$	undefined	$1.25\sqrt{P_n B_n}$	$2.57\sqrt{P_n B_n}$	$\sqrt{2P_n B_n}$

B_i = Impulse BW B_n = Random Noise BW

$P(\alpha)$ = Term Given in Fig. 3.15

3.6.6 APD and Other Statistical Detection Processes

Amplitude Probability Distribution (APD) is not a detector comparable to those just discussed but, rather, is a statistical process of classifying and then plotting EMI in terms of the percentage of time (as abscissa) its envelope exceeds various voltage levels (as ordinates). APD is the measure of noise most commonly required for analyzing the performance of communication systems.[11, 12]

Other statistical processes also are useful in communications design:

Noise Amplitude Distribution (NAD) shows the average frequency with which each ordinate value is exceeded.

Pulse Duration Distribution (PDD) shows the percentage of pulses which exceed various widths in seconds at each of seven amplitude levels.

Average Crossing Rate (ACR) shows the average number of times the noise amplitude crosses various levels and is given as positive crossings per second versus noise amplitude level.

3.6.7 Postdetection Video and Metering

As covered in the functional description of the EMI analyzer in Section 3.1.3, appropriate detection and weighting of the EMI signal is followed by a number of circuits with the basic function of preparing the result for presentation or processing. To preserve accuracy, all postdetection circuits must have bandwidth and dynamic range capabilities commensurate with those available in the predetection stages.

3.7 Using Spectrum Analyzers for EMI Testing

3.7.1 Background and EMI Suitability

Spectrum analyzers differ from EMI analyzers, as introduced above, primarily in that they have untuned front ends without (until recently) preselection, relatively high noise figures and built-in CRT displays. Amplitude calibration is usually achieved through the use of internally generated narrowband signals. This, together with their vulnerability to front-end overload, as discussed above in Section 3.2, makes them relatively unsuitable for measuring coherent broadband EMI and for use in uncontrolled ambient environments where overload from such signals would be a threat. The principal advantage of spectrum analyzers over EMI analyzers is their adaptability to a broader range of applications and their typically lower cost per octave of spectrum coverage.

Spectrum analyzers were developed originally as laboratory instruments for displaying signals and noise over a wide range of frequencies in the frequency domain, as a complement to oscilloscopes which displayed such signals in the time domain. Although EMI testing constitutes only a small part of their total applications, spectrum analyzers are ideal for quick-look assessment of EMI during development stages of new products, prior to EMI qualification testing. They are widely used to examine unknown emissions to determine modulation characteristics and spectrum signatures.

The lack of front-end preselection results in numerous spurious responses which are products of intermodulation and heterodyning among harmonics of the LO and the wider population of signals allowed to reach the first mixer. When preselectors are available as optional accessories, they usually take the form of tracking yttrium iron garnet (YIG) filters which provide tuned preselection above about 2 GHz, or of low-pass filters which are switched in at lower frequencies. Because spectrum analyzers usually also lack RF amplification ahead of their first mixers, they have high noise figures and correspondingly poor RF sensitivities at the IF bandwidths used for EMI testing.

Spectrum analyzers evolved as more general-purpose instruments than EMI analyzers, which were developed specifically to accommodate the unique requirements for EMI testing. Nevertheless, it is possible to obtain useful EMI test results using some of the latest generation of spectrum analyzers, provided adequate attention is accorded the limitations that still remain when these instruments are applied to this task.

To understand these remaining limitations and use EMI-capable spectrum analyzers effectively, it is appropriate to review the basic design of the spectrum analyzer, comparing and contrasting it with that of the basic EMI analyzer discussed above. Before proceeding, however, it is important to emphasize that, despite any shortcomings the spectrum analyzer has for making valid EMI measurements, every EMI laboratory should have one available because of its great value for quickly assessing the general characteristics of unknown EMI.

3.7.2 Functional Description

Figure 3.17 is a simplified functional block diagram of a typical modern RF spectrum analyzer. The RF input is switchable between the input connector (no. 1) (to which various EMI transducers or other sources can be applied) and an internal source (no. 2) of signal(s) for calibration of frequency and amplitude. The input signal is passed through a low-pass filter (no. 3) which attenuates frequency components beyond the tuning range of the instrument to reduce the levels of spurious responses produced by them in the subsequent heterodyning process. Unlike the EMI analyzer discussed in Section 3.1, no preselector or tunable RF amplifier normally is incorporated as a standard component of the spectrum analyzer design. However, as discussed in Section 3.2, preselectors sometimes are available as optional accessories to spectrum analyzers. As in the EMI analyzer, the signal is applied to an RF attenuator (no. 4) which can be set to confine the input signal level to the dynamic capability of the instrument.

To permit scanning over multiple-octave ranges of frequency while maintaining relatively flat frequency response, the incoming signals are up-converted in the mixer (no. 5) by combining them with the output of the local oscillator (no. 6), which is either synthesized digitally or tuned by an analog voltage. The frequency of the LO is sufficiently high that tuning it over an octave range tunes the response to input signals over a range of more than a decade. The resultant IF is fed to the IF amplifier (no. 7) and then down-converted in a mixer (no. 8) by combining it with the output of a fixed tuned LO (no. 9).

The second mixer drives a second IF amplifier (no. 10) and then the signal goes to a series of selectable bandpass filters (no. 11) which offer selectable bandwidths over about four orders of magnitude. The bandwidth-selected output is then coupled to the envelope detector (no. 12), the output of which is amplified either linearly (no. 13) or logarithmically (no. 14), as selected, and then presented to the Y-axis input of the CRT (no. 15).

The sweep generator (no. 16) provides a wide choice of scan speeds and widths (dispersions). Resulting ramp voltages are ap-

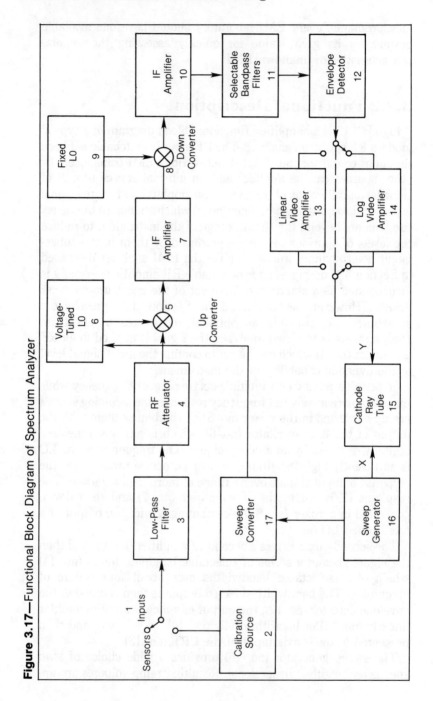

Figure 3.17—Functional Block Diagram of Spectrum Analyzer

plied to the X-axis of the CRT and to a sweep converter (no. 17), which shapes this waveform so as drive the voltage-tuned LO in a manner producing linear excursion of frequency versus sweep on the X-axis CRT drive. In designs for which the LO is frequency synthesized, the sweep generator and sweep converter apply appropriate digital words to the LO and corresponding analog waveforms to the X-axis drive of the CRT.

Some representative modern spectrum analyzers are discussed in Section 3.8.6.

3.8 Representative EMI Instrumentation

This section and the following two chapters include data on a number of available EMI instruments and accessories. All data shown or implied is based on literature of the respective manufacturers and, although believed to be accurate, cannot be guaranteed by the authors; *caveat emptor.*

Modern EMI analyzers are usually designed and classified for operation in three ranges of the frequency spectrum:

1. The range of ELF and LF frequencies from fractions of a hertz to 50 kHz
2. The LF, HF, VHF and UHF frequencies from 10 kHz to 1,000 MHz
3. The UHF and microwave frequencies from 1 GHz to 40 GHz and higher

Capability of the EMI analyzer to operate in automated systems is a common feature and consistent with recommendations of many governing specifications. Sensitivity of this type of instrument is designed to produce accurate readings of EMI at levels somewhat below specified limits, after taking into account the transfer characteristics of the various accessory transducers used to intercept the EMI signals, as discussed in Chapter 4.

Another common feature is a built-in calibrator which furnishes either a narrowband or broadband signal of known amplitude which can be used to normalize the gain of the EMI analyzer. At least two, and preferably three or more, selectable IF bandwidths at each tuned frequency are usually incorporated as are two or more types of detectors. Inclusion of several bandwidths and detector functions enables the instrument to be used for measurements specified by various governing documents and permits selection of a bandwidth and detector function appropriate to the frequency range and type of EMI being measured. An example of this application is the determination of whether EMI is narrowband or broadband, as described in Section 2.3.2.

The inclusion within a single instrument of several properly chosen bandwidths and detector functions, along with adequate dynamic range and other characteristics, permits the EMI analyzer to be used for both military and commercial testing. Early EMI analyzers were designed primarily for testing in accordance with military standards. The differences between these characteristics and those needed for commercial testing, most notably the CISPR recommendations, led to development of converter units which duplicated many functions of the parent EMI analyzer; however, modern EMI analyzers integrate into a single instrument package all the diverse requirements for both types of EMI testing.

3.8.1 Instrumentation for MIL-STD EMI Testing

EMI analyzers designed for tests based on limits of MIL-STD-461 are characterized by carefully designed peak detectors with associated hold-dump circuits as discussed in Section 3.6.1. Another common feature is the inclusion of an impulse generator as the built-in calibrator; the coherent broadband signals of known spectrum amplitude which it produces facilitate accurate measurements of this type of EMI and its comparison to the broadband limits of governing documents.

3.8.2 Instrumentation for CISPR-Based EMI Testing

As discussed in Section 3.6.3, capability of an EMI analyzer to perform EMI measurements in accordance with CISPR recommendations requires imposition of specific parameters onto not only its detector but its predetector bandwidth, its output metering and any circuits affecting its predetector or postdetector overload characteristics.

3.8.3 ELF and LF EMI Analyzers

Shown in Fig. 3.18 is a specialized instrument designed for magnetic-field measurements to frequencies as low as 0.1 Hz and as high as 50 kHz. This instrument is a variation of the variable-mu magnetometer and does not tune frequencies selectively, but registers them on a broadband basis. It gives a response directly proportional to the magnetic field strength, when the accessory ferrite sensor rod or magnetic sniffer probe is used, and to the electric field strength, when the E-field probe is used (see Section 4.3.2).

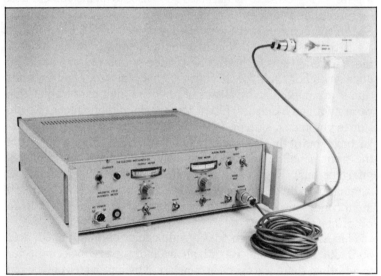

Figure 3.18—EMCO Model 6640 Magnetic Field Intensity Meter, 0.1 Hz to 50 kHz, with Ferrite Rod (courtesy of The Electro-Mechanics Co.)

3.47

In accordance with the variable-mu principle, the ferrite material in the sensor exhibits a change in permeability with any change in the strength of the magnetic field in which it is immersed. This change in permeability is used to affect the inductance of an element in the oscillator tank circuit of the ferrite sensor to produce a shift in its output frequency which corresponds to an increment of change in the magnetic field. The FM signal which results from a time-varying magnetic field is then demodulated to produce a voltage for a meter display which is calibrated to read magnetic field strength. Frequency response of the servo circuit used to feed the resulting voltage back to the sensor to stabilize its performance is tailored to make operation of the instrument independent of the earth's magnetic field.

Figures 3.19 and 3.20 show representative examples of more general-purpose EMI analyzers for use in the range up to 50 kHz. Figure 3.19 shows the modernized successor to an instrument used for more than two decades to measure both conducted and radiated EMI measurements over the frequency range from 16 Hz to 50 kHz. As is the case with other instruments operating in this range of the frequency spectrum, the first stage of conversion is to a frequency higher than the incoming signal, and front-end preselection is accomplished by means of low- and high-pass (rather than variably-tuned bandpass) filters. Consistent with its intended inclusion in automated systems (see Chapter 6), tuning and all other major functions of this instrument can be controlled either locally (from the front panel) or remotely (from a computer via the IEEE-488 interface bus). Regardless of whether the controlling commands originate locally or remotely, a microprocessor built into the instrument conditions and prepares the commands for conveyance to appropriate circuits.

This EMI analyzer provides a wide choice of input impedances: 50 Ω, 600 Ω, 10 kΩ and 100 kΩ, all available at a twinax connector; in addition, there is a special connector which provides both signal and operating power connections to an active high-impedance electric field probe and other accessories. Nine selective bandwidths are provided, ranging from 10 Hz to 5 kHz, in addition to a wideband operating mode in which the instrument bandpass is controlled by selection of the appropriate low- and high-pass filters available at its input. A built-in calibrator provides automatic calibration of the instrument whenever it is activated. In addition to direct and slideback peak, detector functions include true average, true rms and CISPR-recommended quasi-peak. Both frequency and amplitude are displayed in digital LED format. Overload situations are indicated by an LED warning to increase attenuation, and total attenuation inserted is accounted for automatically in the amplitude readout. Included in the instrument is a rechargeable battery module which permits up to six hours of operation disconnected from any source of ac.

Figure 3.19—Electro-Metrics Model EMC-11 Audio/ELF EMI Analyzer, 16 Hz to 50 kHz (courtesy of Electro-Metrics®)

Figure 3.20—Eaton NM-7A EMI/Field Intensity Meter, 20 Hz to 50 kHz (courtesy of Eaton E.I.D.)

The instrument shown in Fig. 3.20 provides both tunable and wideband signal analysis over the frequency range of 20 to 50 kHz. Dynamic range of the instrument is 60 dB without requiring a change in setting of the built-in attenuator and 160 dB when the attenuator is utilized. Frequency resolution at low frequencies in enhanced by the inclusion of two expanded frequency scales covering 20 Hz to 500 Hz and 20 Hz to 5 kHz, respectively. Frequency selection is voltage controlled either from the front panel, from built-in circuitry for automatic scanning or by providing an external 0 to 10 Vdc tuning ramp. The tuned frequency is indicated on the front-panel meter for all three modes of frequency control. A tracking output is provided to which a counter can be connected for highly accurate measurement of tuned frequency. Bandwidths are 10 Hz, 100 Hz and 1 kHz in the selective mode, and 20 and 50 kHz in the wideband mode. A BFO is provided to facilitate signal location and identification.

3.8.4 EMI Analyzers, 10 kHz to 1,000 MHz

Although the amount of EMI testing required at frequencies below and above the range of 10 kHz to 1,000 MHz continues to grow, this segment of the frequency spectrum continues to be the heart of all EMI test requirements. Consequently, at least 60 percent of all EMI analyzers sold cover all or a portion of this fundamental range.

Shown in Figs. 3.21 through 3.24 are representative examples of EMI analyzers designed for coverage of this basic frequency range. Figure 3.21 shows the modernized successor to an instrument used for more than two decades to measure both conducted and radiated EMI measurements over the frequency range of 9 kHz to 1,000 MHz. As is the case with most EMI analyzers in this range of the frequency spectrum, front-end preselection is by means of a tuned RF amplifier which automatically tracks the frequency determined by the first LO and IF. All other major functions of this instrument can be controlled locally or by a computer via the IEEE-488 interface bus.

Three selective bandwidths in decade ratios are provided at each tuned frequency, including those recommended by the SAE for MIL-STD-461/2 and specified by British DEF STAN 59-41. A built-in impulse generator is activated to provide a broadband signal for automatic calibration of the instrument whenever the calibration function is selected. Detector functions include direct peak, slideback peak, rms and true average. Quasipeak detection and all associated CISPR-recommended characteristics are also included. Both frequency and amplitude displays are LED-digital; the frequency display is accurate to ± 0.1 percent, ± 1 count, while the amplitude display is automatically corrected for attenuation and calibration to indicate input voltage to within 2 dB. To facilitate tuning of narrowband signals, the amplitude display is augmented by an analog tuning meter. An optional rechargeable battery module is available for field operation.

The 20 to 1,300 MHz coverage of the test receiver shown in Fig. 3.22 complements that of a companion receiver with coverage from 9 kHz to 30 MHz. Both utilize synthesized LO designs available in corresponding models intended for manual operation, but both incorporate microprocessor systems which enhance their flexibility

Figure 3.21—Electro-Metrics Model EMC-30 Interference Analyzer, 9 kHz to 1 GHz (courtesy of Electro-Metrics®)

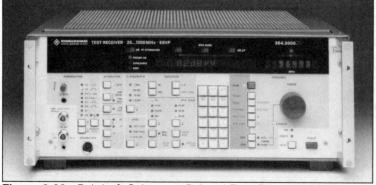

Figure 3.22—Rohde & Schwarz—Polarad Test Receiver ESVP, 20 to 1,300 MHz (courtesy of Rohde & Schwarz)

3.51

and optimize them for computer-controlled operation using the IEC/IEEE interface bus. Both models also can be operated with the companion spectrum monitor shown in Fig. 3.29 to permit high-resolution analysis of received signals. Unique to the model shown in Fig. 3.22 is its front-panel provision for entering of transducer conversion factors.

The instrument shown in Fig. 3.23 covers from 10 kHz to 32 MHz and is complemented by a companion instrument which provides coverage from 30 MHz to 1 GHz. Among its features are four selectable bandwidths and overall measurement range of 160 dB, with 60 dB available on the front-panel meter. Both instruments offer single scan operation for X-Y plotting or repetitive scanning for spectrum display on an oscilloscope, as triggered by a front-panel controls.

Both of the instruments shown in Fig. 3.24 may be operated either in a manual mode or controlled automatically via the IEEE-488 interface bus. With coverage from 9 kHz to 30 MHz and 25 MHz to 1 GHz, respectively, these two instruments are optimized for measurements in accordance with CISPR-based standards and offer optional additional bandwidths for military EMI testing applications.

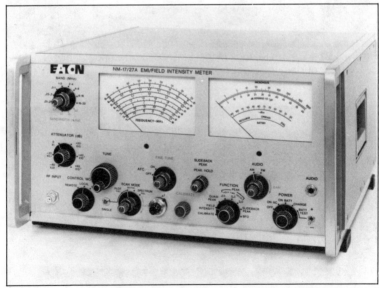

Figure 3.23—Eaton NM-17/27A EMI/Field Intensity Meter, 10 kHz to 32 MHz (courtesy of Eaton E.I.D.)

Figure 3.24—Eaton Emission Measuring Receivers, 3018: 9 kHz to 30 MHz; 3038: 25 to 1,000 MHz (courtesy of Eaton E.I.D.)

3.8.5 Microwave EMI Analyzers, 1 to 40 GHz

Growing usage of the electromagnetic spectrum at microwave frequencies is being accompanied by a corresponding growth in EMI testing in that frequency range. Primarily because they require expensive YIG components in their first LOs and other front-end circuits, the average cost of a microwave EMI analyzer approaches twice that of one with coverage from 10 kHz to 1,000 MHz.

Shown in Figs. 3.25 and 3.26 are representative examples of EMI analyzers designed to cover the microwave frequencies. Figure 3.25 shows an instrument introduced in 1986 to measure EMI over the frequency range from 0.5 GHz to 18.0 GHz, with optional available coverage to 40 GHz. As is the case with most EMI analyzers in

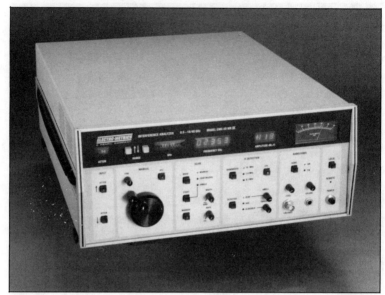

Figure 3.25—Electro-Metrics Model EMC-60 Microwave Interference Analyzer, 0.5 to 18/40 GHz (courtesy of Electro-Metrics®)

Figure 3.26—Eaton NM-67 Microwave EMI/Field Intensity Meter, 1 to 18/40 GHz (courtesy of Eaton E.I.D.)

this range of the frequency spectrum, front-end preselection is provided by tracking YIG filters which are tuned automatically to track the frequency determined by the first LO and IF. To retain sensitivity which might otherwise deteriorate because of losses in long cable runs, the entire front end of the instrument can be moved to a location near the signal source.

Consistent with its intended inclusion in automated systems, tuning and all other major functions of this instrument can be controlled either locally from the front panel or remotely by a computer via the IEEE-488 interface bus. Three selective bandwidths in decade ratios are provided over the entire tuning range of the instrument to optimize its sensitivity to both narrowband and coherent broadband signals. A built-in broadband generator can be activated to provide a broadband signal for automatic calibration of the instrument whenever the calibration function is selected. Detector functions include direct peak, slideback peak and true average. Both frequency and amplitude displays are LED-digital; the frequency display is accurate to ± 1.0 percent, while the amplitude display is automatically corrected for attenuation and calibration to indicate input voltage accurately to within ± 2 dB. To facilitate tuning of narrowband signals, the amplitude display is augmented by an analog tuning meter.

Among the features of the instrument shown in Fig. 3.26 are basic coverage to 18 GHz which is extended to 40 GHz by addition of an optional frequency converter. All control functions and data readouts for the entire 1 to 40 GHz range of frequency coverage are available on the front panel of the basic instrument.

3.8.6 Spectrum Analyzers and Other EMI Instrumentation

As discussed Section 3.7, spectrum analyzers are attractive for use in EMI testing because of their lower cost per octave of coverage, but problematic in that their basic design usually does not incorporate sufficient front-end preselection to permit accurate performance in the presence of impulsive EMI signals. However, despite their limitations, they are widely used and have many legitimate EMI test applications.

Shown in Figs. 3.27 and 3.28 are two typical modern spectrum analyzers which are useful for EMI testing. The unit shown in Fig. 3.27 offers digital storage and signal analysis over the frequency

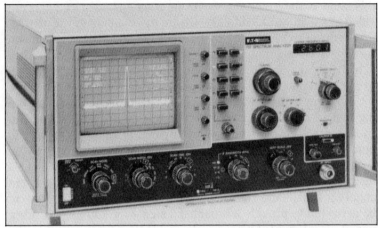

Figure 3.27—Eaton 757 Spectrum Analyzer (courtesy of Eaton E.I.D.)

Figure 3.28—HP 8568B RF Spectrum Analyzer with EMI Accessories (courtesy of Hewlett-Packard)

range from 1 kHz to 22 GHz. For appropriate applications, built-in preselectors covering the range 1.8 to 22 GHz can be bypassed by front-panel control to improve sensitivity by approximately 10 dB.

Shown as the second and third modules from the top of the rack in Fig. 3.28 is a spectrum analyzer functioning as the key element of a computer-automated EMI test system. Its operation is supplemented and enhanced by inclusion in the system of a quasipeak adapter (top module) and an RF preselector (fourth module). A system based on the equipment shown is designed for making military as well as commercial EMI measurements from 100 Hz to 1.5 GHz.

Similar in some respects to a spectrum analyzer, but different in that it operates only as an accessory to an EMI analyzer or other test receiver, is the type of instrument exemplified by that shown in Fig. 3.29. Sometimes also called a **panoramic adapter** or a **spectrum display unit**, this instrument provides a high-resolution display of the spectral contents of the bandpass of the IF output it accepts from the test receiver shown in Fig. 3.22.

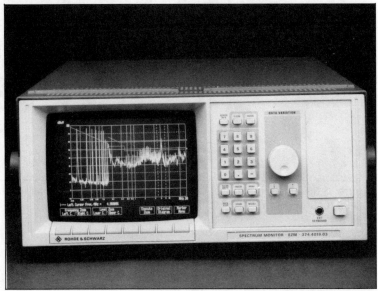

Figure 3.29—Rohde & Schwarz Spectrum Monitor EZM (courtesy of Rohde & Schwarz)

3.8.7 Calibration Instruments and Accessories

As discussed in Section 3.5, an impulse generator can be a very valuable and convenient source of coherent broadband energy which is calibrated in terms of spectrum amplitude, typically microvolts per megahertz. The impulse generators considered in this chapter are designed for calibration and other relatively low-level uses in conjunction with EMI analyzers; similar instruments with higher levels of output are useful for testing susceptibility (see Chapter 5).

Shown in Fig. 3.30 is an impulse generator which provides calibrated broadband spectrum amplitude levels over the frequency range from 10 kHz to 1 GHz. Its output is variable in 1 dB steps from 0 to +90 dBμV/MHz, at repetition rates which are variable in 1 Hz increments from 1 Hz to 100 Hz.

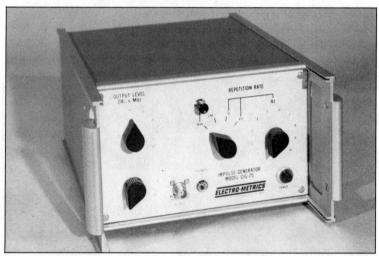

Figure 3.30—Electro-Metrics Calibrated Impulse Generator, Model CIG-25 (courtesy of Electro-Metrics®)

3.9 References

1. NAVSHIPS 94810, "The Radio Frequency Interference Meter," by the staff of the Moore School of Electrical Engineering, University of Pennsylvania, 1962 (available from Government Printing Office, Washington, DC).

2. SAE ARP-1972, "Recommended Measurement Practices and Procedures for EMC Testing," prepared by SAE AE4 Committee on Electromagnetic Compatibility (Warrendale, PA: SAE, January 1986).

3. DEF-STAN 59-41, (Part 3)/2, "Electromagnetic Compatibility; Part 3: Technical Requirements, Test Methods and Limits" (U.K.).

4. Sorger, G.U., "Using Preamp Gain to Improve Sensitivity of Spectrum Analyzers," *Microwaves and RF,* October, 1987.

5. Andrews, J.R. and Arthur, M.G., "Spectrum Amplitude—Definition, Generation and Measurement," NBS Technical Note 699 (Boulder, CO: National Bureau of Standards, October 1977).

6. IEEE Std. 376-1975, "Standard for the Measurement of Impulse Strength and Impulse Bandwidth" (New York: IEEE, 1975).

7. MIL-STD-462, "Electromagnetic Interference Characteristics, Measurement of," 31 July 1967.

8. CISPR (Secretariat) 850E, Report No. 42, "The Determination of the Amplitude Relationship Specified in CISPR Publication 1, 2, and 4," October 1970.

9. Palladino, J.R., "A New Method for the Spectral Density Calibration of Impulse Generators," *IEEE Transaction on EMC,* Vol. EMC-13, No. 1, February 1971, pp. 2-7.

10. Andrews, R.B., Jr., "An Impulse Spectral Intensity Measurement System," *IEEE Transactions on I&M,* Vol. IM-15, No. 4 pp. 209-303, December 1966.

11. Kanda, M. "Time and Amplitude Statistics for Electromagnetic Noise in Mines," *IEEE Transactions on EMC,* Vol. EMC-17, No. 3, August 1975, pp. 122-129.

12. ANSI C63. 12-1984, "Recommended Practice on Procedures for Control of System Electromagnetic Compatibility" (New York: IEEE/ANSI).

13. CISPR 16, "CISPR Specification for Radio Interference Measuring Apparatus and Measurement Methods," second edition, 1987.

Chapter 4

Sensors for EMI Emission Testing

This chapter covers the various sensors and related devices that intercept conducted or radiated EMI and convert it to two-terminal voltages for measurement. Analogous devices for testing EMI susceptibility are covered in Chapter 5.

4.1 Sensors and Accessories for Testing Conducted EMI Current

The sensors and related devices covered in this section are those used for testing conducted current: **current probes**, along with associated inverse amplifiers, capacitors and line impedance stabilization networks (LISNs) which are used as accessory items. Also discussed are **audio isolation transformers**. Figure 4.1 illustrates their basic functions of these devices in the context of a hypothetical test setup.

Although either the current probe or LISN can be used to measure conducted emissions on a power line (or ac mains), one or the other will usually be required by the governing document. Sometimes, as covered in Chapter 10, the two devices are used together. Similarly, either a current probe or a voltage probe will be the appropriate choice for measuring conducted EMI on inter-

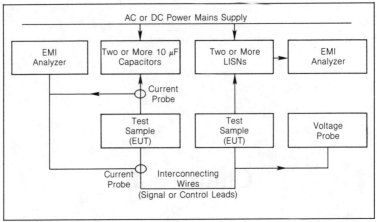

Figure 4.1—Testing Conducted Emissions

connecting signal and control leads and cables. It is important to use the specified sensor if the test results are to be compared to mandated limits; although it is theoretically simple to convert conducted current measurements to equivalent conducted voltage and vice versa, in actual practice this is not usually feasible because accurate values for all of the impedances required for the transposition are not easily determined.

4.1.1 Current Probes and Accessory Devices

Section 2.4.2 discusses the theoretical basis for the current probe, including the use of its transfer impedance to convert its output voltage to the current actually flowing in the conductor under test. Current probes are easy to use since they are simply hinged around one or more conductors and clamped shut. Figure 4.2 shows a typical current probe with its optional compensating amplifier, as discussed in Section 4.1.1.2.

Current probes work on the principle of treating the conductor under test as the primary winding of a transformer, around which the current probe is placed as the toroidal-wound secondary. The voltage induced in the secondary by the lines of flux from the primary is proportional to the permeability of the toroid, its cross-sectional area, its number of turns, the current flowing in the primary and the measurement frequency. Thus, as shown by Fig.

4.3, the transfer impedance increases with frequency at the rate of 20 dB per decade. The design principle also dictates that maximum output voltage for a given level of current will be obtained in a probe by maximizing permeability, number of turns on the toroid and toroidal area while keeping the toroidal radius relatively small.

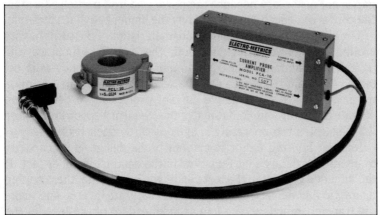

Figure 4.2—Electro-Metrics® Model PCL-10 Current Probe with PCA-10 Amplifier (courtesy of Electro-Metrics®)

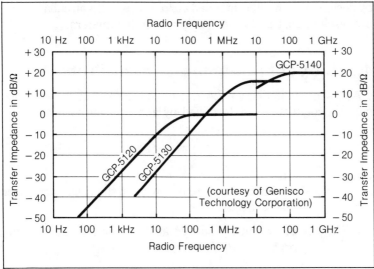

Figure 4.3—Typical Transfer Impedance of Current Probes

As already implied, the toroid is made in two equal halves which are joined by a hinge and clamped together. The mating faces are machined to maintain a small, controlled air gap which functions with the permeability of the core material to concentrate the magnetic field while avoiding core saturation at the power mains frequency. In probes designed for use in the UHF range, this air gap is not necessary because the powdered iron particles forming the core are adequately separated by the binder to avoid saturation.

The size, number and winding characteristics of the turns of wire around the toroid determine both the circuit inductance and parasitic capacitance. The maximum usable frequency falls between the main resonance and the second mode resonance, making it evident that any single current probe can be designed to operate over only a limited range of the frequency spectrum. Figure 4.3 illustrates the operating ranges of three such probes.

Another limiting factor in current probe design is its capacity to operate with large current flow in the conductor under test. If the intended current in the test conductor is too large, the resulting magnetic flux density in the toroid will saturate its core and make the transfer impedance no longer independent of the level of the conducted EMI. Consequently, current probes must be designed to handle the largest currents expected at dc or power-mains frequencies, with a value of 350 A being typical. Special probes can be designed for higher intended currents but with attendant compromises in cost and other performance parameters.

4.1.1.1 Calibrating the Current Probe

As discussed in Section 2.4.2.1, an unknown EMI current flowing in a conductor is determined by applying the formula:

$$I_{in} = V_{out} - Z_T$$

where,

I_{in} = the unknown current flowing in the conductor under test in dBµA

V_{out} = the voltage produced at the output of the current probe in dBµV

Z_T = the transfer impedance of the probe in dB relative to one ohm (1 dBΩ) as supplied by the probe manufacturer

The procedure for determining the transfer impedance, Z_T, is worth noting because it should be applied to confirm the characteristic furnished by the probe manufacturer in the event that damage is suspected. For example, the ferrite toroid could have been saturated or the windings burnt out by excessive current from the power mains. Also, physical damage from being dropped might be apparent, which misaligns the mating surfaces of the toroid or increases the width of the air gap. The calibration should be checked whenever damage is suspected.

Probably the simplest and most obvious check for probe performance is to substitute another probe known to be working properly into the test circuit and to compare current measurements. If such tests are done over the full available range of intended current flow and produce data agreeing to within 1 dB, the probe in question can be considered to be calibrated.

The probe also can be calibrated in a test setup similar to that used by the probe manufacturer. As shown in Fig. 4.4, a signal generator is used to drive a 50 Ω line terminated in a 50 Ω resistor, R_L. The test current, I_i, flowing through the lead to the resistive load is:

$$I_i = V_i/R_L = 0.02 \ V_i \qquad (4.2)$$

From Eq. (4.1), in dB:

$$Z_r = V_i - I_i$$

Thus, at each measurement frequency, the transfer impedance, Z_T, in dB relative to one ohm (dBΩ), is determined by subtracting the current calculated by Eq. (4.2) and expressed in dB relative to one microampere (dBμA), from the corresponding probe output voltage as measured at the input terminals of the EMI analyzer, in terms of dB relative to one microvolt (dBμV). If a high-impedance oscilloscope or RF voltmeter is used instead of an EMI analyzer, its input must be shunted to make it 50 Ω since the probe calibration is based on this load impedance.

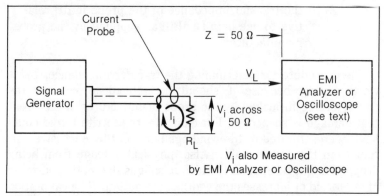

Figure 4.4—Test Setup for Measuring Transfer Impedance of Current Probe under No-Power Load Conditions

Note that in the test setup of Fig. 4.4, no power current is flowing in the conductor under test. Testing the probe under power-current loaded conditions requires special power sources and test equipment since upwards of 350 A of dc or 60/400 Hz ac might be used to drive a load. As tested by the manufacturer, audio and RF transformers capable of handling the load current are used to series inject a known audio-signal current.

4.1.1.2 Using Inverse Filters and Amplifiers with Current Probes

It is apparent from Eq. (4.1) and the accompanying discussion in Section 4.1.1.1 that measurement of the unknown current would be simplified if the transfer impedance, Z_T, were equal to 1 Ω (0 dBΩ) at all frequencies in the usable range of the current probe; i.e. the level of voltage in dBμV would be numerically equal to the current flow in dBμA producing it. Thus it would no longer be necessary for the test engineer or technician to apply a different factor at each frequency of measurement.

Two techniques may be employed to achieve this desired "flat" transfer impedance characteristic:

1. Where the transfer impedance is relatively high (e.g., 0 dB or more), attenuate the output voltage at the rate of 6 dB per octave (20 dB per decade) through a built-in filter consisting of a shunt capacitor and the 50 Ω input impedance of the EMI analyzer.

4.6

2. Where the transfer impedance is relatively low at low frequencies (e.g. – 50 dB at 60 Hz), let the output of the current probe drive an active network with a gain versus frequency characteristic which is the inverse, or complement, of the transfer impedance characteristic. Devices of this type, such as shown in Fig. 4.2, are available as accessories to current probes and provide a 0 dB transfer impedance above 30 Hz.

A 0 dB, or flat, transfer impedance is needed to obtain accurate measurements of coherent broadband conducted EMI because it is not feasible to apply a different correction factor for transfer impedance to each broadband component intercepted within the relatively wide passband needed for such measurements.

4.1.1.3 Ten-Microfarad Capacitor Decoupling

As will be discussed in Chapter 9, various test methods of MIL-STD-462, including CE01 and CE03, call for the use of 10 μF capacitors in conjunction with the current probes discussed immediately above. The intended purpose of the capacitors is to provide a sufficiently low-impedance path at the lowest frequency of interest and thus keep any EMI current from the power mains from being measured along with that from the test sample. Figure 4.5 shows the basic position of the capacitor in a test setup, while Fig. 4.6 illustrates that role more precisely.

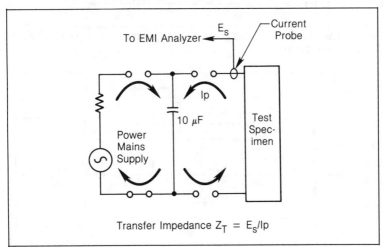

Figure 4.5—Equivalent RF Circuit of a 10 μF Capacitor

As a practical matter, there is a limit to how well the 10 μF capacitor can perform at relatively low EMI frequencies because of the rise in its impedance with decreasing frequency. It can be seen from Fig. 4.6 that the effectiveness of the capacitor for a given level of EMI on the power mains will depend on the relationship between its impedance and those of the power mains and the test sample. This is simple to calculate since the reactance of a 10 μF capacitor is 265 Ω at 60 Hz and 40 Ω at 400 Hz. However, because of the various factors affecting it, the lowest frequency at which the capacitor is effective could range from 1 to 10 kHz and even higher.

To determine experimentally the frequency at which the capacitor is sufficiently effective, with the capacitor grounded as in Fig. 4.6, measure the current in the test sample circuit, I_{tg}, and the current on the power mains, I_{pg}. Then measure the test circuit current again with the capacitor ungrounded (I_{to} in Fig. 4.7).

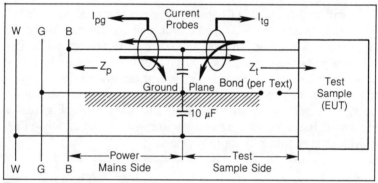

Figure 4.6—Ten-Microfarad Capacitors in Position for Measuring Test Sample RF Currents

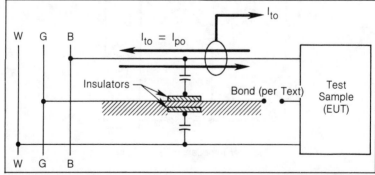

Figure 4.7—Ten-Microfarad Capacitors Insulated from Ground Plane to Determine their Effectiveness

4.8

Analyzing the possible results logically:

1. If $I_{to} \approx I_{tg}$, the capacitor is ineffective and its circuit impedance may be too high.
2. If $I_{to} < I_{tg}$, the capacitor is partly or totally effective.
   a. If $I_{pg} \geqslant I_{tg}$, you may be measuring some EMI current from power mains in the test sample.
   b. If $I_{pg} < I_{tg}$, you are measuring the test sample current

Only condition 2b appears to be valid. Uncertainty develops because both the power mains and test sample impedances are unknown. Also, it is not sufficient to measure the test sample current if its load is not a low impedance.

It has been proposed that only condition 2 be required, in which $I_{to} \leqslant 0.5 \, I_{tg}$. This would be inconclusive, since condition 2a could pertain. Under the circumstances, it appears to be far better than not testing at all. The only other condition which might be added is to omit measurements below 320 Hz where the reactance of the 10 μF capacitor $> 50 \, \Omega$. This offers some assurance that the test sample would appear as a constant EMI current source. A better, higher limit for the reactance for the capacitor might be 1 Ω, which corresponds to 16 kHz. This in part is why it has been proposed to limit the low-frequency power mains tests to a minimum frequency on the order of 10 to 15 kHz.[1]

Alternatively, an inductor may be selected for insertion in the power mains branch. For the lowest frequency, f, to be tested:

$$X_L = X_c, \text{ or } L = 1/(4\pi^2 f^2 C) \tag{4.3}$$

For the 10 μF capacitor, this becomes:

$$L = 2.5 \times 10^3/f^2 \text{ henries} \tag{4.4}$$

Thus:

Test Frequency	Series Inductance	Series Z @ 60 Hz	Comments
100 Hz	250.0 mH	94.0 Ω	Loads < 50 mA
300 Hz	25.0 mH	9.4 Ω	Loads < 500 mA
1 kHz	2.5 mH	1.0 Ω	Loads < 5 A
3 kHz	250.0 μH	Negligible	Loads < 50 A
10 kHz	25.0 μH	Negligible	No Limit

Another method of inserting a series inductor between the power mains and the 10 μF capacitor is to use the audio isolation transformer.* Its secondary is placed in series with the line, and its primary is left open-circuited. For dc circuits, a still better approach is to place the isolation transformer on the test sample side of the 10 μF capacitor. The primary then can be used to measure conducted emission currents at low frequencies (see Section 4.1.2). However, this solution still leaves open the possibility in condition 2a above that some EMI current from the power mains may be measured in the test sample circuit.

---

*See Solar Electronics Application Note AN622001.

4.1.1.4 LISN Decoupling

Although the LISN is primarily a device for testing conducted voltage, as discussed in Section 4.2.1, it is also used to stabilize impedance when using a current probe to test conducted current as shown in Fig. 4.8. The LISN is a two-terminal-pair network with output impedance (looking into the test sample side) stabilized to 50 Ω above a specified frequency, f_L, and below another frequency, f_H, at which parasitic or stray reactances degrade its performance. Between f_L and f_H, the LISN is used, per Notice 3 to MIL-STD-462 (U.S. Army tests), to ensure that all test sample currents are measured for a 50 Ω line source.

A side benefit derived from measuring the EMI current with the line source impedance stabilized to 50 Ω is that this opens the possibility of translating a data base of current measurements to one of voltage measurements and vice versa. This is not a purely

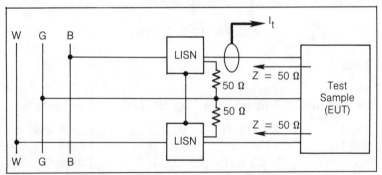

Figure 4.8—Application of LISNs for Stabilizing Test Sample Line Source Impedance to 50 Ω for RF Current Measurements

4.10

hypothetical problem, since some governing specifications, such as those based on CISPR recommendations, require voltage rather than current measurements.

4.1.1.5 Power Line Rejection Filters

As long as the ac mains current sampled by the current probe is less than 20 A or so, the EMI analyzer input circuits probably will not be overloaded by current probe pickup of the line fundamental or harmonic frequencies. However, when the ac mains current approaches the saturation level of the probe, it may be necessary to take measures to reduce the extent to which these signals reach the input of the EMI analyzer.

To alleviate this problem, notch filters and high-pass filters are available commercially for all commonly used power line frequencies and their harmonics. These devices can be inserted between the output of the current probe and the input of the EMI analyzer to reduce the level of the offending frequencies.

4.1.2 Audio Isolation Transformer

For dc power sources, it is possible to overcome the current probe weaknesses of frequency-variable transfer function and low sensitivity at low frequencies by using an audio isolation transformer. The basic circuit is shown in Fig. 4.9, and it provides both increased

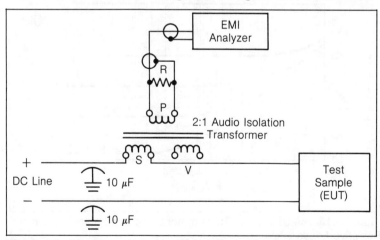

Figure 4.9—Test Setup Using an Audio Isolation Transformer to Measure Low-Frequency, Low-Amplitude EMI Current

sensitivity and relative flatness of response below 20 kHz and transfer of energy over the frequency range 30 Hz to 20 kHz. Curve 1 of Figure 4.10 shows the correction factors required to convert narrowband signals from dBμV, as read at the input to the EMI analyzer, to dBμA. Since the sign of the factor is negative for most of the frequency range, it is apparent that the sensitivity is considerably better than that of conventional current probes. The sensitivity achieved by this technique is better than −46 dBμA at frequencies above 5 kHz when using typical EMI analyzers covering this frequency range.

As shown by curves 2, 3 and 4 of Figure 4.10, by sacrificing sensitivity it is possible to obtain a correction factor curve which is flat over a much greater range of frequencies. Each curve is labeled to show the approximate value of resistor used to achieve the characteristic shown. The dropoff of sensitivity that remains at the lowest frequencies acts as a high-pass filter which reduces power line harmonics.

Problems arise when using the isolation transformer on an ac line (see footnote in Section 4.1.1.3.). Referring to Fig. 4.9, a voltage drop is produced in the test sample winding (S) by the flow of supply current to the EUT. This voltage, in turn, produces twice as much voltage in the output winding (P) at the power frequency. This induced voltage must be kept within the limitations of allowable power

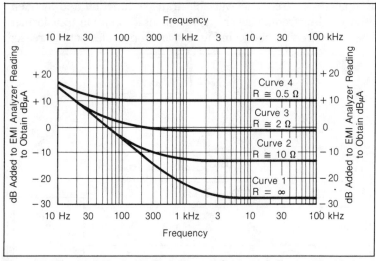

Figure 4.10—Audio Isolation Transformer Correction Factors for Various Resistive Loads

dissipation at the input to the EMI analyzer to prevent damage. Assuming that this limitation is 0.5 W for 400 Hz lines, the power frequency current must not exceed 16 A; also any resistor (R) used across the output winding (P) should have at least a 50 W rating when used with a 400 Hz line and be noninductive to avoid reactance errors.

4.1.3 Circuit Current Probes

Although not designed specifically for EMI testing, circuit current probes such as the one shown in Fig. 4.11 with its associated amplifier and display oscilloscope are often found useful for EMI analysis and troubleshooting. These devices are used with conventional ac voltmeters and oscilloscopes and differ from the EMI current probes discussed above in other ways, one of which is that the intended steady current flow must be limited to a smaller value. In this case, the value is 20 A or less. In the example shown, a variation of the Hall effect is used in the probe element to produce a relatively flat response from dc to 50 MHz. Transfer impedance is selectable in 12 calibrated steps, permitting measurements of current as high as 20 A.

Both the ac and dc components of a signal are accessed for display on an oscilloscope; thus, in a complex circuit, the dc, low-frequency and transient components can be viewed simultaneously.

The probe can also be used to measure the sums or differences of current levels in two separate wires: when the probe is clipped

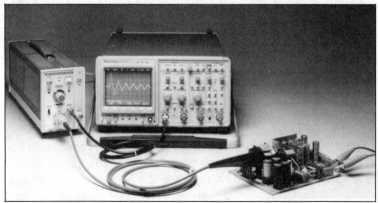

Figure 4.11—Tektronix A6302 Current Probe with Amplifier and Display Oscilloscope (courtesy of Tektronix, Inc.)

around wires carrying current in the same direction, the sum is displayed; by reversing the flow through the probe of one of the wires, the difference is obtained. Thus, currents in the two wires can be balanced by obtaining a zero difference, or null. This capability can be applied in EMC engineering to assess the effectiveness of twisted, shielded pairs used to mitigate magnetic field coupling in LF circuits. The current probe can readily determine the degree to which the balance of the line has been affected by problems from improper grounding or sneak paths. Several loops of the line can be placed through the probe to obtain increased sensitivity.

4.2 Sensors and Accessories for Testing Conducted EMI Voltage

Testing of the EMI voltage which is present on a conductor is required by a number of EMI standards, including that covering compliance to FCC Part 15J on computing devices. The sensors and related devices covered in this Section are those used for testing such conducted voltage: **LISNs, coupling capacitors** and **voltage probes**. Refer to Figure 4.1 for an illustration of their basic functions in the context of a hypothetical test setup.

4.2.1 Line Impedance Stabilization Networks

As introduced by the brief discussion in Section 2.4.3, the LISN is a buffer inserted between the power mains and the EUT. Its multiple functions are to:

1. Stabilize the impedance of the power mains as presented to the EUT
2. Couple to the EMI analyzer, for measurement, any EMI introduced onto the power mains by the EUT
3. Prevent any EMI on the power mains from reaching the EUT or being measured by the EMI analyzer

Referring to Fig. 4.12, which shows a typical LISN used for MIL-STD-462 testing, the LISN provides for direct connection of the 50 Ω terminals of the EMI analyzer to the 50 Ω connector on the LISN. Figure 4.13 shows a representative impedance versus frequency characteristic of such an LISN. The LISN is operated only over that portion of the frequency spectrum for which the impedance presented at its output connector remains close to a specified impedance, in this case 50 Ω. Thus, assuming a two-wire service, a second pair of LISNs would be required for coverage of the band up to 30 MHz, and three pairs are needed to extend coverage up to 400 MHz. Four identical units in each frequency segment are needed for a 3-phase, 4-wire service.

It should be noted on the schematic, Fig. 4.12, that the power leads from the power source and those from the test sample are RF isolated by the series inductance. This component has negligible reactance at 60 and 400 Hz to permit direct coupling of the power source to the test sample. RF noise on the power mains is shunted to ground through C_p. Conversely, any EMI from the test sample on the power leads is coupled to the 50 Ω connector through C_t.

Although use of the LISN and its voltage measurements has been largely phased out of test methods recommended by the U.S. military, it continues to be an important stabilizing element in setups using the current probe. On the other hand, the widely accepted CISPR recommendations continue to specify LISNs, using the term **artificial mains networks**. Figures 10.8 and 10.9 (Chapter 10) show schematics of the LISNs recommended for CISPR-based testing.

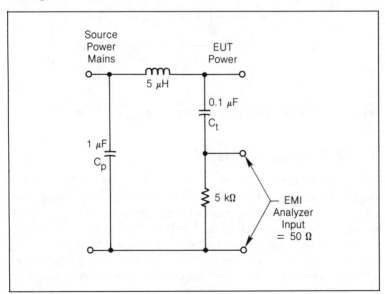

Figure 4.12—Schematic Diagram of a Typical LISN

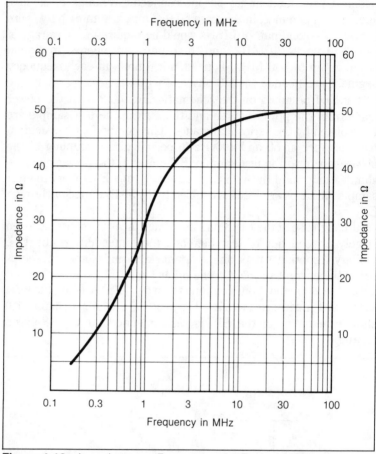

Figure 4.13—Impedance vs Frequency of a Typical LISN

4.2.2 Voltage Probes

Situations exist in which it is not feasible to use LISNs to access the EMI voltages on conductors. For example, the level of intended current flowing in the conductor can be too high for the LISN to handle, the impedance of the LISN can be too low for the high-impedance conductor being tested, or it may not be reasonable or safe to break the conducted path. In such cases a **line probe** or **voltage probe** is very useful, provided that some voltage divider loss of the EMI level to be measured can be tolerated. Figure 4.14 is the schematic of a line probe recommended by the FCC for measuring EMI emissions from computing devices when an LISN with adequate current handling capacity is not available and the calibration factor implied by the attenuation through the 1500 Ω resistor into the 50 Ω impedance of the EMI analyzer is allowable.

Another implementation of the voltage probe is exemplified by a series of **coupling blocks** (still specified by the U.S. Army for reprocurements) covering measurements in accordance with Method CE07 of Notice 3 to MIL-STD-462. These coupling blocks utilize a series capacitor as a high-pass filter to block the dc or power-mains ac and to couple the higher-frequency EMI to the EMI analyzer. They carry nomenclatures CU-891/URM-85 (150 kHz to 30 MHz) and CU-896/URM-85 (20 MHz to 1 GHz).

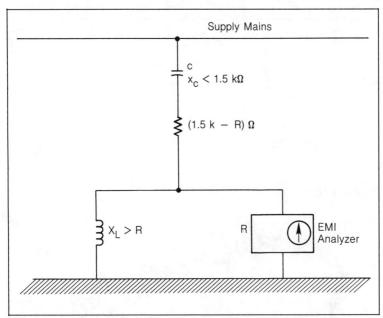

Figure 4.14—Line Probe Schematic for In Situ Measurement of Conducted Emissions

Where higher power-mains voltages are involved, the coupling block also contains a resistive voltage dividing network. The capacitor then series couples into the lower resistance leg of the network. The nomenclature for these devices, which provide a 26 dB coupling loss, is CU-892/URM-85 and CU-897/URM-85. Figure 4.15 shows the schematic of the CU-892/URM-85.

A third type of voltage probe used in EMI testing and analysis is represented by the passive and active probes provided by manufacturers of oscilloscopes. Most passive probes have built-in attenuation (e.g., 20 dB or 40 dB) to reduce circuit loading. Capacitance of typical passive probes when used with an oscilloscope is 2 to 20 pF, depending on probe type and cable length. Typical probe resistance is 10 MΩ. Figure 4.16 illustrates one such probe and its associated elements.

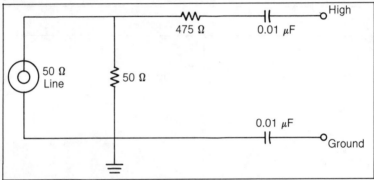

Figure 4.15—Coupling Block, CU-892/URM-85

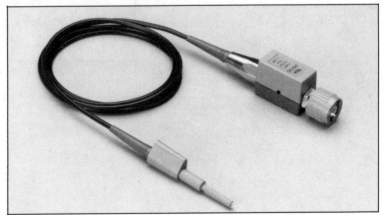

Figure 4.16—Tektronix P6136 Passive Voltage Probe (courtesy of Tektronix, Inc.)

Passive probes with their attendant attenuation cannot be used for measurements requiring maximum sensitivity. Applicable to such situations is an **active** probe, which generally employs a field-effect transistor or equivalent IC elements. Probes of this type, such as that shown in Fig. 4.17, boast low input capacitance, high input resistance and frequency response from dc to 900 MHz, all at unity gain. The probe shown derives its operating power from the associated oscilloscope or from an accessory power supply.

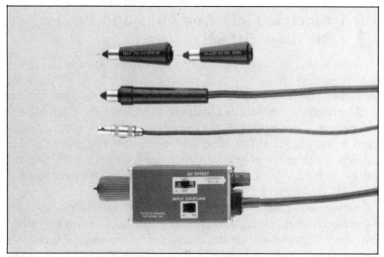

Figure 4.17—Tektronix P6201 Active FET Probe (courtesy of Tektronix, Inc.)

4.3 Antennas for Radiated EMI Emission Testing

This section covers the various antennas used in EMI testing to intercept EMI radiated from an EUT and make it available as two-terminal voltage for measurement by an EMI analyzer. The discussion is arranged by frequency range; for those ranges in which magnetic fields are tested, appropriate magnetic antennas are treated separately from those which measure electric fields. Similar antennas and devices for generating fields used to test EMI susceptibility are discussed in Chapter 5.

EMI testing makes unique demands on antennas because so many measurements are made in the near-field region of the radiating EUT or of the pickup antenna, or both. The fields to be measured are seldom either plane, homogeneous or uniform. The field lines are often curved, the electric and magnetic fields are often out of phase, and the waves that exist are often elliptically polarized.[2] Because of these considerations, each EMI test method must specify uniquely that a particular antenna be used and that it be applied in a precisely defined configuration with respect to the EUT and all peripheral equipment.

4.3.1 Electric-Field Antennas and Probes, 20 Hz to 50 kHz

As discussed in Section 2.5.2, the wave impedance in the near-field region of an electric-field radiator is very high; at the low-frequency end of the 20 Hz to 50 kHz coverage range, this can be on the order of 1,000 MΩ. Accordingly, to measure the electric field without unduly affecting it, the impedance of the antenna should itself be very high. At the same time, the output impedance of the antenna must be suitably low in order for its output voltage to be fed to the 50 Ω, 600 Ω or other relatively low input impedance of the EMI analyzer.

One version of a device developed to satisfy these requirements is the electric-field probe, or capacitive antenna, shown in Fig. 4.18. Two short dipole elements are connected as differential inputs to electrometer circuitry which exhibits suitably high input impedance and low output impedance. This active antenna is powered from its associated EMI analyzer, covers from 20 Hz to 50 kHz and may be oriented for any polarization aspect. Although there is no feasible way to filter its input, the output of this device may be filtered to reduce the amplitude of strong power mains harmonics which might overload the EMI analyzer.

Figure 4.19 is a photograph of a battery-operated, hand-held electric-field antenna with an adjustable rod element. Covering the range 30 Hz to 50 MHz, it is especially suitable for measuring shielding effectiveness of enclosures.

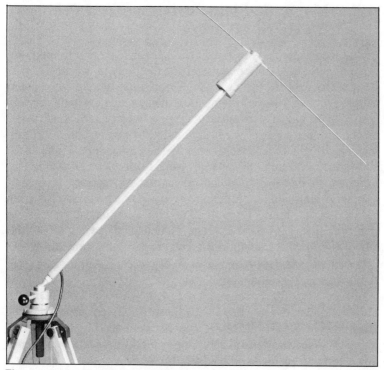

Figure 4.18—Electro-Metrics Model PEF-10/11 Active Electric Field Probe, 20 Hz to 50 kHz (courtesy of Electro-Metrics®)

Figure 4.19—EMCO Model 3301 Battery-Operated Active Electric-Field Antenna, 30 Hz to 50 MHz (courtesy of Electro-Mechanics Co.)

4.3.2 Magnetic-Field Antennas and Probes, 20 Hz to 50 kHz

The loop antenna is useful in the near-field region to intercept the magnetic-field component and substantially reject the electric-field component. Impedance of the loop must be relatively low to couple effectively to the low-impedance magnetic field in this region. The loop antenna satisfies these criteria because it is constructed as one or more turns of wire surrounded by nonferrous metal tubing which shields against electric-field components. Figure 4.20 shows a typical loop antenna covering from 20 Hz to 100 kHz.

Shown in Fig. 4.21 is a loop designed for military testing of magnetic emissions at a distance only 7 cm from the EUT, as detailed in Fig. 11.1 of Chapter 11 and its accompanying text. Note that the device shown incorporates an insulated spacing rod (to the left of the loop) to maintain the correct distance from the EUT.

Ferrite rods provide high permeability for intercepting magnetic fields and permit antenna factors superior to (lower than) loops of equivalent size. The ferrite rod antenna shown in Fig. 3.19 (Chapter 3) is the pickup sensor used with the variable-mu magnetometer described in Section 3.8.1. It can be used for highly sensitive magnetic specification or shielding effectiveness measurements down to frequencies as low as 0.1 Hz.

4.3.3 Electric-Field Antennas, 10 kHz to 30 MHz

Electric-field antennas for the 10 kHz to 30 MHz range are designed so that their physical lengths do not exceed 15 percent of a wavelength at the highest frequency of use, which at 30 MHz would be 1.5 m. Actual lengths and diameters are chosen to give convenient values for effective heights and impedances (see Section 2.5.5.1). Thus, the basic antenna for this range is a rod which is 1 m (41 in.) in physical length, giving it an effective height of 0.5 m. It is available in passive and active versions.

4.3.3.1 Passive Rod Antennas

The passive rod antenna, more commonly termed simply a **rod** or **whip**, is almost universally used for EMI electric-field testing from 10 kHz to 30 MHz, both in open-field and shielded-enclosure

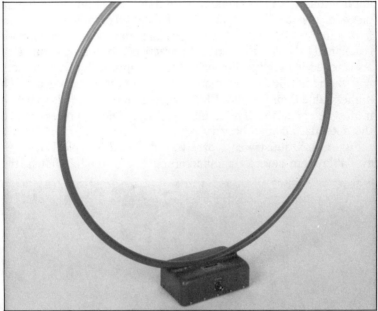

Figure 4.20—Electro-Metrics Model ALP-10/11 Magnetic-Field Loop Antenna, 20 Hz to 100 kHz (courtesy of Electro-Metrics®)

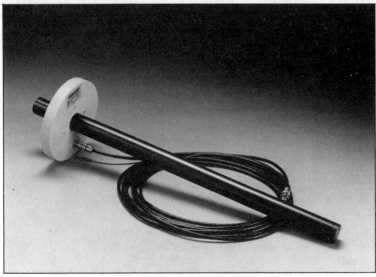

Figure 4.21—Electro-Metrics Model ELS-10 Magnetic Sensor (courtesy of Electro-Metrics®)

4.23

applications. The rod element, with its effective height of 0.5 m, presents an equivalent capacitance of about 10 pF at its base. Thus, it requires a different value of inductance at each frequency for resonance to make it resistive. In practice, a different inductance is switched in on a band-by-band basis to approach this condition, and the resulting combination is nearly resistive but at a much higher value than the 50 Ω EMI analyzer input terminals to which it must be connected. The resulting voltage-dividing process causes the antenna factor to be very high.

Figure 4.22 illustrates a passive rod antenna, typical of those available from several manufacturers. In the model shown, the

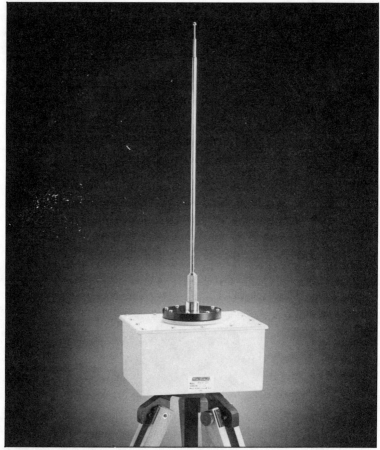

Figure 4.22—Electro-Metrics Model RVR-30 41-inch Passive Rod Antenna, 10 kHz to 30 MHz (courtesy of Electro-Metrics®)

resonating networks are chosen to correspond to the RF bands of the associated EMI analyzer and are relay switched automatically as bands are selected. Other models offer manual switching, and all typically require 10 steps for coverage from 10 kHz to 30 MHz. Figure 4.23 shows typical antennas factors for the same antenna.

The passive rod antenna can also be designed for longer elements and greater sensitivity; however, these are unwieldy to use and are not recommended by any of the most commonly used governing documents. Another version of the passive rod antenna is the electric-field probe. This device, which is used for applications such as searching for leaky enclosure seams, is characteristically small in size, untuned and noncalibrated. As compared to a magnetic probe, however, it is relatively ineffective for finding actual locations of leaks in shields. The relative unsuitability of the rod antenna for susceptibility testing is discussed in Chapter 5.

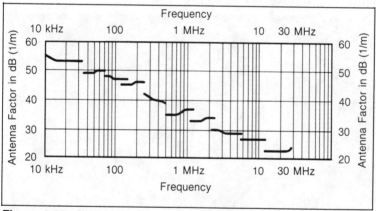

Figure 4.23—Typical Passive Rod Antenna Factors

4.3.3.2 Active Rod Antennas

The active rod antenna is designed to eliminate some of the problems of the passive rod, as identified above. It performs the basic function of accepting the high capacitive impedance of the rod element, amplifying its signal in a low-noise amplifier and then presenting it at a low emitter-follower output impedance for connection to the 50 Ω input terminals of the EMI analyzer. An active rod antenna covering 2 kHz to 100 MHz is shown in Fig. 4.24. Within the 10 kHz to 30 MHz range, its antenna factor is a constant 6 dB, ± 0.5 dB. The battery-operated unit can operate for 16 hours before recharging is required.

bient site surveys near transmitters. Similarly, while the dynamic range for narrowband signals may be 60 dB or greater, the dynamic range capability of the active rod antenna for coherent broadband signals might be as low as 20 dB.

Figure 4.24—Electro-Metrics Model RVA-30 Active Rod Antenna, 2 kHz to 100 MHz (courtesy of Electro-Metrics®)

4.3.4 Magnetic-Field Antennas, 10 kHz to 30 MHz

Loop antennas used for EMI test applications range in diameter from 76 to 914 mm (3 to 36 in.), have multiple turns of wire and are shielded against electric-field components. Although usually round, they also can be diamond-shaped or rectangular. The loop antenna is usually designed so that its diameter does not exceed 5 percent of a wavelength at the highest frequency of use, which would be 0.5 m at 30 MHz. Also, international practice limits the maximum diameter to 60 cm.

The antenna factor of a loop antenna is inversely proportional to the area of the loop, the number of turns on the loop, the magnetic permeability of the core of the loop and the operating frequency. If the loop is loaded with an impedance smaller than its self-reactance, its frequency dependence is eliminated but at the expense of a higher antenna factor.

Shown in Fig. 4.25 is a 635 mm (25 in.) diameter loop antenna used to intercept magnetic components of fields over the range

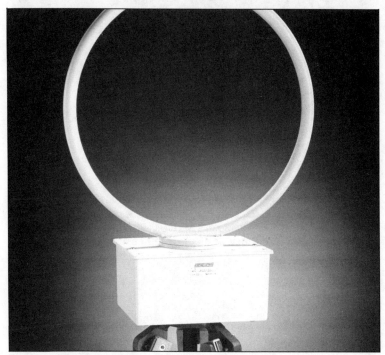

Figure 4.25—Electro-Metrics Model ALR-30 Magnetic-Field Loop, 10 kHz to 30 MHz (courtesy of Electro-Metrics®)

10 kHz to 30 MHz. Analogous to the high-impedance passive rod antenna discussed above, the loop antenna presents an inductive impedance much lower than 50 Ω over most of its operating range which, for optimum efficiency, must be broadly resonated and presented for 50 Ω transfer to the EMI analyzer. As with the passive rod antenna of Fig. 4.22, matching networks are switched in automatically, corresponding to the RF bands of the associated EMI analyzer. Antenna factors, which for the loop antenna are used to convert two-terminal voltage to magnetic field strength, or, in some cases, to equivalent electric field strength, are also relatively high at the lower frequencies, approaching 60 dB(1/m) for conversion to equivalent electric field at 10 kHz.

Magnetic-field ("sniffer") probes such as that shown in Fig. 4.26 are available to assist in locating leakage from shielded enclosures. Three probes, each 76 mm (3 in.) in diameter, collectively cover from 10 kHz to 230 MHz. As with the corresponding electric-field probe, these devices are untuned and noncalibrated.

Figure 4.26—Electro-Metrics Models MFA/B/C-25 Magnetic-Field Probes, 500 kHz to 30 MHz (courtesy of Electro-Metrics®)

4.3.5 Dipole-Based Electric-Field Antennas, 20 MHz to 1 GHz

In the frequency range from about 20 MHz to 100 or 200 MHz, some form of dipole antenna is usually used. This may be either a tuned, resonant dipole or a dipole with a broadened range of frequency coverage. In any case, the design includes a **balance to unbalance transformer (balun)** which has the purpose of matching the balanced output impedance at the feed point of the dipole to the unbalanced connector to which a coaxial cable can be attached for transmission to the EMI analyzer.

Above 100 or 200 MHz, complex-array antennas and aperture antennas often are used because of their higher gain compared to simple dipole antennas. However, because of the narrower antenna patterns which accompany their higher gain, they cannot be used too close to the EMI source being tested. A simple but conservative approximation relating the maximum usable gain for an antenna to the measurement distance at which it can be used is:

$$g \leqslant d\pi/\lambda \qquad (4.5)$$

where,

  g = maximum allowable gain
  d = measurement distance
  λ = wavelength of the field being measured

and,

  d and λ are in the same units

4.3.5.1 Tunable Dipoles

Tuned dipole antennas that are resonant at one-half wavelength are a special case of the general dipole antenna. Under proper conditions, these "half-wave" dipoles have certain theoretically predictable characteristics. Their effective length is λ/π when the antenna is immersed in a **plane-wave** field,[3] and the feed-point impedance is purely resistive if the antenna is far enough removed from ground or other obstacles. This purely resistive impedance is about 73 Ω for an infinitely thin antenna but ranges from 55 to 65 Ω in actual practice, depending on the length-to-diameter ratio of the elements.

If the antenna is removed from free-space conditions and brought to within a few wavelengths of ground, it begins to couple its image to the ground, causing its feed-point impedance to vary cyclically with increasing amplitude around the free-space value as it is brought closer to ground. Finally, when the antenna is closer than $\lambda/4$ from ground, the impedance decreases rapidly and can drop to a few ohms when the antenna is less than one-tenth wavelength (one meter at 30 MHz) above ground for horizontally polarized antennas, for which the effect is most pronounced. This may be seen in Fig. 4.27. In typical EMI measurements below 100 MHz,

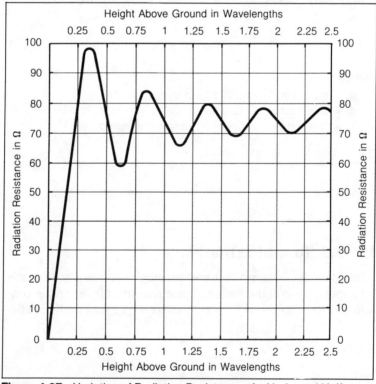

Figure 4.27—Variation of Radiation Resistance of a Horizontal Half-wave Dipole with Height Above Metallic Ground Plane

the antenna heights usually are less than a wavelength. Below 50 MHz, they are less than one-half wavelength, so the large impedance variations implied by Fig. 4.27 can cause significant changes in antenna factors.

The tunable dipole is a dual telescoping-arm antenna which is adjusted in length to be half-wavelength resonant at the test frequency. This adjustment is usually made from about 35 MHz to 1 GHz as the dipole becomes too long for shielded-room applications below about 35 MHz. For use below the lowest frequency of adjustment, an appropriate antenna factor is furnished by the manufacturer, taking into account the resultant performance degradation.

Over its range of adjustment, the tunable dipole is an excellent standard against which other antennas may be calibrated with regard to gain and antenna factor. However, it is of limited use in routine testing since its relatively narrow useful range at a given adjustment is incompatible with the automatic frequency scanning practices of modern EMI testing. The tunable dipole is also susceptible to errors at the lower end of its intended range of use because its length of about 5.5 m puts its ends about 3 m from the EUT when its center is only the prescribed 1 m from the EUT. Also, at low frequencies, the tips of the antenna elements are frequently so near the walls of the shielded enclosure that the dipole is capacitively loaded and detuned. Because of such considerations, the tuned dipole is no longer used for MIL-STD-461 or other EMI testing based on 1 m spacing in shielded enclosures. However, the tunable dipole continues to be useful in open-area EMI testing at spacings of 3 m or more from the EUT, whenever its inherently narrowband response can be tolerated.

Figure 4.28 shows a typical set of tuned dipoles, and Figure 4.29

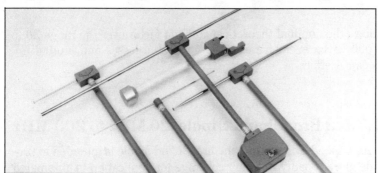

Figure 4.28—EMCO Model 3121 Adjustable Element Dipole Antenna Set, 28 MHz to 1 GHZ (courtesy of Electro-Mechanics Co.)

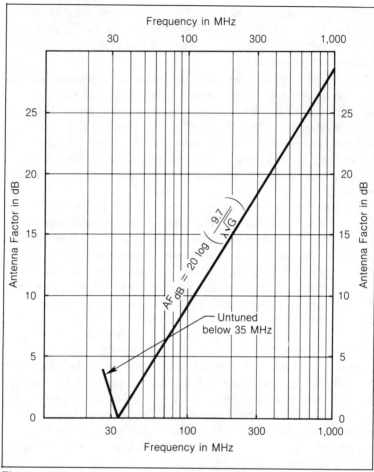

Figure 4.29—Antenna Factor for a Tuned Dipole

shows the nominal theoretical antenna factor over the range 30 to 1,000 MHz, exclusive of cable and balun losses and mutual impedance effects.

4.3.5.2 Broadband Dipole, 20 MHz to 200 MHz

As implied by its name, the broadband dipole is intended to provide more broadly resonant coverage for application to automated testing and thus overcome the narrowband limitations of the tuned dipole. This is accomplished by making the dipole elements much larger in diameter and by broadening the response of the accompanying balun. One or two sets of additional elements are furnished, to be attached to extend coverage to lower frequencies. Each fixed length of the antenna is useful over approximately three octaves of frequency coverage, providing a considerable advantage over a tunable dipole for automated testing.

Figure 4.30 shows antenna factors for a typical broadband dipole antenna, both with and without its two sets of extensions. As long as overall sensitivity is adequate, it is obviously advantageous to accept the accompanying degradation in antenna factor and use the

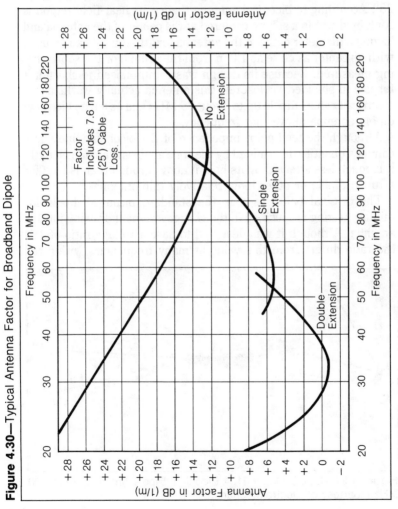

Figure 4.30—Typical Antenna Factor for Broadband Dipole

antenna over the maximum range possible without adding the extensions. Although superseded by the biconical antenna for MIL-STD-461 testing, the broadband dipole is still used when older specifications apply.

4.3.5.3 Biconical Dipoles, 20 MHz to 300 MHz

The biconical dipole illustrated in Fig. 4.31 has the typical antenna factor shown in Fig. 4.32 and is one of those specified by MIL-STD-462. It is about 1.38 m long and has a cone angle of about 26°. According to biconical antenna theory, its near-field region is contained within a sphere centered at the center of the antenna and having a diameter equal to the antenna length; thus, it can be used with its center as close as 1.0 m from the ground or the source being measured. Because its design was compromised to shorten it for use in shielded enclosures, this antenna actually works as an electrically short dipole up to about 75 MHz and as a true biconical dipole antenna above that frequency.

Although the feed-point impedance of the biconical dipole is a complex quantity determined by the cone angle and antenna length, it is much less affected by its height above ground than is true for a tuned dipole or other long, relatively thin antennas.[2]

The original balun used in the standard biconical dipole for military testing is specified in the U.S. government drawing for this antenna. Although it was designed to have a voltage ratio of 1:1, the ratio differs from this value at many frequencies within the

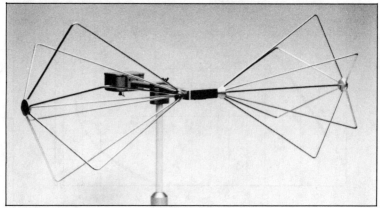

Figure 4.31—EMCO Model 3104 Biconical Dipole Antenna, 20 to 200 MHz (courtesy of Electro-Mechanics Co.)

coverage range of the antenna, making any accurate prediction of its performance impractical. As discussed in Ref. 4, a reliable program of measurements is the only practical way to determine antenna factors for the biconical dipole.

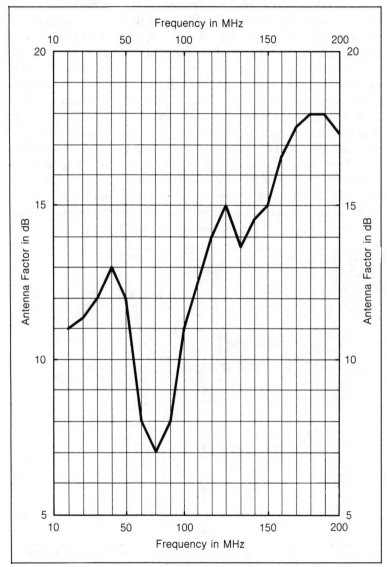

Figure 4.32—Typical Antenna Factor for Biconical Dipole

4.3.5.4 Log Periodic Dipole Array Antennas, 200 MHz to 1 GHz

The log periodic dipole array antenna is another special version of the general dipole antenna. Because it is usually designed for use at frequencies above 100 MHz, its relatively small physical size makes it usable relatively nearer to ground and other obstacles. The gain is usually 7 to 8 dB relative to isotropic, or 5 to 6 dB referred to an ideal half-wave resonant dipole. This means that the pattern is more concentrated than that of a simple dipole, making these antennas similar in operation to aperture antennas. The beamwidth, or angle subtended by the half-power points in the main pattern lobe, is typically 70 to 80 degrees in the plane of the elements (E-plane) and 120 to 150 degrees in the plane perpendicular to the elements (H-plane). The front-to-back gain ratio ranges from 10 to 30 dB, and the antenna output is designed to present a VSWR of much less than 2:1 to a 50 Ω unbalanced load.

Figure 4.33 shows a log periodic array dipole antennas of this type, while Fig. 4.34 shows typical antenna factors.

Figure 4.33—EMCO Model 3146 Log Periodic Antenna, 200 MHz to 1 GHz (courtesy of Electro-Mechanics Co.)

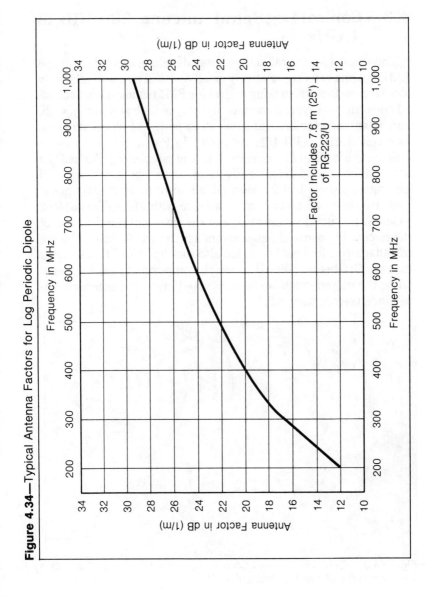

Figure 4.34—Typical Antenna Factors for Log Periodic Dipole

4.3.6 Conical Log Spiral Antenna, 200 MHz to 1 GHz

The conical log spiral antenna was developed as a broadband EMI antenna offering relatively small physical size and relatively low antenna factors, making it ideal for EMI testing within shielded enclosures. A typical antenna of this type is shown in Fig. 4.35, and its antenna factors and some other pertinent characteristics, as given in MIL-STD-461, are shown in Fig. 4.36.

Since the conical log spiral antenna is circularly polarized, its antenna factors, as given in Fig. 4.36, should be increased by 3 dB when the field being measured is known to be linearly polarized. However, all testing in accordance with MIL-STD-461/462 assumes no such foreknowledge of the field and requires use of the circularly polarized-based antenna factors as furnished by the manufacturer. It should be noted also that VSWR of this antenna exceeds 3:1 below 300 MHz, which complicates measurements when the output cable is not terminated in its characteristic impedance (see Section 8.2.1).

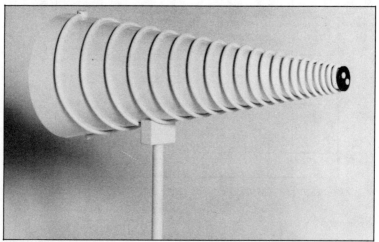

Figure 4.35—EMCO Model 3101 Conical Log Spiral Antenna, 200 to 1,000 MHz (courtesy of Electro-Mechanics Co.)

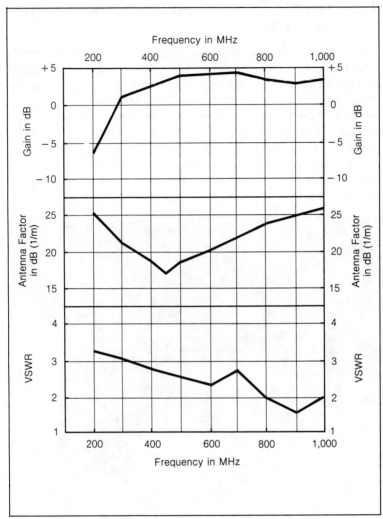

Figure 4.36—Typical Performance Data for Conical Log Spiral Antenna

4.3.7 Double-Ridged Guide Antenna, 200 MHz to 2 GHz

As illustrated in Fig. 4.36, the double-ridged guide antenna is basically a microwave horn which employs double-ridged waveguide to expand its bandwidth to more than three octaves, as compared to typically less than one octave for a conventional waveguide horn. A further benefit of using the ridged waveguide is to reduce the physical size from that which would otherwise be realized for operation at such relatively low frequencies. The superior performance of this antenna can be deduced from a quick inspection of Fig. 4.38, which shows its antenna factor and gain characteristics.

Figure 4.37—Double-Ridged Guide Antenna, 200 MHz to 1 GHz

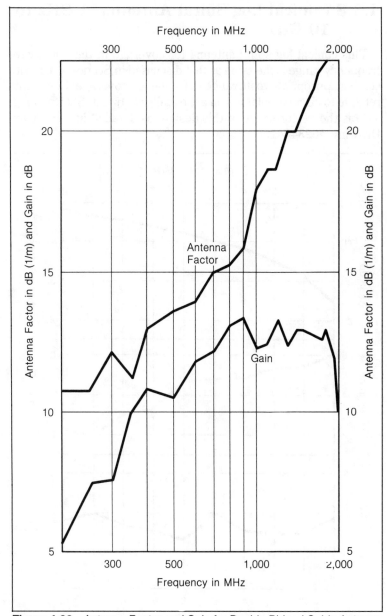

Figure 4.38—Antenna Factor and Gain for Double-Ridged Guide Antenna

4.3.8 Conical Log Spiral Antenna, 1 GHz to 10 GHz

This conical log spiral antenna for coverage in the microwave frequency range is the same as that discussed in Section 4.3.5, with scaling appropriate to its range of frequency coverage. Comments relative to circular polarization are equally pertinent. Shown in Fig. 4.39 is the performance of this design, as detailed in U.S. Army Drawing #6234041.

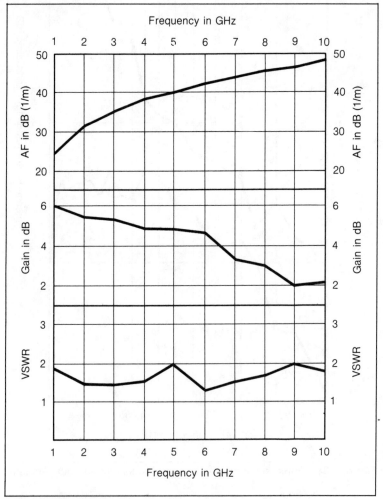

Figure 4.39—Typical Performance of Conical Log Spiral Antenna

4.3.9 Double-Ridged Guide Antenna, 1 GHz to 18 GHz

The double-ridged guide antenna for coverage in the microwave frequency range, as shown in Fig. 4.40, is a scaled-down version (in size) of that discussed in Section 4.3.7. As can be seen in Fig. 4.41, its performance characteristics are superior to those of the conical log spiral antenna discussed above.

Figure 4.40—EMCO Model 3115 Double-Ridged Guide Antenna, 1 to 18 GHz (courtesy of Electro-Mechanics Co.)

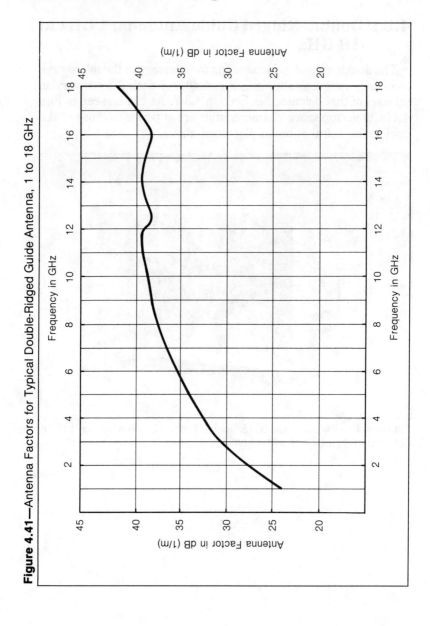

Figure 4.41—Antenna Factors for Typical Double-Ridged Guide Antenna, 1 to 18 GHz

4.3.10 Horn-Fed Parabolic Dish Antennas, 12 GHz to 40 GHz

A 457 mm (18 in.) diameter dish illuminated by a small horn is specified for harmonic and spurious test in accordance with Method RE03 of MIL-STD-462, involving radiated emissions from test items in the open field. Typical antenna factor for this antenna is 19 dB.

A version of this antenna scaled down to a 305 mm (12 in.) dish is used with either of two separate horns to cover 18 to 26 GHz or 26 to 40 GHz, with typical antenna factors of about 23 dB.

4.3.11 Use of the Antenna Factor

As discussed and analyzed in Section 2.5 of Chapter 2, the antenna factor, AF, is a convenient term which converts a two-terminal voltage at the output terminals of the antenna, as measured into a specified load, into the field strength of the electromagnetic field producing that voltage. Therefore, the operator need only determine the output voltage, V, and apply the antenna factor, AF, to obtain the field strength, E:

$$E = V \times AF \qquad (4.6)$$

where,
E = electric field strength in μV/m
V = antenna terminal voltage in μV
AF = antenna factor, in units of 1/m

In dB terms, with E in dBμV/m, V in dBμV and AF in dB (1/m):

$$E = V + AF \qquad (4.7)$$

However, as shown in Fig. 4.42, precautions must be taken to assure that the voltage to which the antenna factor is applied is actually that appearing at the antenna terminals; i.e., before any loss in the transmission path to the EMI analyzer. For convenience, Tables A.3 and A.4 (Appendix A) give typical attenuations of coaxial and waveguide transmission lines, respectively, which can be used to approximate this loss.

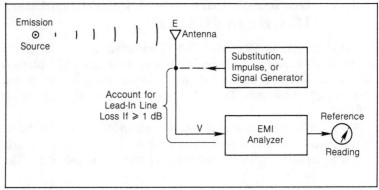

Figure 4.42—Role of Cable Attenuation in Radiated Measurements

Table 4.1 summarizes typical antenna factors for some of the electric field antennas discussed in this chapter. As is apparent from Eqs. (4.6) and (4.7), the lower the antenna factor, the more effective the antenna, i.e., the higher the voltage produced by a given field strength.

Table 4.1—Representative Antenna Factors

Antenna Type	Frequency Range	AF in dB
Active Electric-Field Probe	20 Hz to 50 kHz	23 to 33
1 m (41-inch) Passive Rod	10 kHz to 30 MHz	24 to 54
Active Rod	14 kHz to 30 MHz	0 to 6
Tuned Dipole	28 MHz to 1 GHz	−1 to 33
Broadband Dipole	20 MHz to 200 MHz	0 to 17
Biconical Dipole	20 MHz to 300 MHz	12 to 19
Log Periodic Dipole Array	200 MHz to 1 GHz	10 to 25
Conical Log Spiral	200 MHz to 1 GHz	18 to 26
Double-Ridged Guide	200 MHz to 1 GHz	11 to 18
Double-Ridged Guide	1 GHz to 18 GHz	24 to 43
Horn-Fed Parabolic Dish	12 GHz to 40 GHz	19 to 23

4.3.12 Conversion between Field Strength and Antenna-Induced Voltage

If a data base for radiated EMI has been built on an older specification calling for units of antenna induced voltage, it can be converted to units of field strength by using the relationship established in Section 2.5.5.1 of Chapter 2: $E = V_o/h_e$, where V_o is the antenna induced voltage and h_e is the effective height of the antenna used to accumulate the original data. For a 1 m (41 in.) rod with E in dBμV/m and V_o in dBμV, the equivalency is:

$$E = V_o + 6 \text{ dB} \qquad (4.8)$$

For a tunable dipole, it is:

$$E = V_o - 20 \log (\lambda/\pi) \qquad (4.9)$$

It must be observed, however, that the effective field strength obtained by applying these equations is that which existed at the distance from the test sample at which the antenna induced voltage was originally measured. Thus, if the original antenna induced voltage was measured at 305 mm (1 ft.) distance as required by MIL-I-6181D, the field strength thus calculated would also be that at the 305 mm distance and not at the 1 m MIL-STD-461/2 distance. Further, the field strength cannot be simply extrapolated to the longer distance because the measurements are in the near-field region (length $< \lambda/2\pi$) for frequencies up to 150 MHz.

Shown in Fig. 4.43 is a setup for determining the ratios between the field strength at the two distances. The ratio of the 1 m field strength, E_2, to the 305 mm field strength, E_1 is:

$$\frac{E_2}{E_1} = \frac{V_{L2} \times (AF_2)}{V_{L1} \times (AF_1)} \qquad (4.10)$$

or,

$$E_2 = \frac{E_1 \times V_{L2}(AF_2)}{V_{L1}(AF_1)} = \frac{V_{01} \times V_{L2}(AF_2)}{h_e \times L_{L1}(AF_1)} \qquad (4.11)$$

where,

$$V_{01} = \text{the antenna induced voltage at 305 mm (1 ft.)}$$
$$V_{L1}, V_{L2} = \text{the loaded antenna output voltages}$$
$$(AF_1), (AF_2) = \text{the antenna factors for the antennas spaced at 305 mm (1 ft.) and 1 m, respectively}$$

4.47

If it is assumed that $(AF_1) \approx (AF_2)$, Eq. (4.11) becomes:

$$E_2 = \frac{V_{01} \, V_{L2}}{h_e \, V_{L1}} \qquad (4.12)$$

For the 1 m (41-inch) rod, with E_2 in dBμ/m and V_{01} in dBμV:

$$E_2 = V_{01} + 6 \text{ dB} + 20 \log(V_{L2}/V_{L1}) \qquad (4.13)$$

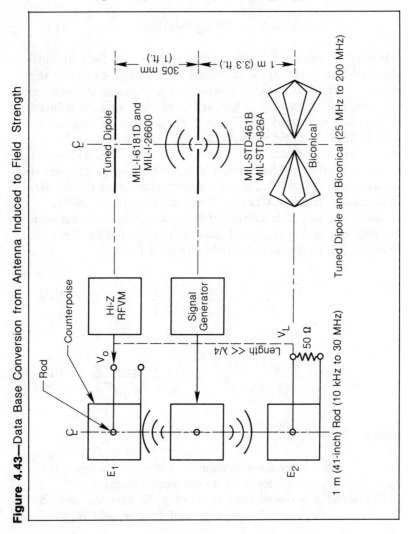

Figure 4.43—Data Base Conversion from Antenna Induced to Field Strength

The voltage produced by each of the two receiving antennas should be measured with the other receiving antenna present and then absent. If there is a significant loading effect difference, i.e., 2 dB or more, then the voltages should be measured with the other antenna absent. Also, the two antennas should produce equal voltages when equidistant (either 305 mm or 1 m) from the source.

A similar procedure is used to convert antenna induced data based on a tuned dipole antenna at 305 mm to electric field strength at 1 m. The procedure is likely to be less uncertain, however, if the setup in Fig. 4.43 is used in which the center of the MIL-STD-462 antenna is aligned with the center of the tunable dipole antenna. To preclude continuous tuning of a dipole during measurements, it is normally fix-tuned in half-octave steps. In accordance with Eq. (4.11):

$$E_2 = V_{01} - 20 \log (\lambda/\pi) + 20 \log [V_{L2}(AF_2)/V_1(AF_1)]$$

$$(4.14)$$

Here, V_{L2} and (AF_2) would be based on use of the biconical antenna from 20 to 200 MHz and on the conical log spiral antenna from 200 to 1,000 MHz. The lengths of antenna cables should be the same to avoid introducing error. Because the dipole is tuned to 35 MHz when making measurements from 25 to 35 MHz, it may be better to use the first part of Eq. (4.11), rather than the second.

4.3.13 Antenna Performance Condition

Despite the fact that they are usually passive devices, EMI measurement antennas must be handled carefully to avoid damage which alters their electrical characteristics. The center pins of coaxial connectors can become disconnected from their cable center conductors or completely dislodged. Sometimes a damaged antenna can still provide an output voltage, as from capacitive coupling at higher frequencies. Rod antennas can develop poor switch contacts or have tuned inductors altered in value by overloading during use for susceptibility testing. This vulnerability to physical damage makes it imperative that the calibration of EMI antennas be checked periodically.

The simplest way to check an antenna is to substitute another of the same manufacturer and model number into the same physical position in the setup and determine whether the same EMI analyzer reading is obtained. This check typically is made at three frequencies per octave, and differences between antennas at each frequency should not exceed 1 dB.

4.4 Other Devices for EMI Emission Testing

4.4.1 Absorbing Clamp, 30 to 1,000 MHz

The absorbing clamp was developed in Switzerland by de Stadelhofen and is recommended by the CISPR for measurement of **radiated** EMI from ac-powered appliances in the frequency range 30 to 1,000 MHz.[5] Impetus for its development was the need to overcome difficulties associated with finding or creating interference-free ambient environments which were suitable for making radiated EMI measurements at VHF and UHF frequencies.

Application of the absorbing clamp is based on the fact that low-frequency EMI from an EUT is mostly radiated from its ac power cable. A device capable of measuring such EMI energy off the cord would obviously provide an attractive alternative to actual radiated measurements. The absorbing clamp shown in Fig. 4.44 is such a device.

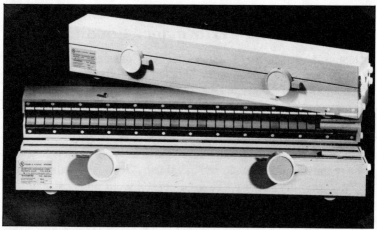

Figure 4.44—Rohde & Schwarz MDS-21 Absorbing Clamp, 30 to 1,000 MHz (courtesy of Rohde & Schwarz)

As shown in Fig. 4.45, the absorbing clamp consists essentially of three components:

1. A number of ferrite rings surrounding the ac power cable of the EUT; these serve to absorb any EMI from the power mains and to stabilize the mains impedance presented to the EUT to about 150 Ω
2. A coupling transformer at the EUT end of the absorbing rings; this produces an output proportional to the EMI current flowing in the ac line
3. A number of ferrite rings designed to prevent unwanted currents from flowing on the surface of the coaxial cable that connects the transformer to the EMI analyzer

The ferrite rings of components 1 and 3 are split into half rings, with each half in the jaws of the clamp so that the ac power cord can be inserted within the channel of rings without having to remove its plug. The EUT is placed on an insulating support and its ac line cord is held horizontally at the same height, the clamp being arranged so that it can be moved up and down the cord on its rollers. As the clamp is shifted along the cable away from the EUT, the EMI analyzer indicates various maxima and minima as a result of the standing waves present on the cord. The EMI level

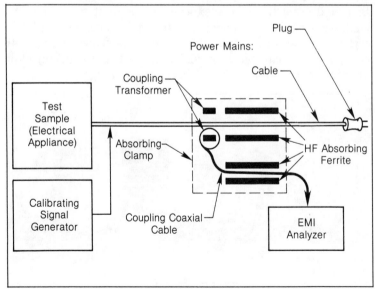

Figure 4.45—Basic Elements of Absorbing Clamp

is measured at the first maximum unless the plug prevents this; in that event it is measured at the second maximum using an extension cord. The largest of the peaks is taken as the measurement of record.

The output of the coupling transformer (component 2) into 50 Ω is a voltage which is proportional to the EMI current and EMI power developed in the 150 Ω impedance of the ac line.

4.4.2 RF Rejection Networks

When measuring harmonic and spurious EMI conducted on antenna terminals or radiated from an antenna integral to the EUT, it is often necessary to suppress the intended signal to avoid erroneous measurements as a result of overloading the front end of the EMI analyzer. Although low-pass filters can sufficiently reject strong harmonics of the fundamental, rejection of the fundamental itself (so that possible signals close to it in frequency can be measured) requires the use of highly selective, tunable rejection filters such as the commercially available unit shown in Fig. 4.46.

Unless sufficient rejection of the fundamental frequency is achieved, the EMI analyzer is likely to generate spurious responses or indicate improper readings as a result of masking. Since no more than 60 dB rejection can be expected in the front end of the EMI analyzer itself, it is not uncommon to require an additional 60 dB rejection ahead of its input. The three units shown in Fig. 4.46 collectively are capable of providing as much as 100 dB rejection over the entire 10 kHz to 1 GHz frequency range.

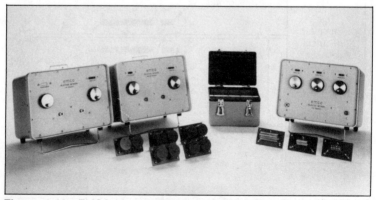

Figure 4.46—EMCO Model 3011 Rejection Networks

4.5 References

1. Notice 3 (Army) to MIL-STD-462, Method CE02.
2. Bronaugh, E.L., "Antennas for EMI Measurements"; *RF Design*, November/December, 1986.
3. Greene, F.M., "NBS Field-Strength Standards and Measurements (30 Hz to 1,000 MHz)," *Proceedings of the IEEE*, Vol. 55, No. 6, June, 1967, pp. 970-981.
4. Bronaugh, E.L., "Open-Site Verification of EMC Antenna Factors," *Electro/83 Record*, Session B, New York, April 19-21, 1983.
5. Publication 16, "CISPR Specification for Radio Interference Measuring Apparatus and Measurement Methods," second edition, (Geneva: Bureau Central de la Commission Electrotechnique Internationale, 1987).

Chapter 5

Instrumentation and Transducers for EMI Susceptibility Testing

This chapter discusses instruments used to generate and amplify EMI test signals and the various injectors, antennas and related devices which conduct or radiate those signals to the equipment under test (EUT) to measure its EMI susceptibility. All of the basic instruments and accessory devices needed to perform EMI susceptibility testing are discussed in this chapter, while specific configurations of them into practical systems for testing conducted and radiated susceptibility are covered in Chapters 12 and 13, respectively.

Caution: Extreme care must be taken to protect both personnel and measurement instrumentation against the high levels of power and radiated fields produced by most of the instruments and field generators discussed in this chapter!

5.1 Test Signal Sources for EMI Susceptibility Testing

Test signal sources for testing EMI susceptibility fall into two basic categories:

1. Generators of sine wave signals, both CW and modulated, including sweepers
2. Generators of special waveforms, including pulses and damped sinusoids

All of the instruments discussed in this section either drive directly or feed power amplifiers which, in turn, drive:

1. Signal injectors (see Section 5.2.1) for conducted EMI susceptibility testing of power mains or signal and control leads
2. Antennas or special structures (see Section 5.2.2) which generate electric or magnetic fields for radiated susceptibility testing of various test samples

5.1.1 CW and Modulated Sine Wave Generators

5.1.1.1 Sweep Oscillators

Requirements for testing susceptibility to CW and modulated CW signals extend from 30 Hz to over 10 GHz. Because of the relatively low efficiencies of antennas and other radiated-field generators over much of this range, the power required from the sources feeding them is well in excess of the +4 to +10 dBm level available from standard signal generators. Thus, RF sweep oscillators, termed **sweepers**, were developed especially for EMI susceptibility testing. They feature outputs greater than +10 dBm and are capable of being swept over many octaves of frequency. However, the subsequent development and ready availability of general-purpose signal generators capable of sweeping over many decades of frequency with leveled outputs, and of wideband amplifiers capable of amplifying those outputs to the required levels of power, led to their combined use as a replacement for most EMI-dedicated sweepers.

5.1.1.2 Power Oscillators and Amplifiers for EMI Susceptibility Testing

When selecting instrumentation and field generators for testing radiated susceptibility to field strengths from 1 V/m to 100 V/m, paramount consideration should be given to selection of the most efficient field transducer; each dB of increase in field strength is much more costly when it must be achieved through higher amplifier output power as compared to higher effectiveness in the field transducer (higher transmitter antenna factor: see Section 2.7.1.1).

Other considerations which should be observed when choosing the components of an EMI susceptibility test system include the following:

1. Since the respective frequency ranges of the various components will seldom match, careful selection of each is necessary to assure that there are no gaps in coverage and that the number of equipment changes is minimized.
2. With regard to the choice of amplifiers, it is generally true that the higher the power output capability of the amplifier, the smaller the frequency range over which that power can be achieved.
3. The signal sources and leveling preamplifiers that feed the power amplifiers should have the widest possible bandwidths. Only one or two sources and two leveling preamplifiers should be needed for coverage from 10 kHz to 1,000 MHz.
4. The input/output (I/0) impedances and power requirements of the signal source and the leveling/power amplifiers it is feeding must be compatible. The gain of the power amplifier must be sufficient to drive its output to maximum at each frequency.
5. The power amplifier must be designed to operate into a wide range of load impedances. It must be able to absorb the power reflected from high voltage standing wave ratio (VSWR) loads without losing stability or shutting down.
6. Power amplifier specifications must be analyzed very carefully to determine the maximum power actually available at each frequency in its coverage range. If a guaranteed power output capability is not specified, it may be necessary either to obtain a commitment from the manufacturer or to deduce it from the available specifications for maximum output, nominal output and output flatness.

5.1.1.3 Representative Power Oscillators

The **power oscillator** is arbitrarily defined to be a source of RF power of 1 W or more which is tunable over at least one octave of frequency. Figure 5.1 is a photograph of a power oscillator which produces triangular, square and sine waves at 100 W levels with selectable sweep rates or manual control over the frequency range from 15 Hz to 150 kHz. Frequency is variable over a range of 10:1 in each of four selectable steps. A calibrated tuning dial covers the range for manual tuning, while an automatic sweep selector switch provides a choice of sweeping at a rate of either once or 10 times per minute. A rear-panel connector provides a voltage suitable for driving the X-axis of an X-Y plotter.

Figure 5.1—Solar Electronics Model 6550-1 Power Sweep Generator, 100 W, 15 Hz to 150 kHz (courtesy of Solar Electronics)

5.1.1.4 Representative Power Amplifiers

Figure 5.2 shows a 100 W audio amplifier which was specifically designed for use with the audio isolation transformer shown in Fig. 5.10 for making susceptibility tests required by several military specifications. Although intended primarily for that specific application, this unit provides flat response (± 1 dB) at reduced power levels from 30 Hz to 100 kHz.

Power amplifiers generally are used to boost the output from lower-level signal generators and sweepers. The combination of a low-level source and a power amplifier is the appropriate choice for most susceptibility testing, especially if a suitable low-level source is already available.

Modern broadband RF power amplifiers typically require an input signal level of only 1 mW and produce CW power levels ranging

Figure 5.2—Solar Electronics Model 6552-1A 100 Watt Audio Amplifier (courtesy of Solar Electronics Co.)

from 1 W to 10 kW or more. In general, the higher the output power, the smaller the bandwidth over which that amount of power can be delivered. Figure 5.3 shows a unit which is capable of delivering 10 W at any frequency in the range from 10 kHz to 1,000 MHz, while that shown in Fig. 5.4 is rated at 2 kW from 10 kHz to 220 MHz. Both units shown are arbitrary selections from a broad range of products offered by their respective manufacturers.

Figure 5.3—IFI Model 5500 Wideband Amplifier, 10 W, 10 kHz to 1,000 MHz (courtesy of Instruments for Industry, Inc.)

Figure 5.4—Amplifier Research Model 2,000L RF Power Amplifier, 2 kW, 10 kHz to 220 MHz (courtesy of Amplifier Research)

In the microwave portion of the spectrum, traveling-wave tube amplifiers are generally used to produce outputs up to 1 kW at 10 GHz and 1 W or greater up to 40 GHz. Also available are solid-state power amplifiers which can provide up to 100 W at 40 GHz.

The characteristics required of an amplifier are, of course, determined by the applicable EMI specification, the power input available from the source and the effectiveness of the test field transducer in producing the required field strength. Table 5.1 shows power outputs required to produce several field-strength levels when using various transducers as discussed more fully in Section 5.2.2.7.

Insertion of a leveling preamplifier (such as that shown in Fig. 5.5) between the signal source and the power amplifier is a desirable modification to the basic test setup, especially for radiated susceptibility testing. When fed from a field sensor of the type discussed in Section 5.2.4, the leveling preamplifier completes a closed-loop system by automatically adjusting the level it feeds to the power amplifier as necessary to maintain a constant field strength versus frequency. The unit shown can accept inputs from, and base its output on upper control limit settings of, as many as eight sensors.

Figure 5.5—IFI Model LPA-2A Leveling Preamplifier (courtesy of Instruments for Industry, Inc.)

5.1.1.5 Power Output Requirements

As stated in Section 5.1.1.2, it is far less costly to increase field strength for EMI testing by increasing the TAF of the test field transducer as compared to increasing the power level fed to it. This section discusses the performance considerations involved in selecting power sources and test-field transducers to obtain required levels of field strength. Figure 5.6 illustrates the basic relationship between the sources of power and the two types of transducers used to produce the radiated susceptibility test fields.

The output power, P_t, required to produce a voltage, V_t, at the input to the field-producing antenna is simply:

$$P_t = V_t^2/R \quad \text{watts} \tag{5.1}$$

where,

R = the antenna input impedance, assumed to be 50 Ω

The TAF for the antenna in use, as developed in Section 2.7.1.1, is then used to relate V_t to the electric field, E, produced at a distance of 1 m:

$$\text{TAF} = E/V_t \quad \text{V/m per volt input} \tag{5.2}$$

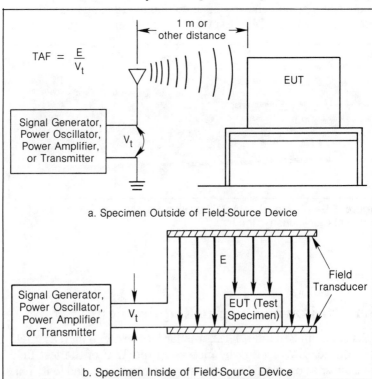

a. Specimen Outside of Field-Source Device

b. Specimen Inside of Field-Source Device

Figure 5.6—The Two Types of Transducers Used to Produce Radiated Test Fields

Thus, the power required to produce a desired field strength is obtained by substituting Eq. (5.2) into Eq. (5.1), yielding:

$$P_t = \frac{E^2}{TAF^2\, R} \quad \text{watts} \qquad (5.3)$$

The power thus calculated must be increased by the amount of loss in the transmission line connecting the power source to the field producer. Such loss may exceed 1 dB for a 3 m (10 ft) length of RG-223/U cable at frequencies above 400 MHz and reach values of 13 dB at 10 GHz unless a suitable waveguide is used in place of coaxial cable.

When the correct mating antenna from Table 5.2 is chosen, and its worst-case TAF for the 1 m distance is substituted in Eq. (5.3), the power requirements shown in Table 5.1 are obtained for the field strengths shown. Loss in 3 m of RG-58A/U cable was included in the calculations.

Table 5.1—Power Oscillator/Amplifier Power Required for Various Field Generators

Antenna/ Field Generator	Frequency Range	EUT Size	For Field Strength of:		
			1 V/m	3 V/m	10 V/m
Cage	DC-1 MHz	large	≈23 dBm	3 dBW	13 dBW
Parallel Plate	DC-30 MHz	small	13 dBm	23 dBm	3 dBW
Long-Wire	DC-30 MHz	med.	20 dBm	0 dBW	10 dBW
Parallel-Line	0.01-50 MHz	large	15 dBm	25 dBm	5 dBW
Broadband Dipole	30-200 MHz	large	25 dBm	5 dBW	burnout
Biconical	20-200 MHz	large	0 dBW	10 dBW	burnout
Strip-Line	DC-200 MHz	small	5 dBm	15 dBm	25 dBm
Tunable Dipole	30-				
	1,000 MHz	large	20 dBm	0 dBW	10 dBW
Conical Log Spiral	0.2-1 GHz	large	27 dBm	7 dBW	17 dBW
Log Periodic	0.2-1 GHz	large	17 dBm	27 dBm	7 dBW
Ridged Guide	0.2-1 GHz	large	12 dBm	22 dBm	2 dBW
Conical Log Spiral	1-10 GHz	large	20 dBm	0 dBW	10 dBW
Ridged Guide	1-10 GHz	large	10 dBm	20 dBm	0 dBW
20 dB Horns	1-10 GHz	large	0 dBm	10 dBm	20 dBm

5.1.2 Waveform Generators

This section covers the instruments used to generate the high-power spikes, damped sinusoids and other special waveforms needed to test EMI susceptibility.

5.1.2.1 Spike Generators

Characteristics of the typical spike, or transient waveform, required for EMI susceptibility testing to military specifications are shown in Fig. 5.7. The pulse width at 3 dB down is approximately 5 μs; therefore, as discussed in Section 2.3.4.2, most of its spectral energy is contained in the frequency domain between DC and $1/\tau$ = 1/5 μs $\approx$ 200 kHz. Thus, this spike waveform is sometimes referred to as a **low-frequency** transient. Instruments that are capable of generating the required waveform are readily available from commercial sources.

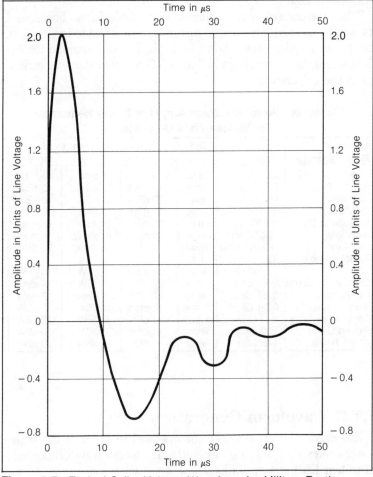

Figure 5.7—Typical Spike Voltage Waveform for Military Testing

5.1.2.2 Damped Sinusoid Generators for EMP Testing

Damped sinusoid generators are used to produce waveforms such as that shown in Fig. 12.19, with peak currents as shown in Fig. 12.20, for injection into the interconnections and cables of various equipments and systems to determine their susceptibility to electromagnetic pulse (EMP).[1,2] A commercially available example of a sinusoid generator for this application is shown in Fig. 5.8.

The unit shown utilizes a number of plug-in modules, such as that shown on top of the main unit, to produce the damped sinusoidal waveforms required for conducted testing to U.S. military standards. This generator also accepts other plug-in modules (such as the one shown already installed) to produce exponential waveforms which simulate transients induced on long cables.

The basic operation of this general type of simulator typically involves charging a capacitor to a relatively high voltage, such as 30 kV, and then discharging it through a controlled value of inductance and resistance in series with the capacitor, thus producing

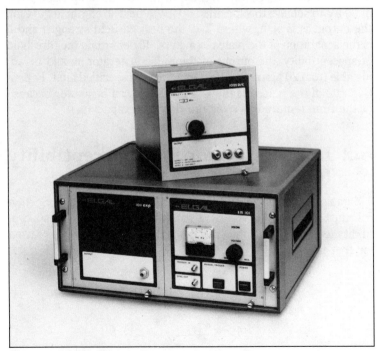

Figure 5.8—Elgal EM101 Transient Generator System (courtesy of Elgal Instrumentation and Systems Ltd.)

5.11

the required waveform across the resistor for transmittal to the injection device. Frequency of the oscillatory waveform is either fixed at a single frequency or made variable over various segments of the spectrum from 10 kHz to 100 MHz as required. Resistance in the circuit is selected to produce a Q of about 15, as required for the required exponential decay; output amplitude is specified for a 100 Ω resistive load.

5.1.2.3 EMP Transient Pulse Generators

The EMP transient pulse generator is designed to generate a high-voltage pulse which is applied to a special version of the parallel-plate line (discussed in Section 5.2.2.2) to produce a high-field-strength waveform such as that shown in Fig. 13.12. Characteristics of both the generator and the parallel-plate line are covered by the applicable military specification.[2]

The generator is designed to operate into a parallel-plate line with a characteristic impedance of 100 Ω, ±10 Ω. For a parallel-plate spacing of 1 m, the generator must furnish a peak amplitude pulse of 50 kV to achieve the specified 50 kV/m field strength; in general, the output is E × h, where E is the desired field strength and h is the separation of the plates in meters. To determine the threshold of susceptibility, the output of the pulse generator should be adjustable from 20 percent to 100 percent of the specified limit. Repetition rate of the pulse ideally is 1 Hz, but it can be slower because of the time required to recharge the main capacitor.

5.2 Transducers for EMI Susceptibility Testing

Signals generated by the instrumentation discussed in Section 5.1 must be applied to the EUT for radiated or conducted susceptibility testing. This section discusses the various transducers used for that purpose.

5.2.1 Injection Devices for Conducted EMI Susceptibility Testing

5.2.1.1 Audio Isolation Transformer

Application of the audio isolation transformer for EMI emission measurement was discussed in Section 4.1.2. Figure 5.9 shows its application to susceptibility testing. The transformer secondary is designed to carry both the injected audio-frequency signal and the power-source currents at levels up to 50 A, ac or dc, without saturation. Figure 5.10 shows a commercially available isolation transformer used for injection of susceptibility signals. It can handle 100 W of audio power over the frequency range 30 Hz to 250 kHz. The turn ratio provides a two-to-one voltage step down to the special secondary winding. Another secondary is connected to a pair of binding posts suitable for isolated connection of a voltmeter as required by some test procedures.

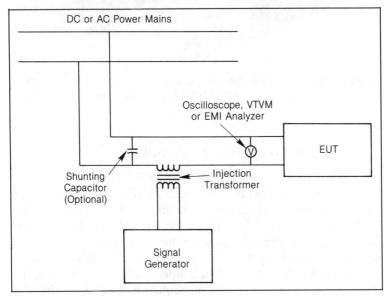

Figure 5.9—Application of Audio Isolation Transformer to Testing Conducted Susceptibility

Figure 5.10—Solar Electronics Model 6220-1A Audio Isolation Transformer for Injecting Susceptibility Signals (courtesy of Solar Electronics Co.)

5.2.1.2 RF Isolation Networks

For some receiver conducted susceptibility tests (see Section 12.2), it is necessary to provide at least 20 dB of isolation between signal generators to avoid intermodulation and other interactions. As illustrated in Fig. 5.11, an isolation network is needed to combine the outputs of two signal generators into a common port. One method of doing this is to use a common type-N coaxial T connector and two 10 dB pads. Although broadband in performance, the placement of two 50 Ω generator outputs in parallel results in a VSWR of 2:1 at the network output. However, as seen from each signal generator, the 10 dB attenuator pad in its path buffers the mismatch down to a VSWR of 1.23:1 and contributes to a total isolation of 20 dB between the generators. The arrangement shown in Fig. 5.12 can be used to avoid this mismatch problem; by placing a 16.7 Ω resistance in each arm, VSWR is reduced to about 1.1:1.

5.14

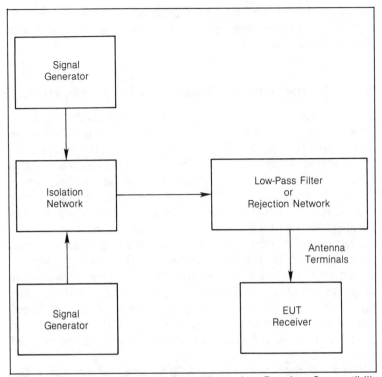

Figure 5.11—Application of Isolation Network to Receiver Susceptibility Tests

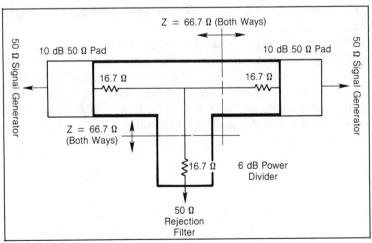

Figure 5.12—Matching Three-Port Network and Power Divider

Also available for this application are hybrid junctions which provide the required isolation without the power loss associated with these resistive networks.

5.2.1.3 Injectors for Testing EMP Susceptibility

Direct injection of the damped sinusoidal conducted EMP waveform of Section 5.1.2.2 onto discrete pins or terminals requires that a special test jig be built for the specific EUT. However, a more standardized device can be used for injection onto a cable or cable bundle to test common-mode susceptibility to the EMP-simulation waveform. Such indirect coupling can be accomplished either capacitively or inductively using commercially available devices designed for this function.

The capacitive coupling device is essentially a conductive tubing which surrounds the test cable. Efficiency of the coupling is dependent on how closely the outside diameter of the cable approaches the diameter of the inside conducting surface of the device: the tighter the fit, the better the coupling. The resulting distributed capacitance appears to the output of the generator as a capacitor in series with the effective impedance to ground of the inserted cable.

The device for inductive coupling is reciprocal in operation to the current probe discussed in Section 4.1.1. In this case, the test cable is a single-turn secondary, while the number of turns in the multiple-turn primary determines its transfer efficiency and frequency response.

Inductive coupling is generally preferred for frequencies up to about 10 MHz, while capacitive coupling is usually more effective at higher frequencies. However, the selection of coupling method and numerous other details, some of which are considered in more detail in Chapter 12, are dependent on the type of cable being tested and the need to simulate as closely as possible the EMP vulnerability of the EUT.

5.2.2 Antennas and Structures for Producing Electric Fields

5.2.2.1 Low-Frequency Parallel-Plate Antenna

Sometimes referred to as a **cage** antenna, the low-frequency parallel-plate antenna is ideal for measuring susceptibility to electric fields of relatively large EUTs. As shown in Fig. 5.13, the EUT is placed between the parallel plates which are fed from a signal generator or power oscillator to produce the desired electric field strength. Operation is in the dominant transverse electromagnetic (TEM) mode. The areas of the plates are chosen to be several times larger than the cross-sectional area of the EUT, and the plate separation, h, is chosen to be about twice the height of the largest EUT to be tested. Essentially, this antenna is simply a physically-large capacitor to which is connected the 50 Ω output line from the signal generator or power amplifier.

The equivalent capacitance of this structure will vary from about 10 to 100 pF, with values of 30 pF being typical for a 0.93 m^2 (10 ft^2) plate area and a 2.44 m (8 ft) height. Since this value corresponds to a shunt reactance of about 500 Ω at 10 MHz imposed across the 50 Ω terminated line, it can be seen that this capacitance

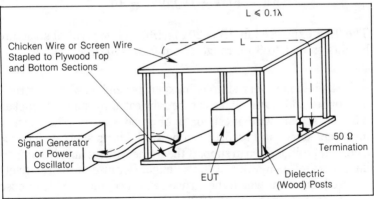

Figure 5.13—Low Frequency Parallel-Plate Antenna

is not the limiting factor in determining the highest frequency at which this structure is usable. Of much greater significance is the equivalent inductance of the feed and termination which, at about 1 μH, imposes a series reactance of 50 Ω at about 8 MHz.

The low-frequency parallel-plate antenna will work well from dc up to a frequency for which the total length, L, shown in Fig. 5.13, is less than about 0.1λ. For signal-generator-to-antenna coaxial line lengths of about 3 m, plate dimensions of about 3 m and height of 1 to 4 m, the total length, L, is about 10 m. Thus, the maximum usable frequency, for which L $\approx$ 0.1λ, would be about 3 MHz; however, in practice, other parasitic and resonance effects limit the maximum frequency of use to slightly higher than 1 MHz. The larger the structure, the lower its maximum usable frequency. Because the transmission line from the signal source is terminated in its characteristic impedance, typically by a 10 W, noninductive resistor, the resultant characteristic electric field strength versus frequency is essentially as flat as that of the signal source output over the entire usable range of the antenna.

This field-generating structure is relatively efficient in terms of the transmitter antenna factor as defined in Section 2.7.1.1; i.e., it develops a reasonably high field strength for each volt applied from the signal source. For a plate separation, h:

$$\text{TAF} = E/V_t = (V_t/h)/V_t = 1/h$$

The TAF expressed in dB is 20 log(1/h) and, for typical structure heights from 1 to 3 m, ranges from 0 to −10 dB.

This antenna is very simple, inexpensive and easy to construct. The upper and lower plates can be fabricated by stapling chicken wire or screen wire mesh onto plywood sheets. The vertical members shown in Fig. 5.13 can be studding as small as 5 cm × 5 cm and positioned so to support the frame without unduly hampering access to the interior of the antenna. Because of the relatively low frequencies at which the structure is used, metal nails impose no problem. Also, because of the frequency range of usage, only modest precautions need be taken with the feed and termination lines. Thus, coaxial line from the generator can be connected by soldering its shield to the bottom plate and soldering its center conductor to 1 cm wide strips of copper or brass foil. The foil is then connected to the top plate. The same type of foil can be used to connect the terminating resistor, as shown in Fig. 5.13.

Although the structure just discussed will permit testing of EUTs as large as a dual-bay, 19" console, it is sometimes necessary to test even larger specimens. Reference 3 describes development and construction of an extrapolation and refinement of the basic low-frequency cage which permits testing either magnetic- or electric-field susceptibility of specimens ranging in size up to that of a small tank or truck, at frequencies up to 3 MHz. Field strengths up to 100 V/m are achievable, and fields are uniform over a spherical volume 6.1 m (20 ft) in diameter. Splitting of the input power to drive both ends through baluns introduces the capability to choose either in-phase drive (resulting in high-impedance electric fields) or opposite-phase drive (producing low-impedance magnetic fields).

5.2.2.2 Parallel-Plate Line, DC to 30 MHz

The parallel-plate line is very effective in developing high electric field strengths from relatively low input power at frequencies up to 30 MHz. Figure 5.14 shows construction details of a parallel-plate line suitable for testing EMI susceptibility in accordance with MIL-STD-461/462. The physical size of an EUT which can be tested in this particular parallel-line structure is limited to about 30 cm × 30 cm × 1 to 3 m in length.

The parallel-plate line structure can be considered an extrapolation of the lower-frequency structure discussed in Section 5.2.2.1. The important difference is that the combined length of the line and its feeder cable significantly exceeds 0.1 λ at the upper range of its application frequencies. The line is essentially a large, air-dielectric capacitor when used at frequencies up to about 1 MHz; as frequency increases, however, it functions increasingly like a transmission line. Thus, unless precautions are taken, impedance mismatches between the line and source or load can cause standing waves that invalidate measurements.

The characteristic impedance of the structure is determined by the width and separation of the plates with an air dielectric. The length of coaxial cable driving the line is unimportant provided that an impedance match is maintained throughout the system. Although insertion of the EUT disturbs the field between the plate and introduces some mismatch, these effects are not significant as long as the height of the EUT does not exceed one-third of the plate separation, h. Figure 5.15 shows the relationship between VSWR and the EUT upper-plate spacing for various surface areas of the EUT face nearest to the upper plate.

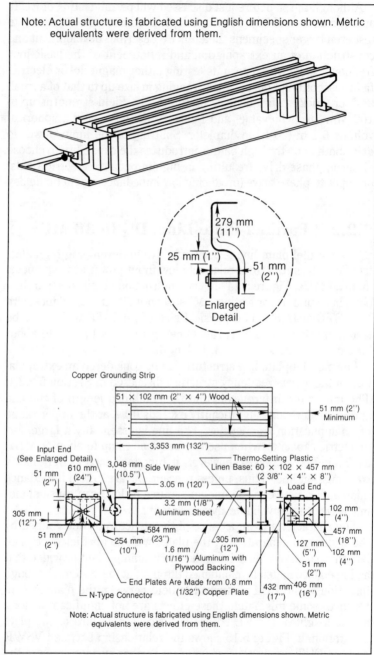

Figure 5.14—Parallel-Plate-Line Antenna for MIL-STD-461/2 Testing

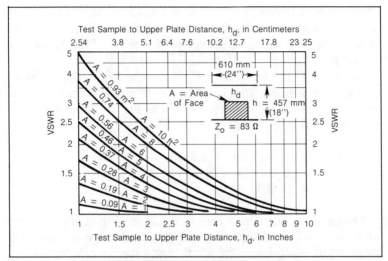

Figure 5.15—Parallel-Plate VSWR versus EUT Spacing from Upper Plate for Various EUT Surface Areas

Impedance of the line shown in Fig. 5.14, with 610 mm (24") plate widths and 457 mm (18") plate separation, is about 83 Ω. Therefore, it is necessary to use a 50 Ω to 83 Ω impedance-matching network such as that shown at the left side of Fig. 5.16. Shown at the right side of the figure is a network that can be used as a terminating load and which also attenuates the applied voltage for monitoring by an RF voltmeter or EMI analyzer. Such monitoring is convenient for this line because the field strength is simply the applied voltage divided by the plate separation of 457 mm, producing a field

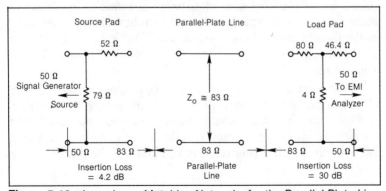

Figure 5.16—Impedance Matching Networks for the Parallel-Plate Line

5.21

strength of 2.19 V/m for each volt actually applied to the line. However, because the 30 dB pad attenuates the voltage by a factor of 31.6, the field strength, E, expressed in terms of the voltage out of the pad, V, is E = 2.19 × 31.6 V = 69.2 V.

As shown at the left side of Fig. 5.16, the loss in the matching pad is 4.2 dB. If the TAF is defined in terms of voltage into that pad, the TAF for the structure shown in Fig. 5.14, for which the plate separation, h, is 457 mm, becomes:

$$
\begin{aligned}
\text{TAF} &= 20 \log (1/h) - 4.2 \text{ dB} \\
&= 20 \log (1/0.457) - 4.2 \\
&= 2.6 \text{ dB}
\end{aligned}
\tag{5.4}
$$

The parallel-plate line provides a valuable method of generating an electric field for susceptibility testing because, within limits of mechanical feasibility, its physical length can be extended as far as required, as long as it continues to be terminated in its characteristic impedance.

5.2.2.3 The Long-Wire Chamber, DC to 30 MHz

The long-wire chamber field generator described in this section is installed in a shielded enclosure as a center conductor which functions with the walls of the enclosure as the outer conductor to create a large TEM cell. Also called the **open wire line (OWL)** antenna or **Beverage** antenna, it can be installed within a relatively short time and requires no complicated construction features.

As shown in Fig. 5.17, a wire is drawn taut along the longest dimension of the enclosure after being attached to insulators installed on opposite walls at between two-thirds and three-fourths of the floor-to-ceiling height. American Wire Gauge (AWG) no. 12, single-strand bare copper wire is a suitable choice for the application.

The concentric feeder line shown in the figure consists of 25 mm (1") copper tubing with bare AWG no. 16 wire installed concentrically as a center conductor using two or more short, nonconductive bushings. This feeder is installed at the source end of the long wire, but initially it is not connected to it. However, the bottom end is

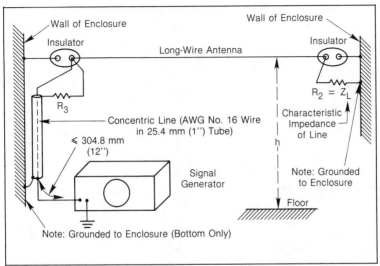

Figure 5.17—Installation of the Long-Wire E-Field Generator

connected to the signal generator as shown. The characteristic impedance of the concentric feeder line, Z, is:

$$Z = 138 \log (d_1/d_2) \qquad \Omega \qquad (5.5)$$

where,

d_1 = inside diameter of the tube
d_2 = diameter of the center conductor

For AWG no. 16 wire and 2.5 cm tubing, $Z \approx 150 \ \Omega$.

With the output of the feeder line still open-circuited, adjust the signal generator for that frequency at which the concentric line is one-quarter wavelength. This condition is achieved when a high input impedance voltmeter such as a vacuum tube voltmeter (VTVM), connected at the output end of the concentric line as shown in Fig. 5.18, indicates a maximum while input to the line from the signal generator is held constant. A second indication is a dip in the output of the signal generator, as monitored by a VTVM, because of the nearly short circuit which is reflected to that point.

Figure 18 — 236

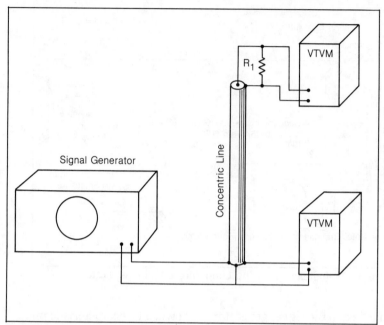

Figure 5.18—Test Setup for Determining Characteristic Impedance of the Concentric Line

Next, a terminating impedance, R_1, equal to the characteristic impedance of the feeder line, as calculated from Eq. (5.4), is connected across the output of the feeder line. To verify the correctness of the resistive value of R_1, set the output of the signal generator to zero and zero-adjust both VTVMs shown in Fig. 5.18. As the output of the signal generator is increased, the VTVM readings should rise together and indicate the same reading at both ends of the feeder line, if the choice of resistance value for R_1 is correct. If the voltage reading at the upper end of the line is higher than the reading at the lower end, the resistance value is too high; conversely, a lower reading at the top indicates too low a resistance. The resistance value should be changed until the readings are equal. Once the proper value is found and installed, this procedure should be repeated at lower frequencies to confirm that the choice is correct.

The next step is to select the correct termination resistor, R_2, for the long wire. The approximate trial value for the resistance is determined for whichever of the following two cases more closely matches the situation:

Case 1: Distance of wire to ceiling is less than one-third the room height:

$$Z = 138 \log (4D/d) \quad \Omega \qquad (5.6)$$

where:

D = distance of wire to ceiling
d = diameter of wire (2.06 mm, or 0.081" for AWG no. 12)

Case 2: Distance of wire to ceiling is greater than one-third and less than one-half the room height:

$$Z = 138 \log (h/d) + 5 \quad \Omega \qquad (5.7)$$

where,
h = height of enclosure
d = as given for case 1

For typical enclosures 2.4 m high, and wire location one-third of room height from ceiling, Eqs. (5.5) and (5.6) give $Z = R_2$ values of about 430 Ω.

With a tentative value of R_2 as determined from the applicable equation, installed as shown in Fig. 5.19, the procedure given above for finding the optimum value for the feeder line now is used to optimize the value of R_2. This process is implemented with R_1 removed from the top of the concentric feeder line and with the signal generators and VTVMs connected as shown in Fig. 5.19. Once the proper value is found, R_2 is installed permanently.

Finally, to determine the final value for the resistance, R_3, to be installed at the top of the concentric line as shown in Fig. 5.17, the resultant parallel combination of R_3 and R_2 is calculated and set equal to R_1:

$$R_1 = (R_2 \times R_3)/(R_2 + R_3)$$

or,

$$R_3 = (R_1 \times R_2)/(R_2 - R_1) \qquad (5.8)$$

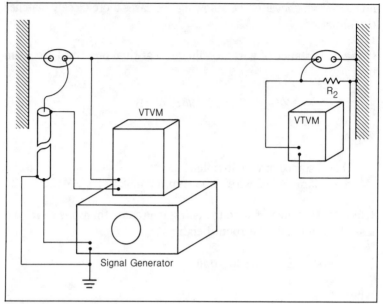

Figure 5.19—Test Setup for Determining Characteristic Impedance of the Long-Wire Chamber

With the installation of this value of R_3, the construction of the long-wire chamber is complete.

It should be noted that R_1 and R_3 can be completely eliminated if a transformer is used to match 50 Ω to the approximately 450 Ω impedance of the OWL, thus making the TAF much higher. See SAE J1338 and a related paper by Bronaugh and McGinnis.[4,5]

Figure 5.20 shows the electric-field lines in the transverse plane of the shielded enclosure for a specific installation in which the wire is strung 1.22 m (4 ft) above the edge of a metal-top test bench which is grounded to the wall of the enclosure. For this specific situation, for an input voltage to the wire of V, the field strength above the edge of the bench is V/1.22 V/m. Thus, to produce the 21 V/m field strength shown in Fig. 5.20, the voltage applied to the long wire, V, must be 1.22 × 21, or 25.6 V, implying a TAF of 21/25.6 = 0.82 = −1.7 dB(1/m). For the more centrally located wire position discussed above and enclosure heights of 2.44 to 3.66 m (8 to 12 ft), it can be similarly shown that the TAF ranges from 0 to −6 dB(1/m).

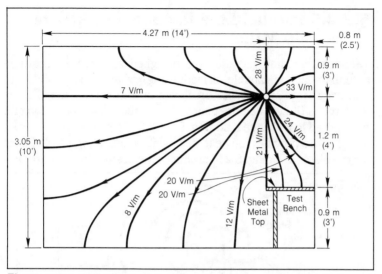

Figure 5.20—Electric Field Configuration Within a Shielded Enclosure for a Long-Wire Voltage of 25.6 V

5.2.2.4 TEM Cells, 10 kHz to 200 MHz

Figure 7.12 (Chapter 7) shows a cutaway view of a TEM cell as used for susceptibility testing. Important advantages of the TEM cell for radiated susceptibility testing include its ability to support both the electric-field and magnetic-field components and its complete containment of energy. This eliminates the need for a shielded enclosure. The principal disadvantages are its relatively complex and costly construction and its size, which is double that of a parallel-plate line for accommodating the same EUT.[6] The electric field strength, E, at the center of the cell, midway between the septum and lower or upper wall ideally is:

$$E = V/b \quad V/m \tag{5.9}$$

where,
  V = input voltage to the cell in volts
  b = the floor-to-septum separation of the cell in meters

Thus, the TAF of a TEM cell would be approximately:

$$TAF = E/V = (V/b)/V = 1/b \tag{5.10}$$

Thus, for a floor-to-septum spacing of 0.5 m, the TAF would be 1/0.5 = 2, or approximately +6 dB.

5.2.2.5 Parallel-Line Radiator, 10 kHz to 30 MHz

The parallel-line radiator was designed as a readily movable antenna which is capable of testing the radiated susceptibility of relatively large specimens. As shown in Fig. 5.21, if the EUT is too large to fit between the plates of a parallel-plate line, it can still be exposed to its fringe field (Fig. 5.21a). Opening the line as shown in Fig. 5.21b provides the next step, while substituting parallel lines for the plates as in Fig. 5.21c produces the desired basic configura-

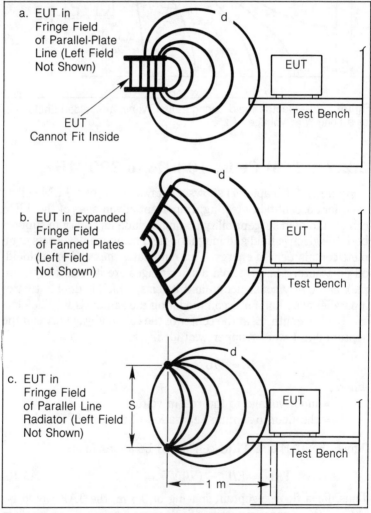

Figure 5.21—Evolution of Parallel-Line Radiator

tion. For a spacing of 1 m from the EUT, the path length of the electric field component intercepting the EUT is approximately the circumference of circle with a diameter of 1 m, which is π, or approximately 3 m.

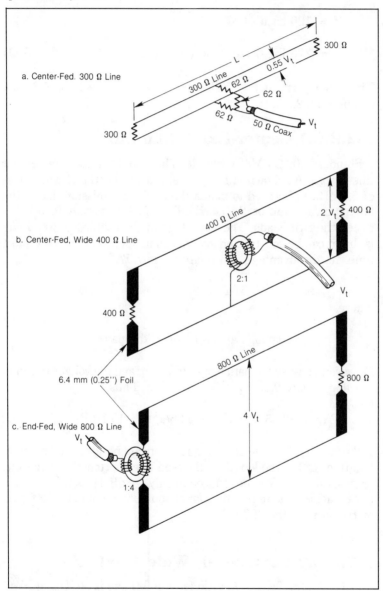

Figure 5.22—Three Configurations of the Parallel-Line Radiator

Figure 5.22 illustrates three practical implementations of the basic configuration, each of which exhibits a characteristic impedance based on the relationship between the spacing between the line elements, s, and the diameter of the radiating elements, d:

$$Z = 120 \cosh^{-1}(s/d)$$

$$\approx 276 \log (2s/d) \quad \text{for s/d} \gg 1 \qquad (5.11)$$

The three parts of Fig. 5.22 are discussed in Sections 5.2.2.5.1 through 5.2.2.5.3.

5.2.2.5.1 Center-Fed, 300 Ω Line

Standard 300 Ω FM/TV twin-lead line can be used to implement this design. As shown in Fig. 5.22a, a balanced L-pad with a loss of 5.2 dB can be used to match the 50 Ω transmission line to the antenna; each volt on the coaxial line appears as only 0.55 V between the twin leads. The advantage of the center-fed 300 Ω line is that it can be constructed and placed in operation in a very short time. Its disadvantage is a relatively low TAF:

$$TAF = E/V_t$$

where,

$$V_t = \text{voltage at the input to the pad}$$

However, because the path length of E is π, and the voltage reaching the line is only 0.55 V_t, E = 0.55 V_t/π. Thus:

$$TAF = (0.55 \ V_t/\pi)/V_t = 0.55/\pi, \text{ or } -15.1 \text{ dB}$$

If the two 300 Ω line-terminating resistors are removed and the total length of L/2 + the length of the feed line shortened to 1 m (3 ft) or less, this factor can be reduced to only −4 dB. However, this may not be achievable unless the signal source is mounted on a frame or tripod near the 300 Ω line.

5.2.2.5.2 Center-Fed, Wide 400 Ω Line

From Eq. (5.10), the s/d ratio for a 400 Ω line is 56. Using AWG no. 10 bare copper wire (d ≈ 2.5 mm or 0.10") for the parallel line, the separation is about 142 mm (5.6"). The two 400 Ω terminating resistors present a 200 Ω impedance at the center which can be matched to 50 Ω coaxial feeder line by a wideband toroidal transformer as shown in Fig. 5.22.

The TAF for this line is $2/\pi = -4$ dB(1/m), and there is no restriction on the length of the feeder since all lines are impedance matched.

5.2.2.5.3 End-Fed, Wide 800 Ω Line

From Eq. (5.10), the s/d ratio for an 800 Ω line is 1,800. Using AWG no. 30 bare copper wire (d = 0.25 mm or 0.010") for the parallel lines, the separation needed is 457 mm (18"). The 800 Ω terminating resistor presents an impedance of 800 Ω at the driven end. This is impedance matched to the 50 Ω coaxial line with a wideband toroidal transformer as shown in Fig. 5.22.

The TAF of this line is $4/\pi = +2.1$ dB(1/m), with no restrictions on the length of the feeder line since all lines are impedance matched. Thus, this configuration is superior to the other two.

5.2.2.5.4 Length and Termination Considerations

To illustrate the rationale for determining the maximum allowable length of this type of line, Fig. 5.23 shows a plan view of the parallel line positioned 1 m away from an EUT. To have all the incremental elements of this end-fed line make contributions essentially in phase, the maximum permissible phase differences via paths BT and BACT is set equal to λ/8 at the highest design frequency:

$$L + \sqrt{1\ m^2 + (L/2)^2} = \sqrt{1\ m^2 + (L/2)^2} + \lambda/8 \qquad (5.12)$$

or,

$$L = \lambda/8 \qquad (5.13)$$

For an end-fed line and a maximum frequency of 30 MHz, λ = 10 m and L = 1.25 m (4.1 feet).

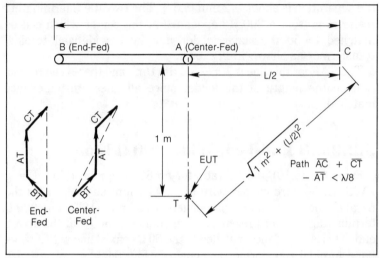

Figure 5.23—Plan View of Parallel-Line Radiator Deployment Relative to EUT

To assure good performance of either the 400 or 800 Ω line shown in Fig. 5.22, the line termination(s) should use a resistor card. For a 142 mm (5.6") spacing of the 400 Ω line, a 100 Ω/sq cut to a width of 36 mm (1.4") can be used to obtain 400 Ω of distributed load. For a 457 mm (18") spacing of the 800 Ω line, a 100 Ω/sq resistor card cut to a width of 57 mm (2.25") can be used to produce 800 Ω.

To remove any lead inductance effects from the toroid transformer to the line in either the 400 or 800 Ω design, copper foil about 6.4 mm (0.25") wide should be used. The foil is soldered over its entire width on the line and is cut to a 30° taper on the toroid before soldering it to the toroid leads.

The toroid transformer may be built using Rutherford techniques or purchased commercially. Two transformers may be required, with a crossover frequency of about 1 MHz.

5.2.2.6 Large Air Strip Lines, DC TO 1 GHz

The large air strip line can be considered an extrapolation of the basic design of the parallel-plate line discussed in Section 5.2.2.2. For EUTs approximately the size of this book, it is possible to construct a line which is usable to at least 200 MHz and which provides sufficient electric field strength for many tests using low-power signal generators as sources. Figure 5.24 shows the design of this type of structure, while Fig. 5.25 illustrates the TEM field within the line, both with and without the EUT inserted. The line operates in its dominant TEM mode from dc to over 200 MHz. Since insertion of the EUT produces an impedance mismatch, the cross-sectional area of the EUT should not exceed 20 percent of the w × h area of the line to maintain a VSWR of less than 2:1.

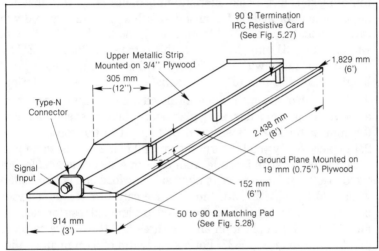

Figure 5.24—A 90 Ω Strip Line for Susceptibility Testing

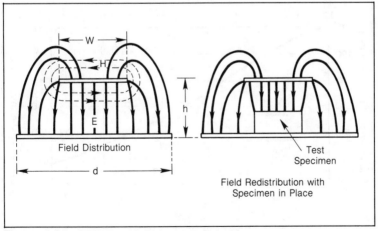

Figure 5.25—TEM Field Within 90 Ω Strip Line

5.33

The cross section of the line dimensions can be calculated from the graph of characteristic impedance versus w/h ratio shown in Fig. 5.26; the width of the ground plane should be at least 3(w) for the graph to apply. The useful range of w/h ratios for susceptibility testing is from about 1 to 5 (Z ≈ 125 Ω to Z ≈ 50 Ω). A ground plane width, d, of 1 m (3 ft) is chosen to correspond to the depth of a test bench or table top within a shielded enclosure on which the strip line is likely to be located. Although it would be tempting to select a characteristic impedance of 50 Ω to match a signal generator and 50 Ω transmission line, for the required w/h ratio of 5 and w of d/3 = 305 mm (12"), the height of the line, h, would be only 61 mm (2.4"). Since this is too small for most EUTs, a 90 Ω impedance with its w/h ratio of 2 is chosen, resulting in a height, h, of 152 mm (6"). This satisfies the book-size criterion.

The length of the line is not critical and is chosen for convenience, as long as its impedance is matched. Thus, a sheet of metal 0.8 mm in thickness is screwed or bonded to the top of a 1 × 2.4 m piece of plywood to form the ground plane. As shown in Fig. 5.24, the upper strip is made from the same sheet metal stock affixed to a 0.3 × 1.8 m piece of plywood. The load end is terminated with a 90 Ω resistive card; the resistive card provides a superior impedance match at VHF as compared to a lumped resistor. Recommended for this application are the three 270 Ω resistive cards in parallel shown in Fig. 5.27. For a strip width of 51 mm and an in-

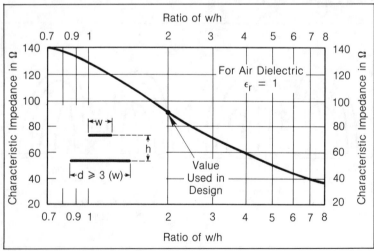

Figure 5.26—Strip Line Characteristic Impedance versus w/h Ratio

ternal height of 152 mm (191 mm O.D.), the card impedance used is 90 Ω/sq. The cards have a power rating of 0.16 W/cm^2 (1 W/in^2) and can be purchased in 51 mm strip widths and 90 Ω/sq impedance value. Other combinations of card value can be used to obtain the desired 90 Ω load.

The driving end of the upper 0.3 m strip is tapered to a blunt point as shown in Fig. 5.24 and fixed in place. A type-N female bulkhead connector (UG-58 A/U) is secured to the center of the ground plane end as shown in the detail sketch, Fig. 5.28. Its outer

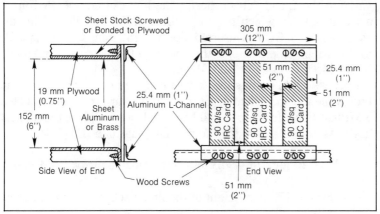

Figure 5.27—Construction Details for Securing 90 Ω/sq Card to form 90 Ω Load

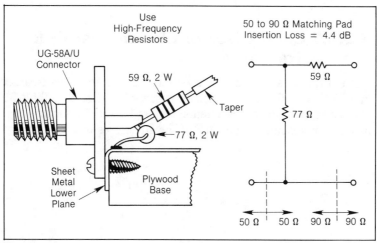

Figure 5.28—Detail of 50 to 90 Ω Matching Pad and Taper Line Feed

conductor, 19 mm (0.75") away from the end of the taper, is connected to the taper by soldering in place a 2 W, 59 Ω resistor. The center conductor is also connected to ground by a 77 Ω shunt resistor. All lead lengths should be kept as short as possible. This L-pad, shown schematically in Fig. 5.28, provides a match from the 50 Ω connector to the 90 Ω taper and strip line; its insertion loss is 4.4 dB.

If reasonable care is taken in its construction, the VSWR of the strip line should be less 1.2 up to 200 MHz. Higher VSWR implies either a construction flaw or the need for a slightly different resistor value in the L-pad. Theoretically, the line can be operated up to a frequency for which $h = \lambda/2$, above which it will multimode, especially if an EUT is inserted. For $h = 152$ mm, $\lambda/2$ corresponds to 985 MHz. In practice, if the line is well constructed, it should be usable up to 400 or 500 MHz.

Because of its small spacing between elements, this large strip line is the most efficient of all transducers for producing radiated EMI test fields from dc to 200 MHz and thus displays the highest TAF. As was the case for the parallel-plate line (Eq. 5-4):

$$TAF = 20 \log 1/h - \text{dB loss of the matching pad (4.4 dB)}$$

Thus, for the 152 mm height of the line discussed in this section:

$$TAF = 16.4 - 4.4 = +12 \text{ dB}$$

5.2.2.7 Comparison of Electric Test Field Transducers

All of the passive antennas used for emission testing, discussed in Section 4.3, also can be used for susceptibility testing. Table 5.2 compares the transmitter antenna factors for these popular antennas at 1 m spacing to the TAF of the structures discussed above.

Table 5.2—Transmitter Antenna Factors of Popular Transducers

Antenna Type or Structure	Frequency Range	TAF @ 1 m* in dB (1/m)
Low-Frequency Parallel-Plate (Cage)	DC-1 MHZ	−10 to 0
Parallel-Plate Line	DC-30 MHz	+2.6
Long-Wire Chamber	DC-30 MHz	−6 to 0
Parallel-Line	DC-50 MHz	−4 to +2
Strip-Line	DC-200 MHz **	+12
TEM Cells	DC-200 MHz	0 to +6
Passive 41-Inch Rod	10 kHz-30 MHz	−25 to −5
Tunable Dipole	35 MHz-1 GHz	−3
Broadband Dipole	20-200 MHz	−10 to −3
Biconical Dipole	20-200 MHz	−14 to −3
Conical Log Spiral	200 MHz-1 GHz	−13 to +1
Log Periodic Dipole	200 MHz-1 GHz	−8 to +6
Double-Ridged Guide	200 MHz-2 GHz	+3 to +10
Conical Log Spiral	1-10 GHz	+3 to −1
Double-Ridged Guide	1-12 GHz	+7 to +10

*Spacing not applicable to encompassing structures
**Special configuration available for DC to 1 GHz; TAF = +16 dB

Some observations and recommendations can be deduced from analyzing this table:

1. The passive-rod antenna is highly inefficient (TAF = −25 to −5 dB) and should be avoided.
2. Either the parallel-plate or strip-line chambers should be used below 30 MHz for relatively small test samples; either the long-wire or parallel-line antennas should be used for larger test samples. The TEM cell may be used for either large or small EUTs.
3. The biconical antenna should be avoided at its low-frequency end (TAF ≈ −14 dB) and either a strip-line chamber (for small EUTs), TEM cell or parallel-line antenna should be used from 30 to about 60 MHz.
4. The conical log spiral antenna is 9 to 16 dB poorer than the double-ridged guide antenna below 1 GHz, and the former should not be used unless there is power to spare.

5.2.3 Antennas and Structures for Producing Magnetic Fields

5.2.3.1 Low-Frequency Loop Antenna, 30 Hz to 30 kHz

Shown in Fig. 5.29 is the basic construction of a commercially available loop antenna specified by the military for generating magnetic fields for susceptibility testing in the 30 Hz to 30 kHz frequency range. This 12 cm diameter loop is intended for positioning 5 cm from the EUT, at which distance the flux density, B, is 5×10^{-5} tesla for each ampere of current in the loop. Maximum continuous current rating is 5 A, with 50 A permitted intermittently.

Figure 5.29—EMCO Model 7603 Magnetic Field Generating Coil 20 Hz to 50 kHz (courtesy of Electro-Mechanics Co.)

5.2.3.2 Helmholtz Coil Field Generator, 60 Hz to 30 kHz

The Helmholtz coil is useful for determining the susceptibility of automotive electronics to magnetic fields generated by power transmission lines and generating stations.[6] The test field is produced between two identical coils in a series-aiding connection. With the coils spaced a distance equal to the radius of the coils, the magnetic flux density in tesla at the center of the space between them is:

$$B = \mu H = 8.991 \times 10^{-7} \, (NI/R)$$

where,

N = number of turns on the coil
R = coil radius in meters
I = coil current in amperes

The radius of the coils is determined by the size of the test sample. The extent of the uniform field, within 1 dB, produced by this coil is illustrated in Fig. 13.7 (Chapter 13). The self-resonant frequency of the coils should be higher than the highest test frequency. This coil should not be operated in a shielded enclosure or in the proximity of large metal objects, and care should be taken to protect both personnel and test instrumentation from the high-level field produced. This type of coil is available commercially as illustrated in Fig. 5.30.

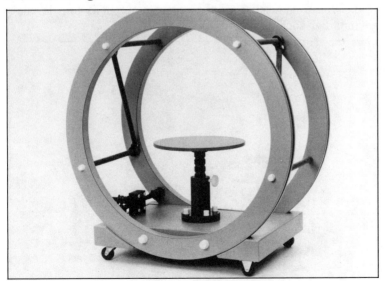

Figure 5.30—EMCO Model 6400 Helmholtz Coil (courtesy of Electro-Mechanics Co.)

5.2.4 Field Sensors for Radiated EMI Susceptibility Testing

Although structures of the encompassing type discussed above permit accurate knowledge of the field strength actually generated, based on their geometries, this is not true of the various antennas discussed, especially if they are used in shielded enclosures with their myriad attendant reflections of the radiated energy. Thus, it is necessary in many instances to use a calibrated sensor which responds to the generated field at the location of the EUT; this is especially important when the frequency of the field is being swept to level the generator output and thus achieve a degree of automation.

The most commonly used type of **field sensor** employs either a monopole or a special isotropic pickup to feed a broadband voltmeter or power meter; either can, in turn, provide an output to level the signal from the power source. Figure 5.31 illustrates such an instrument. It can provide direct readings of field strength from 1 to 300 V/m over the frequency range from 10 kHz to 220 MHz. Included in the photograph is its companion fiber optic transmitter and receiver. These eliminate the need for conductive interconnecting cables and their attendant distortion of the radiated field. Typical connection of the receiver output is to a leveling preamplifier such as that shown in Fig. 5.5.

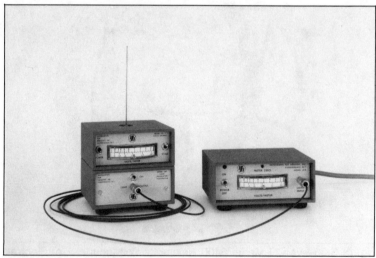

Figure 5.31—IFI EFS-1 E-Field Sensor with LMT/LDI Light Modulator/ Demodulator (courtesy of Instruments for Industry, Inc.)

Measurement of the field strength actually produced between the parallel plates by application of the EMP transient pulse discussed in Section 5.1.2.3 requires use of a **D-Dot (derivative) sensor** and an **integrator**, or of a single self-integrating **D-sensor** which combines the two functions. The D-Dot sensor responds to the first derivative of the field strength; this response must then be integrated to recover the radiated transient waveform. The integrator and monitoring oscilloscope are located in a shielded enclosure, along with any other sensitive test equipment. Figure 13.14 illustrates the setup utilizing these devices.

5.3 References

1. MIL-STD-461C, "Electromagnetic Emission and Susceptibility Requirements for the Control of Electromagnetic Interference," 1 April 1986.
2. MIL-STD-462, "Interim Notice 5 (Navy), Military Standard, Electromagnetic Interference Characteristics, Measurement of," Methods CS10, CS11 and RS05, 1 April 1986.
3. Grinoch, A., "Picatinny Arsenal, Electromagnetic Hazard Simulation Chamber," *Proceedings of the IEEE Southeastern Regional EMC Symposium*, (New York: IEEE, October, 1969).
4. SAE J1338, "Open Field Whole-Vehicle Radiated Susceptibility 10 kHz-18 GHz, Electric Field," (Warrendale, PA: Society of Automotive Engineers, 1981).
5. Bronaugh, E.L. and McGinnis, W.H., "Whole-Vehicle Electromagnetic Susceptibility Tests in Open-Area Test Sites: Applying SAE J1338," *SAE Transactions*, Vol. 92.
6. SAE J1113, "Electromagnetic Susceptibility Measurement Procedures for Vehicle Components (Except Aircraft)," draft of January 28, 1987.

Chapter 6

Automated EMI Testing

This chapter covers automation in EMI emission and susceptibility testing. Wherever appropriate, the advantages achieved through automation are weighed against both the economic cost to achieve them and the technical limitations which remain. Any remaining limitations in performance, and other disadvantages such as the relatively high cost of computer control, are usually outweighed by the significant improvements achieved in repeatability of data and savings of time and labor. Sections 6.1 through 6.3 deal with the various degrees of automation for testing EMI emissions, while Sections 6.4 through 6.6 cover the application of automation to EMI susceptibility testing.

6.1 Automating EMI Emission Tests

This section reviews the basic techniques used to automate EMI Emission tests. Also discussed are various considerations which limit the degree to which automation can actually be achieved, either because of some unique properties of the EMI to be measured or because of constraints imposed by the specifications that govern those measurements.

6.1.1 Evolution of Automatic Emission Tests

The subject of automating EMI emission tests can be approached most conveniently by reviewing the evolution of automation as applied to the generic EMI analyzer that was discussed in Section 3.1 and diagrammed in Fig. 3.1.

The most elementary degree of automation is achieved by having the EMI analyzer feed two basic signals to an X-Y plotter:

1. An X-axis drive voltage corresponding to its tuned frequency
2. A Y-axis voltage corresponding to the reading on its front-panel meter

The EMI meter is then scanned over the selected band of frequency coverage to produce a plot of EMI level versus frequency. Such scanning is facilitated in the modern EMI analyzer by designing its first local oscillator to be voltage tunable in response to a ramp voltage waveform which could either be generated internally or applied from an external source.

As discussed more fully in Section 6.2, this most basic degree of automation can be enhanced by adding some voltage offsets to the X and Y axes. Such offsets can be used to cover correction factors for input attenuation and pickup devices. They also permit plotting of multiple RF bands on a single sheet of paper.

Computer automation of EMI emission tests, as covered in Section 6.3, provides significant further advantages as compared to the X-Y plotter level of automation. Repeatability is improved as a result of decreased human involvement, and the length of time required to perform a test is reduced significantly because all correction factors are inserted automatically and readout data are presented in a processed form ready for incorporation in the final test report. With suitable software, the entire verbiage of the test report can be produced by the computer.

6.1.2 Scan Speed Limitations in EMI Testing

Limitations on the speed with which a segment of the frequency spectrum can be scanned while testing for EMI emissions arise from a number of factors.[1] Whether the EMI analyzer is being scanned in analog fashion or stepped in digital increments, sufficient time must be allowed for each response to attain full amplitude in its measurement circuitry. The first limitation factor to be considered applies to measurement of continuous-wave (CW) signals and is fundamentally based on the bandwidth of the EMI analyzer or spectrum analyzer. It is necessary that:

$$t \geq (0.96/\sqrt{\alpha^{-4} - 1}) (\Delta f/B_6^2)$$

where,

    t = the scan time in seconds

    α = the EMI analyzer IF response relative to that for a stationary signal without sweeping

    Δf = frequency segment being scanned in Hz

    B_6 = the 6 dB bandwidth of the analyzer in Hz, which is also approximately its impulse bandwidth, B_i

When the factor in the first set of parentheses equals unity, the formula becomes:

$$t > \Delta f/B_i^2 \qquad\qquad (6.1)$$

However, for this factor to be unity, $\sqrt{\alpha^{-4} - 1} = 0.96$, making $\alpha = 0.8493$, which is down by 1.42 dB from full response. This loss of response should always be accounted for when this simplified formula is used.

This approximation implies that, using a bandwidth of 100 kHz, the entire frequency segment from 30 Hz to 1,000 MHz could be swept in about 0.1 s. Realistically, however, scan times of more than one hour are required for some practical combinations of detector function and characteristics of the EMI signal, and of the instrumentation being used to measure it.

An example of a limitation resulting from unique characteristics of the EMI signal being measured is that of pulsed CW occurring at irregular intervals which can only be intercepted and measured by suitably slowing or stopping the scanning process.

Important restrictions on scanning speed are frequently determined by performance limitations of the particular automated system. For example, the system might have to delay further scanning until it is finished with a particularly lengthy or sophisticated processing of intercepted EMI signals. Such processing could include that needed to determine whether a signal is narrowband (NB) or broadband (BB).

Another type of limitation is that imposed by the governing specifications. An example of this type is that introduced by quasipeak detection and its relatively long detector time constants as required for conformance to CISPR recommendations.

6.1.3 Broadband/Narrowband Signal Determination

For some MIL-STD-461 testing it is necessary to determine whether each EMI signal response is narrowband or broadband to compare it to the appropriate limit (see Section 2.3.1). Such a determination can become complex for certain types of EMI because of ambiguities, e.g., emanations from a switching power supply. The basic task in automated testing remains that of applying to the signal the criteria of Table 2.1 (Chapter 2), either through critical analysis of plotted responses by the operator, dual-pen X-Y plotting of simultaneous responses to peak and average detection (see Section 6.2.2.3) or software-controlled application of RF tuning or other criteria in a computer-automated EMI test system.

6.1.4 Detector Functions

Of the various detector functions discussed in Section 3.6, direct peak is most commonly used for automated EMI emission testing. Because of its short charge time, the direct peak detector is best suited for achieving full response to the amplitude of EMI emissions as segments of the frequency spectrum are scanned.

However, despite the advantages inherent in the use of peak detection during automatic scanning, there are situations, such as the need for CISPR-recommended quasipeak detection mentioned in Section 6.1.2, in which other detector functions are mandated. Otherwise, the use of detector functions other than direct peak is usually confined to situations in which they are needed for analytical purposes such as application of the Table 2.1 (Chapter 2) criteria to determine whether an EMI response in narrowband or broadband.

As illustrated below, in conjunction with X-Y plotting, a great deal of information relative to an unknown emission can be derived from its simultaneous peak and average detection. Characteristics of these two detector functions are detailed in Section 3.6.

If it is assumed that the time constant of the average detector is long relative to both the modulation rate of the emission being measured and the RF window dwell time of the EMI analyzer as it scans through the emission, then the average detector will read the average level of the modulation envelope. Thus, the peak and average detectors will give the same reading for an unmodulated CW signal since the peak detection function in EMI analyzers is calibrated to read the rms value of a sinewave with a peak amplitude equal to that of the waveform being measured. However, for 100 percent sinewave amplitude modulation, the peak detector will read 6 dB higher than the average detector. In general, for a sinewave-modulated AM signal, the difference, Δ, in dB, between the outputs of peak and average detectors for a given percent modulation, m, will be:

$$\Delta = 20 \log(1 + m/100) \tag{6.2}$$

$= 0$ dB for CW emissions (m $= 0$ percent AM)

$= 2.3$ dB for m $= 30$ percent AM

$= 3.5$ dB for m $= 50$ percent AM

$= 6.0$ dB for m $= 100$ percent AM

The difference between peak and average detector readings is also useful in identifying other emissions. For example, for a computer clock having a 50 percent on/off cycle, the difference in readings between the two detectors will be 6 dB, corresponding to a 50 percent duty factor. For this to hold, however, the clock rate must be less than one-half the impulse bandwidth of the EMI analyzer. In general, for a pulsed CW of constant amplitude, the difference in dB between peak and average will approximate:

$$\Delta = 20 \log \delta \tag{6.3}$$

where,

δ = duty factor = $\tau \times f_r$

τ = pulse width

f_r = average pulse repetition rate

6.1.5 Importance of Planning

It should be apparent from the preceding sections that careful planning is essential to obtain accurate, reliable EMI data from an automated system. The measurement techniques and scan speeds suitable for one type of EMI emissions are not necessarily suitable for others. Often, different measurement techniques and scan rates are needed for different segments of the frequency spectrum.[1]

6.2 X-Y Plotter-Automated EMI Emission Testing

As discussed in Section 6.1.1, the most elementary degree of automation is achieved by having the EMI analyzer feed to an X-Y plotter an X-axis drive voltage corresponding to its tuned frequency and a Y-axis drive voltage corresponding to the reading on its front-panel meter. The EMI meter is then scanned over the selected band of frequency coverage to produce a plot of EMI level versus frequency.

6.2.1 Calibration and Normalization

As the X-Y plotter is being scanned over various segments of the frequency spectrum to produce a hard-copy recording of the readings of the EMI analyzer, it is desirable to maintain on this recording the inherent accuracy of the EMI analyzer in both frequency and amplitude. Although there are many EMI test situations in which the maximum achievable accuracy is not required (such as preliminary scans), it will be assumed in the following discussion that the X-Y plot is suitable for inclusion in a test report.

The basic technique used to achieve maximum accuracy most efficiently is to prepare a master grid for the plotter based on its response, in both axes, to a particular EMI analyzer and then to reproduce, while taking care to maintain linearity, as many copies as are likely to be used before the EMI analyzer is scheduled for its next routine calibration. Modern X-Y plotters designed for use with EMI analyzers provide controls for normalizing the scaling of the plot back to that of the master whenever one of the copies is inserted before a run; typically, offset voltages are applied to match two diagonally opposite corners of the plotting area of the copy to corresponding corners of the master. Paper size is typically either 22 × 28 cm or 28 × 43 cm (8.5" × 11" or 11" × 17"), with the plotting area occupying up to two-thirds of the total writing surface.

6.2.1.1 Frequency Calibration

Figure 6.1 shows a plotter format onto which frequency grid lines have been drawn for a hypothetical test system. Each frequency grid line along the X-axis is determined by tuning the EMI analyzer to the desired frequency and by then drawing a vertical line on the paper at the position attained as the plotter tracks that tuning. If maximum possible accuracy is desired, the Y-axis can be allowed to respond to a signal fed to the EMI analyzer from a suitably accurate frequency source such as a comb generator; the vertical lines then are drawn at each point of maximum Y-axis response. Similarly, such an external source can be used to check the frequency accuracy of any subsequent plots. When automatic scanning is used, care must always be taken to scan sufficiently slowly so as to avoid inertial errors which might result from the slewing speed and acceleration limitations of the plotter.

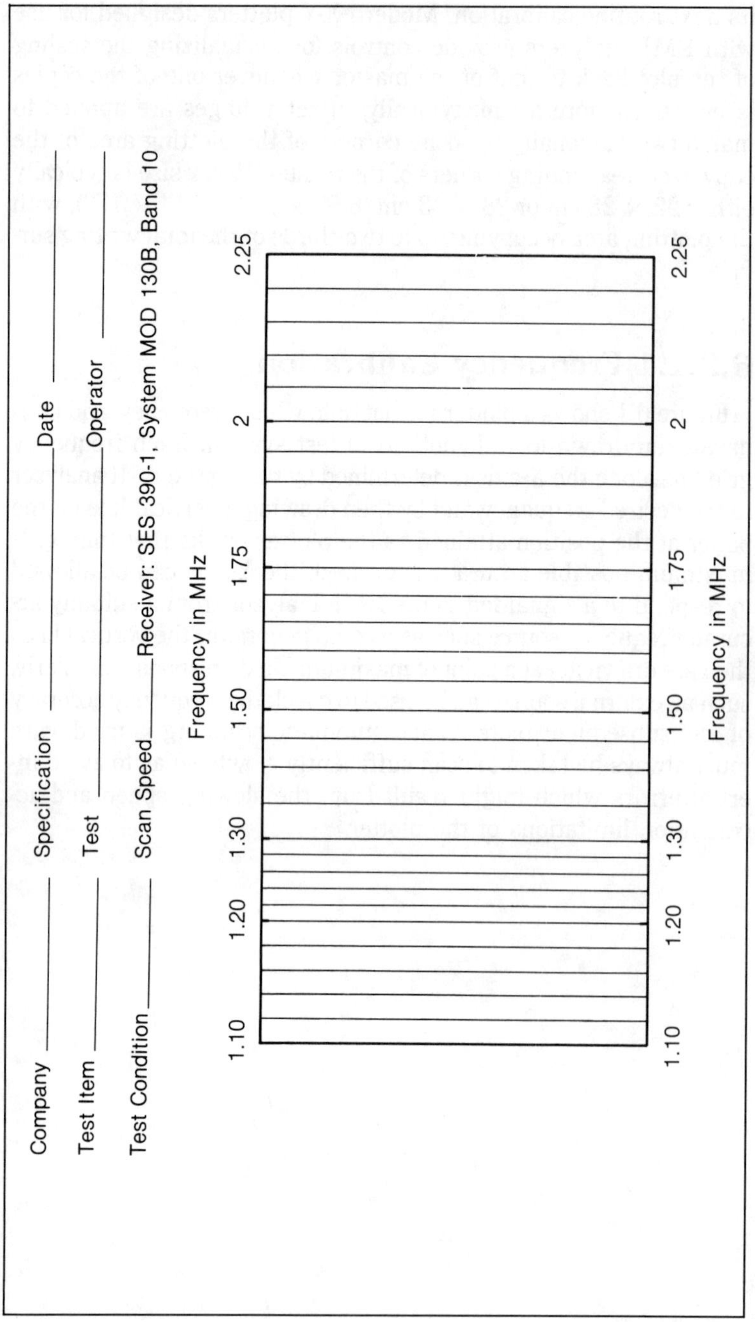
Company
Specification
Date
Test Item
Test
Operator
Test Condition
Scan Speed
Receiver: SES 390-1, System MOD 130B, Band 10
Frequency in MHz
1.10
1.20
1.30
1.50
1.75
2
2.25
1.10
1.20
1.30
1.50
1.75
2
2.25
Frequency in MHz

Figure 6.1—X-Y Plotter Paper with Frequency Grid Lines

6.2.1.2 Amplitude Calibration

Some modern EMI analyzers have front panel meters with display ranges of 60 to 80 dB and also include metered slideback peak as a detector function. In this case, an amplitude-calibrated master can be produced simply by normalizing a frequency-calibrated copy and then running multiple plots with the slideback voltage set to produce a reading at each 10 dB increment on the scale of the EMI analyzer front-panel meter. The result is a series of parallel horizontal lines corresponding to the full dynamic range of the front-panel meter of the EMI analyzer. Once this master grid is produced and copied for each frequency segment (band) of interest, running a plot becomes simply a matter of normalizing the copy to the master (as discussed in Section 6.2.1) and then activating the EMI meter to scan the respective frequency band.

The resulting plot is a hard-copy recording, plotted against frequency, of the same readings which would be registered by the front-panel meter of the EMI analyzer, and it has about the same degree of accuracy. If the RF band being scanned is amplitude calibrated at only one frequency before beginning the scan, the accuracy of both the meter reading and the plotted amplitude will deteriorate because of the lack of flatness in gain over that band.

A more conventional and inherently more accurate method of calibrating the plotter presentation with respect to amplitude is to plot the actual response of the EMI analyzer to calibrated levels of EMI fed to it as it is scanned over the frequency band of interest. The resulting master plot might then appear like that shown in Fig. 6.2. Each of the plotted levels is essentially a known substituted calibration signal against which each unknown recorded EMI level can be visually compared or interpolated.

It should be noted in Fig. 6.2 that the ordinate of the plot is calibrated in the broadband terms of spectrum amplitude at the left, and in the narrowband terms of voltage at the right. The calibrated levels shown are developed by the following procedure:

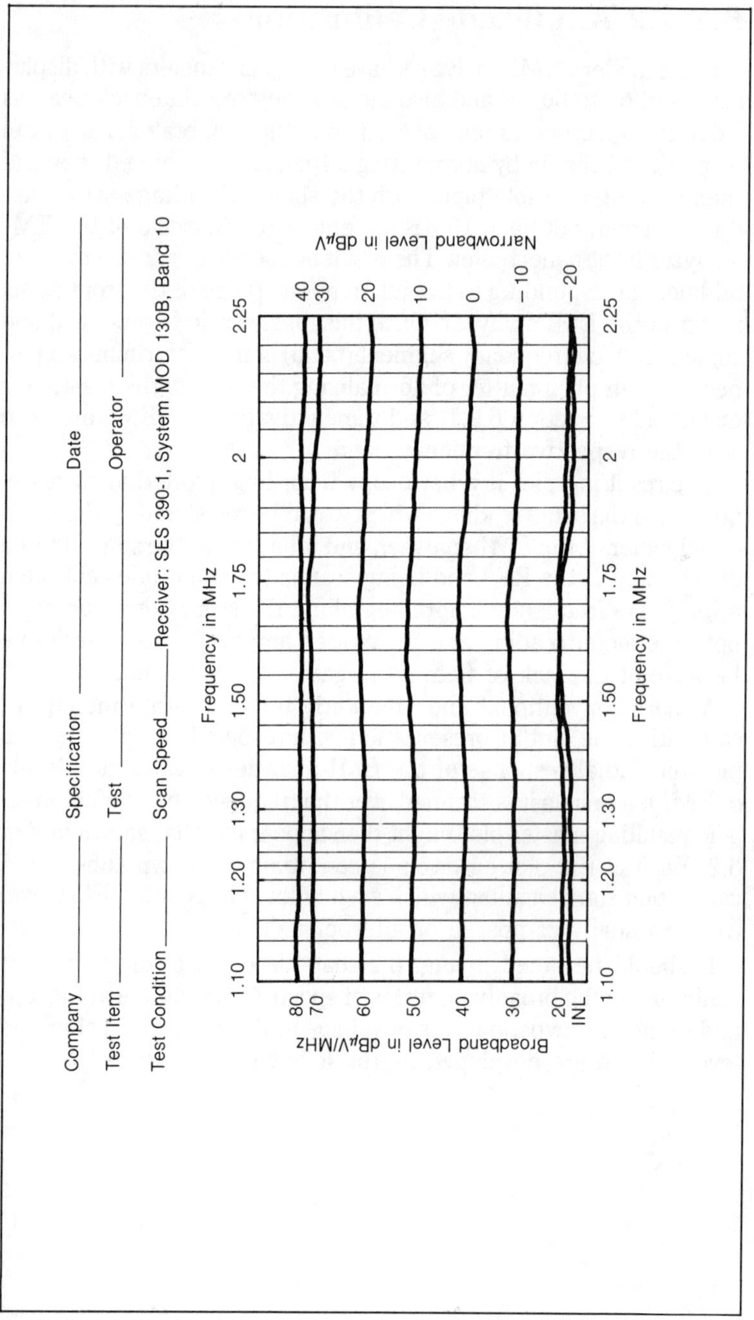

Company ______ Specification ______ Date ______
Test Item ______ Test ______ Operator ______
Test Condition ______ Scan Speed ______ Receiver: SES 390-1, System MOD 130B, Band 10
Frequency in MHz
1.10
1.20
1.30
1.50
1.75
2
2.25
Narrowband Level in dBμV
40
30
20
10
0
– 10
– 20
Broadband Level in dBμV/MHz
80
70
60
50
40
30
20
INL

Figure 6.2—Master X-Y Grid Plot Calibrated for Frequency and NB/BB Amplitudes

Broadband Calibration (Left Ordinate):

1. Insert a blank piece of frequency-calibrated paper, as shown in Fig. 6.1, onto the platen of the X-Y plotter and normalize the X-axis zero adjustment and gain settings.
2. With a calibrated impulse generator (IG) connected to the input terminals of the EMI analyzer, adjust the IF gain of the EMI analyzer and the Y-axis controls of the plotter so that the complete dynamic range of receiver response to the impulse generator, from internal receiver noise to saturation, occupies the full height of the plotting area.
3. Reduce the output level of the IG to zero and scan the EMI analyzer to plot its internal noise level (INL). Label the resulting plot as shown in Fig. 6.2.
4. Increase the IG output in 5 or 10 dB increments to the lowest level which increases Y-axis deflection above the amplitude of the INL line; then plot and label the result as that level in dBμV/MHz.
5. Continue to increase the IG in desired increments, plotting and labeling each level until saturation occurs. Care should be taken to avoid excessive levels beyond saturation for which vertical displacement might "fold back" and create ambiguities with lower levels.

Narrowband Calibration (Right Ordinate):

Labeling of calibrated narrowband levels is based on the relationship expressed in Eq. (3.22) of Chapter 3. The level of sinewave signal, V_s, in dBμV required to produce the same EMI analyzer meter reading as produced by a given broadband level, S(f), in dBμV/MHz is obtained by adding to that broadband level the impulse bandwidth of the EMI analyzer, B_i, as expressed in dBMHz:

$$V_s = S(f) + B_i \qquad (6.4)$$

Therefore, the narrowband label for each of the plotted levels is determined by measuring the impulse bandwidth, B_i, of the EMI analyzer as discussed in Section 3.5.2.7, and by adding 20 log B_i to the number labeled for each broadband level at the left ordinate.

For example, suppose that B_i were determined to be uniformly 10 kHz (0.01 MHz) across the frequency segment covered by plot of Fig. 6.2. Since 20 log 0.01 = −40 dB, each of the labeled numbers at the right ordinate, for narrowband signals, would be 40 dB lower than its corresponding number labeled for broadband signals at the left ordinate.

If the impulse bandwidth of the EMI analyzer is not sufficiently uniform across the frequency segment to permit convenient labeling of plotted BB levels for NB, a calibrated signal or comb generator can be used to plot NB levels, which can then be connected to create a grid which is independent of the BB levels.

6.2.1.3 Reconfirming Amplitude Calibration

Although confirmation of frequency calibration is seldom necessary for EMI testing, it can always be checked by using a frequency-accurate signal source.

Amplitude calibration, on the other hand, is much more vulnerable to alteration from various causes including physical abuse of the instrumentation, inadvertent adjustment of control settings and drift in gain from inadequate temperature compensation. A check of the amplitude calibration typically is done near the beginning of the test day, after initial equipment warm-up. After normalizing the plotter to the grid copy onto which test results are to be recorded and adjusting the gain of the EMI analyzer as necessary to restore its calibration, a calibrated IG is set to feed one of the plotted broadband levels into the EMI analyzer. If, in response to this level, the plotter pen falls on the proper line, the same check should be repeated at another frequency within the band of interest and at another IG level. Plotter gain and control settings should be adjusted as necessary to make the levels correspond. If correspondence cannot be achieved, several possibilities must be considered:

1. The plotted calibration data is incorrect as the result of a previous error.
2. The impulse generator has developed a fault.
3. The EMI analyzer has a problem.

Sometimes it may be found that the proper level is registered in one part of the frequency range but departs materially (by more than ±2 dB) in another. This indicates that the EMI analyzer is at fault and in need of alignment or repair. Once this is completed, a new master grid should be generated since it is likely that some characteristics of the repaired unit will have been altered. On rare occasions, this type of error can result from a malfunctioning IG.

6.2.2 Adding Specification Limits and Transducer Factors

The master grids for X-Y plotting discussed so far simply record the voltage levels fed into the respective EMI analyzer and do not take into account any transducer conversion factors. Neither do they facilitate any assessment of whether specification limits on levels of EMI have been exceeded. This section covers additions to the master grids which overcome these omissions.

6.2.2.1 Factors and Limits for Conducted Testing

Since some military specification limits are rated in terms of current as measured using a current probe, it is necessary to take into account the transfer impedance of the probe (see Section 2.4.2) to superimpose lines which represent the specification limits onto the voltage levels of the X-Y plotter grid. Thus, for a given narrowband specification limit in terms of current, I_n, the corresponding level of voltage, V_n, is:

$$V_n = I_n + Z_T \qquad (6.5)$$

where,

V_n = narrowband or right-margin voltage in dBμV

I_n = specification-limit current in dBμA

Z_T = transfer impedance of the current probe in dBΩ

Similarly, for the broadband limit:

$$V_b = I_b + Z_T \qquad (6.6)$$

where,

V_b = broadband or left-margin voltage in dBμV/MHz

I_b = broadband specification-limit current in dBμA/MHz

6.13

Prior to adding the specification limits to the master grid, it is convenient to tabulate the pertinent data. Table 6.1 shows resulting data for the adjusted narrowband and broadband conducted specification limits over two RF bands of a hypothetical EMI analyzer, one of which is the same covered by the plot shown in Fig. 6.2.

Table 6.1—Adjusted Limits Derived from Addition of Transfer Impedance, Z_T, of Typical Current Probe to Specification Limits for NB and BB Conducted EMI

Freq.	RF Band	NB Limit in dBμA	BB Limit in dBμA/MHz	Z in dBΩ	Adjusted Limits NB: dBμV	BB: dBμV/MHz
30 Hz	1	120	124	−52	68	72
400 Hz	1	120	124	−34	86	90
1 kHz	1	103	124	−21	82	103
3 kHz	1	84	124	−18	66	106
—	—	—	—	—	—	—
1.1 MHz	10	24	60	0	24	60
1.6 MHz	10	21	54	0	21	54
2.2 MHz	10	20	50	0	20	50

Figure 6.3 shows the plot of Fig. 6.2 with the adjusted specification limits from Table 6.1 added. Note that the relationship shown between the NB and BB levels applies only to the 10 kHz bandwidth of the hypothetical EMI analyzer on which the plot is based. It should also be noted that the insertion of the adjusted specification limits is based on the values shown in parentheses along both ordinates. The 20 dB difference represented by these values accounts for the insertion of 20 dB attenuation in the front end of the EMI analyzer to allow a 30 dB margin above the specification limits for documenting any out-of-specification conditions.

6.2.2.2 Factors and Limits for Radiated Testing

The procedure for applying adjusted specification limits for radiated emission testing is quite similar to that described immediately above for conducted testing. The counterparts to Eqs. (6.4) and (6.5), but based on electric field strengths and antenna factors, are as follows.

Figure 6.3—Master Grid Plot with Adjusted NB and BB Conducted Limits

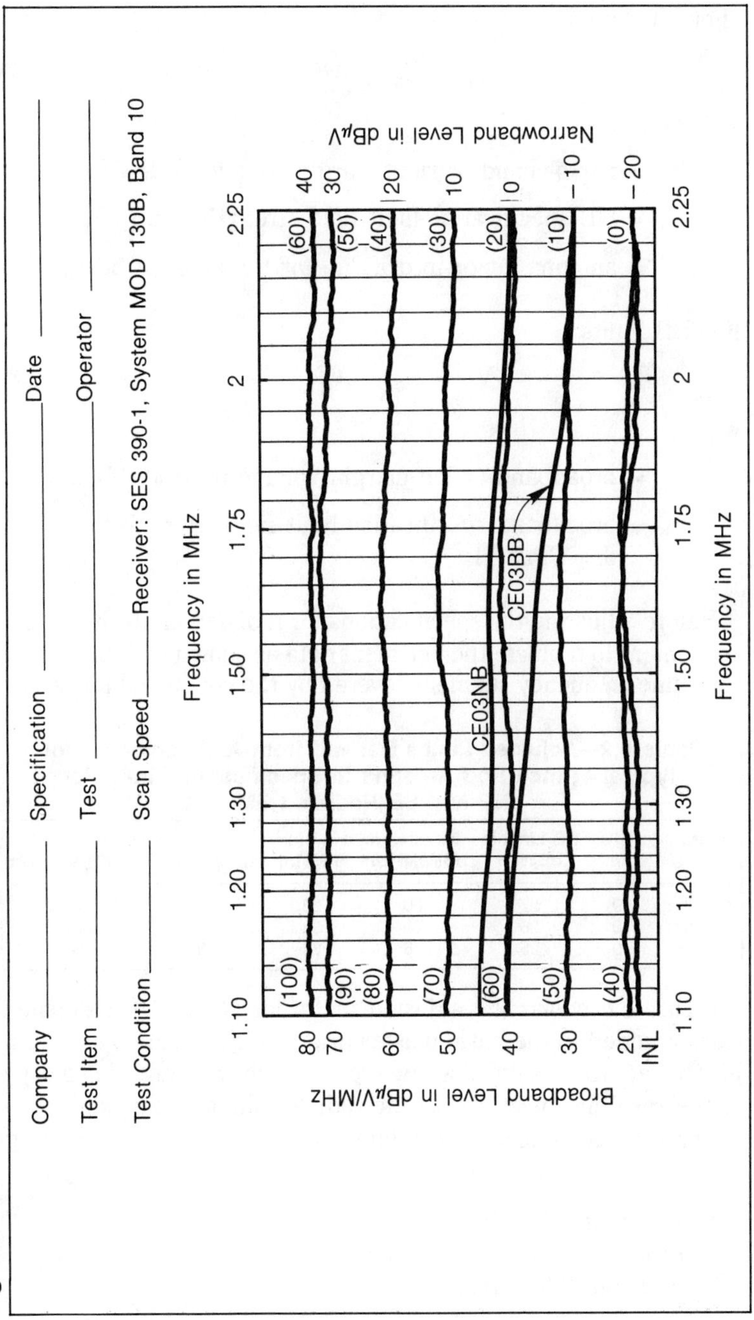

Company —————— Specification —————— Date ——————

Test Item —————— Test —————— Operator ——————

Test Condition —————— Scan Speed —————— Receiver: SES 390-1, System MOD 130B, Band 10

Narrowband Level in dBμV

Broadband Level in dBμV/MHz

Frequency in MHz

CE03NB

CE03BB

For NB limits:

$$V_n = E_n - AF \qquad (6.7)$$

where,

V_n = narrowband or right-margin voltage in dBμV

E_n = NB specification-limit field strength in dBμV/m

AF = antenna factor in dB(1/m) for the antenna being used

For BB limits:

$$V_b = E_b - AF \qquad (6.8)$$

where,

V_b = broadband or left-margin voltage in dBμV/MHz

E_b = broadband specification-limit field strength in dBμV/m/MHz

Before adjusting the specifications for radiated limits, it is again convenient to tabulate the pertinent data as shown in Table 6.2 for the same frequency segment covered by the conducted test scan.

Table 6.2—Adjusted Limits Derived from Addition of AF for Typical 41-Inch Rod Antenna to Specification Limits for NB and BB Radiated EMI

Freq.	RF Band	NB Limit in dBμV/m	BB Limit in dBμV/MHz/m	AF in dB(1/m)	Adjusted Limits NB: dBμV/m	BB: dBμV/MHz/m
1.1 MHz	10	27	80	33	−6	47
1.6 MHz	10	26	78	33	−7	45
2.2 MHz	10	25	76	34	−9	42

Figure 6.4 shows the adjusted limits for NB and BB radiated testing added to the basic master grid of Fig. 6.2. Also shown in Fig. 6.4 are the results of a single plot which was run using a copy of the resulting master with the radiated limits included.

Three radiated emissions of interest are shown on the resulting plot:

1. At about 1.19 MHz
2. From about 1.4 to 1.85 MHz
3. At about 2.04 MHz

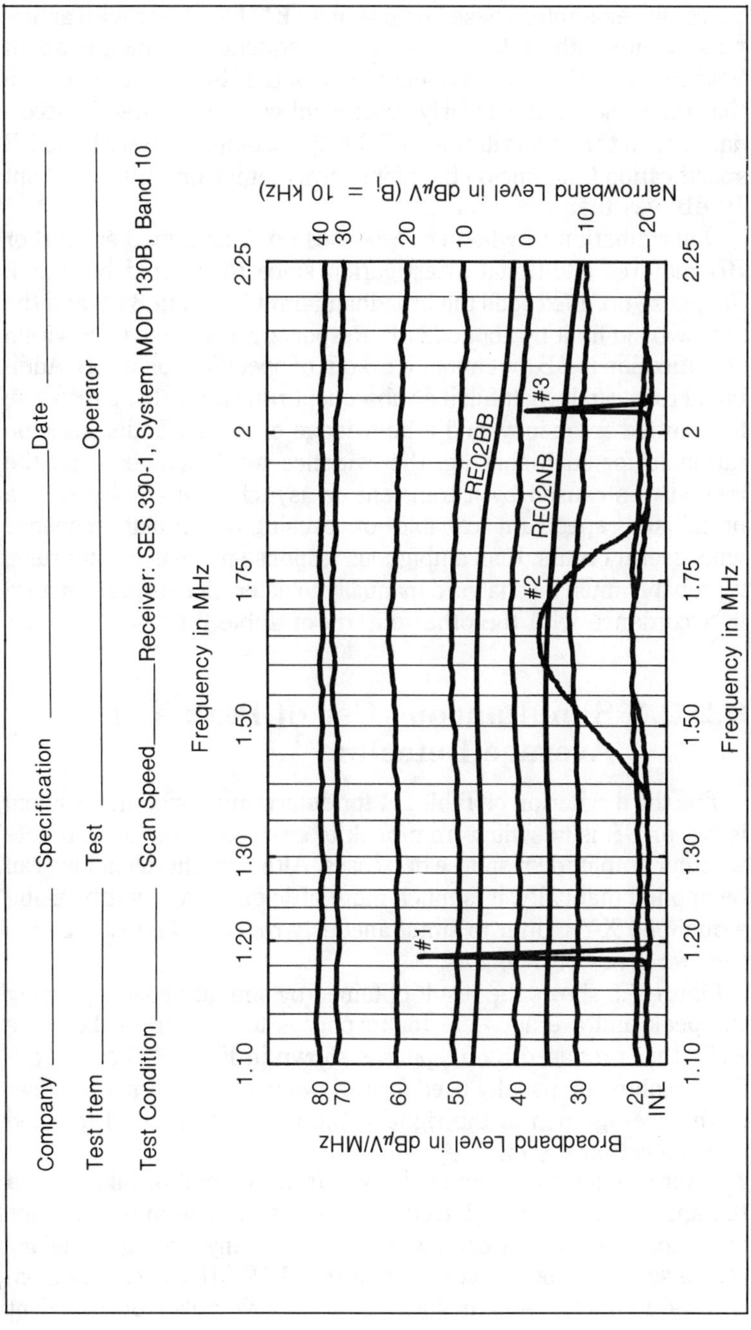
Company
Specification
Date
Test Item
Test
Operator
Test Condition
Scan Speed
Receiver: SES 390-1, System MOD 130B, Band 10
Frequency in MHz
1.10
1.20
1.30
1.50
1.75
2
2.25
Narrowband Level in dBμV (B_i = 10 kHz)
40
30
20
10
0
– 10
– 20
Broadband Level in dBμV/MHz
80
70
60
50
40
30
20
INL
RE02BB
RE02NB
#1
#2
#3

Figure 6.3—Results after One Run Using Copy of Master Grid Plot with Adjusted NB and BB Radiated Limits

Since this example is based on use of an EMI analyzer with an impulse bandwidth of 10 kHz at these frequencies, which is about 0.9 percent of the total frequency span of the X-axis, it can be seen that response no. 2 is clearly broadband when evaluated in accordance with the first criterion of Table 2.1. Comparison with the BB specification limit line on the plot shows that its amplitude is about 10 dB less than the limit.

Determination of whether responses no. 1 and no. 3 are NB or BB requires additional investigation since they could be either. Response no. 1 exceeds the broadband limit by about 8 dB and the narrowband limit by about 22 dB. Response no. 3 is a few dB within specification if BB, but about 5 dB out of specification if NB. Additional runs can be helpful: if a subsequent run shows that a response has shifted frequency, and a knowledge of the EUT discloses no rationale for such shifting, the evidence would suggest that the response is caused by a transient or asynchronous pulse with a broadband spectrum capable of causing a similar response whenever it occurs. If an ambiguous response persists in later runs, it probably must be analyzed manually to determine its performance in accordance with the other criteria of Table 2.1.

6.2.2.3 Simultaneous Use of Peak and Average Detectors

The third criterion of Table 2.1 for determining whether a signal is NB or BB is to switch from peak to average detection and note whether amplitude response decreases. Although this technique can be applied manually, it is much more efficient to apply it by using a dual-pen X-Y plotter to simultaneously register the responses to the two types of detectors.

Figure 6.5 shows the result obtained by simultaneously plotting the peak and average detector responses to EMI from the same EUT that produced the responses shown in Fig. 6.4. Pens of different colors are usually used for the two detectors. A slight offset of the average pen to the right of the peak pen is used to avoid mechanical interference.

Several conclusions can be derived from the plot of Fig. 6.5 and the analysis of relative detector responses in Section 6.1.4. Since there apparently is a complete absence of any average detector response, the peak detector response at 1.19 MHz is clearly from a low-duty-factor source such as a narrow pulse or transient

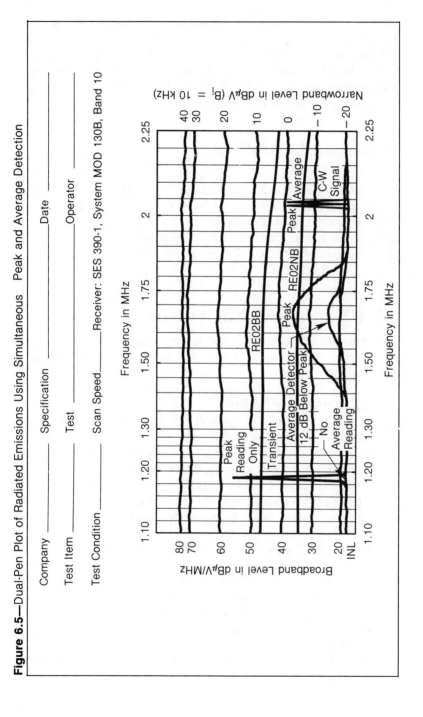

Figure 6.5—Dual-Pen Plot of Radiated Emissions Using Simultaneous Peak and Average Detection

waveform. The previously recognized BB response from 1.4 to 1.85 MHz is now accompanied by an average detector response which is 12 dB lower. This response appears to be due to a data line radiation having about a 25 percent duty factor. Since both the peak and average detectors plot at the same amplitude level, response no. 3 apparently is due to a CW emission.

6.2.3 Multiband Plotting

Before widespread availability of low-priced computers capable of serving as controllers for automated EMI testing, X-Y plotting of multiple RF bands on a single sheet of paper provided a significant advance over plotting of a single band at a time. However, this form of automatic testing now has been almost completely superseded by computer-controlled systems which offer both superior performance and economy.

6.2.4 X-Y Plotting Limitations

As a preface to the discussion of computer-controlled automation, it is appropriate to summarize the weaknesses of the X-Y plotting technique:

1. **Limited Repeatability**
   Although, ideally, the operator should leave all equipment settings fixed from one spectrum scan to the next, there is a finite probability that settings will be altered, either deliberately or inadvertently. Thus, multiple runs on the same EUT might not be directly comparable, and the existence of discrepancies in the setup might not be recognized until much expensive test time has been wasted.

2. **Excessive Impact of Equipment Changes**
   Preparation of the master grid plots incorporating spec limits is still a relatively time-consuming process. Substitution of a pickup transducer with different correction factors requires the generation of a new master.

3. **Excessive Time for Data Analysis and Test Reports**
   Once the data are plotted, they must still be analyzed and interpreted, e.g., for NB/BB determination.

6.3 Computer-Automated EMI Emission Testing

6.3.1 Advantages

A properly designed computer-automated EMI emissions test system can overcome nearly all limitations of the X-Y plotter technique cited in Section 6.2.4:

1. Repeatability is excellent because each test run is executed identically, under software control. To any minor extent that the operator is involved during the test run, he can be reminded via interactive dialogue of the proper settings for any accessible controls.
2. The adverse impact of equipment changes is drastically lessened because new correction factors for input transducers can be easily substituted and automatically accounted for by the computer.
3. The time required for data analysis and preparation of test reports is also drastically reduced because the system can automatically apply all correction factors, make crucial decisions such as whether a signal is NB or BB and present the corrected EMI data in a readily assessable format for incorporation into a final test report. Total time required for testing and reports can be reduced by as much as 80 percent.

6.3.2 Basic Functions for EMI Emission Testing

The basic objective in designing a computer-controlled EMI test system is to remove from operator responsibility all routine, time-consuming aspects of the testing, without compromising in any way the ability of the operator to exercise sound judgment based on previous test experience. The essential automatic tasks of the system are to:

1. Tune each EMI analyzer over its appropriate portion of the total selected range of frequency coverage
2. Provide inputs to each EMI analyzer from appropriate transducers

3. Obtain an EMI analyzer reading for each response of interest and apply to it all pertinent correction factors
4. Compare each processed response to the appropriate test limit
5. Present the resulting data in a format suitable for easy assessment and incorporation into a test report

6.3.3 System Hardware

Design details of each system will be determined by many factors, but especially by whether the EMI analyzers have the capability to be tuned directly by digital commands. The ability of the EMI analyzers to respond in this manner without the interposition of an intermediary interface unit to provide digital-to-analog (D/A) conversion and control enables the system to be designed with greatest efficiency and economy.

Figure 6.6 shows a functional block diagram of one such system. The system examined here is relatively elaborate because it includes three EMI analyzers and operates over the entire frequency range from 20 Hz to 40 GHz; any reduction in the operating range that would eliminate the need for one or two of these EMI analyzers would correspondingly simplify the system.

Shown in the lower right corner of Fig. 6.6 is the system controller, which comprises a computer and various peripherals. The choice of a computer for controlling the system is a major factor in determining the overall system capability. This selection must be based not only on the maximum capabilities of the central processing unit (CPU) itself but on the availability of compatible peripherals which satisfy the data presentation requirements unique to the EMI testing task. Typical capability and peripherals would include a 10 MHz, 16-bit processor; both floppy-disk and hard-disk drives; a full-capability keyboard; interfaces for both the IEEE-488 and RS-232 buses; a high-resolution color monitor; a hard-copy printer; and a digital X-Y plotter.

Three EMI analyzers which collectively cover the frequency spectrum from 20 Hz to 40 GHz are controlled from the computer via the IEEE-488 interface bus. These EMI analyzers, in turn, exchange appropriate power and control signals with various accessory devices as shown to their left in Fig. 6.6. Each of the EMI analyzers furnishes RF tuning information to a **transducer control inter-**

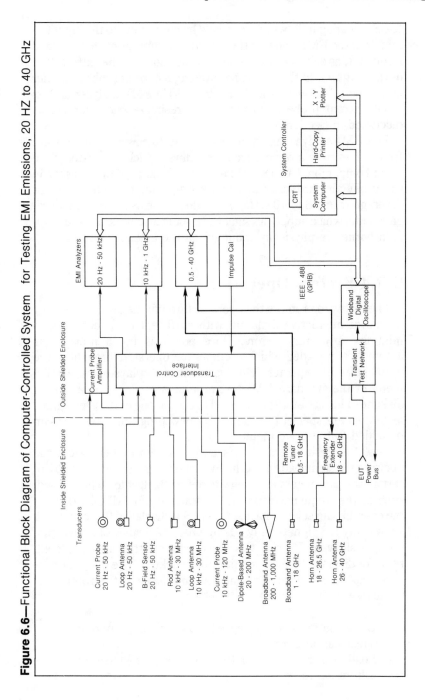

Figure 6.6—Functional Block Diagram of Computer-Controlled System for Testing EMI Emissions, 20 HZ to 40 GHz

face switching unit, which responds by connecting to the input terminals of the EMI analyzer the transducer appropriate to the tuned frequency, as selected from among those shown at the extreme left of the diagram. In this particular system, a current probe amplifier is interposed between the 20 Hz to 50 kHz EMI analyzer and its input current probe to give it a flat response characteristic as discussed in Section 4.1.1.2.

The EMI analyzer used in this system to cover the microwave frequencies uses a remote front-end tuner which is situated close to its companion 1 to 18 GHz antenna. This minimizes losses in the connecting cable. Similarly, its frequency extender unit, for coverage from 18 to 40 GHz, is also located close to the standard-gain horns which supply its signals. In some instances, the standard-gain horns are physically mounted on the extender unit.

6.3.4 System Operation

The software prompts the operator through the test sequence by means of interactive dialogue with sufficient error checking to minimize any entry errors. Once power is up, a program is automatically loaded which prompts the operator throughout the initial start-up sequence. The system then displays on the CRT a menu of the standard EMI test programs available on a system diskette. The operator is instructed to choose one of these programs or to create a special program. Any new program generated can be added to the basic menu.

Once the desired program is either chosen or generated, the operating system loads a routine which prompts the operator to insert all the parameters necessary to define the test to be performed, such as the frequency range to be scanned. For MIL-STD tests, the operator can select a format for graphic display of the data which shows only NB signals, only BB signals, or a display of both signal types as shown in Fig. 6.7. Once all operator entries are completed, they are displayed on the monitor for checking. The operator concurs that the entries are satisfactory, and the executive routine activates a series of subprograms which:

1. Draw the graphic display formats including appropriate specification limits
2. Load into the processor the pertinent transducer and calibration factors

3. Activate the instrumentation to perform the desired tests
4. Plot the fully corrected and processed data onto the appropriate graphic display format for easy comparison to the specification limits

Once the scan is complete, the operator can obtain a copy of the completed plot from the digital X-Y plotter, or, if desired, from the hard-copy printer. Also obtainable from the printer is a listing of the frequencies and amplitudes of all narrowband and broadband signals. This listing also shows the correction factors for the transducer used, for the cable loss encountered and for (BB signals only) the bandwidth, along with a numerical comparison of each signal amplitude to the specification limit. In addition, the operator can choose to have the data stored on a disk, which provides the option of subsequent recall in an expanded format for further analysis.

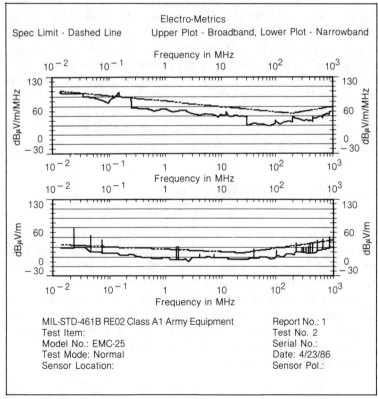

Figure 6.7—Dual-Graphic Display of BB and NB Responses

6.3.4.1 The Scanning Process

By means of commands conveyed over the IEEE-488 bus, the appropriate RF band of the EMI analyzer is selected. The EMI analyzer is then tuned to the median frequency of that band, and an internal automatic amplitude calibration is performed. Once calibration is successfully completed, the computer tunes the EMI analyzer to the start frequency and begins the scan. Using the peak detector function, two readings are taken at each of three frequencies, for a total of six, within each frequency increment equal to the impulse bandwidth of the EMI analyzer. Any significant difference between the two readings taken at the same frequency, including the complete absence of a response at one of the readings, indicates the probability that the higher reading resulted from a transient event.

At the end of the scan for each RF band, the computer analyzes the acquired data. For MIL-STD testing, the NB/BB RF tuning criterion from Table 2.1 is applied; the NB signal levels thus determined are processed to add the appropriate correction factors and then plotted on the NB graph. The remaining signals are similarly processed as BB and then plotted on the BB graph. The program also stores the resulting data in a matrix for storage on a diskette after the scan is complete. Upon the completion of a scan for each RF band, the next higher-frequency band or EMI analyzer is activated by the computer and the scanning process resumed.

6.3.4.2 Entry of Data from Nonautomated Tests

A small percentage of EMI emission tests are not amenable to automation and must be performed manually by the operator. The software of the system being discussed allows the operator to enter into the computer the raw data that have been collected manually, along with pertinent transducer factors and other test parameters. The system can then provide plots of the data automatically corrected for these factors. This data can also be stored on diskette and subsequently accessed in the same manner as for data collected automatically by the system.

6.4 Automating the Testing of EMI Susceptibility

Primarily because of the relative complexity of evaluating the threshold at which an EUT begins to malfunction, the degree of operator involvement in automated EMI susceptibility testing is inherently greater than that required for automated EMI emission testing. However, when implemented properly, automation can be applied to susceptibility testing to decrease significantly the likelihood of errors due to operator factors such as inattention, improper adjustment of test instrumentation, inability to duplicate test conditions and misplacement of test data.[2]

6.4.1 Selection of Scan Speed

Selection of appropriate rates at which to scan the frequency of the EMI energy being conducted or radiated is determined largely by the unique characteristics of each potentially susceptible EUT. In some instances, scan speed can be accelerated by using higher-than-threshold levels for initial determination of the frequencies at which the EUT is most susceptible; more thorough testing can then be concentrated at those frequencies.

Some pertinent considerations relative to limitations on scan speeds are given in SAE information report J1507 on the use of anechoic chambers for testing the radiated susceptibility of motor vehicles.[3] Since some EUTs have relatively slow thermal or electrical time constants (or both) or long cycle times, the sweep rate must be compatible with the reaction-interaction time of the EUT to the radiated test field or the conducted test energy. There are two aspects to this reaction time:

1. The time required for the EUT to respond at a given frequency
2. The frequency bandwidth over which the response can occur

This bandwidth of vulnerability can be used to define a "Q" for the response; i.e., $Q = f/B$, where f is the center frequency and B is the 3 dB bandwidth. Typical values of Q range from 2 to 40 but can be as high as 100.

If the response is the result of a resonance, unaffected by other EUT considerations, then the response time t_r can be approximated by $t_r \approx 0.35$ Q/f. Furthermore, the maximum scan speed, SS_m, can be approximated by $SS_m \leqslant 1.73$ $(f/Q)^2$. This will not apply, however, when the response occurs only during a portion of the operating cycle of the EUT; in this case the scan speed must be much slower than SS_m. If a field sensor is used in conjunction with automatic leveling of the radiated field, the time required for stabilization may be the determining factor. The maximum scan speed, SS_m, as limited by the Q of wiring resonances, is proportional to the square of the frequency as can be seen from the above. It may be as slow as 0.16 Hz/s at 30 Hz, but as fast as 1.7×10^7 GHz/s at 10 GHz. To determine the required scan time, the scan speed relationship must be integrated over the frequency range to be scanned. Then, a piece-wise approximation must be made for scan speeds over the bands covered by the signal generating equipment. This is explained in more detail in Section 9.4.6.

To assure that all responses are found in automated systems which increment the frequency in steps, the maximum step size should be less than f/1.65 Q. Also, all known clock and other EUT operating frequencies should be specifically addressed. Finding the appropriate step size and time required to cover the test frequency range is also discussed in detail in Section 9.4.6.

6.4.2 Other Considerations

Ambiguities can result from harmonics of intended frequencies being fed from the signal generators or power amplifiers. Although potential confusion can be minimized somewhat by scanning each RF band from high end to low end, it is frequently necessary to utilize low-pass filters at the outputs of the culprit sources. In many wideband power amplifiers, the second harmonic may be only 15 dB down from the fundamental. At a 200 V/m level of the fundamental, this is a significant 35 V/m.

6.4.3 Monitoring the EUT

The need for operator monitoring to note any degradation of EUT performance is the most significant constraint in the automation of EMI susceptibility testing. Constant monitoring by the operator, such as viewing a CRT, is subject to errors induced by boredom and fatigue. Thus, any automation of this EUT monitoring which can be achieved represents a major advance in the entire process of EMI susceptibility test automation.

6.5 Swept Signal Source Automated EMI Susceptibility Testing

Various sources of signals for testing EMI susceptibility were discussed in Chapter 5, including swept signal generators and power oscillators. The most elementary degree of automation in testing EMI susceptibility is to frequency sweep such a source of conducted or radiated susceptibility signal at increasing increments of output level and to note that level at which the EUT first exhibits a malfunction. The rate of sweeping must not be too rapid, since the potential EUT malfunction might require that the interfering signal dwell for some minimum length of time within a relatively narrow passband centered at an unknown critical frequency.

Another factor that determines the feasibility of using a swept signal source for susceptibility testing is the extent to which a malfunction of the EUT can be automatically recorded. If the X-axis of an X-Y plotter can be driven by an accurate analog of the sweep generator frequency, with the Y-axis vertically offset for successively higher output levels and one of the axes further affected in response to a malfunction of the EUT, the resulting simple system can be very useful for recording the approximate level of EUT susceptibility. The frequency sweep can be repeated at successively higher levels until a malfunction occurs, with the recorded sweep lines being labeled to show the level of generator output.

6.6 Computer-Automated EMI Susceptibility Testing

The degree of automation ultimately achievable in EMI susceptibility testing in accordance with U.S. military procedures is inherently limited by the high degree of intervention and decision making required of the human operator. Some test methods require that the operator perform various tasks manually, depending on the computer only for data compilation and reduction, while other test methods can be automated to a degree comparable to that realized for emission testing as discussed in Section 6.3. Therefore, a paramount consideration in designing a computer-controlled system for EMI susceptibility testing is to provide the greatest possible degree of computer assistance to the operator. In addition to its maximum possible involvement in word processing, record keeping and data processing, the computer is used to perform automatic calibration and adjustment of signal levels and otherwise assist the operator in executing the tests.

6.6.1 System Hardware

Shown in Fig. 6.8 is a functional block diagram of a computer-controlled system capable of performing EMI susceptibility tests at frequencies from 30 Hz to 18 GHz. At the left side of the diagram are shown the controlling computer and its peripherals which are interconnected by the IEEE-488 interface bus to various signal sources and a switching controller. Also connected to the computer via the bus are the power sensors, including the interface with the optical link field sensors, and the safety and interlock alarm system for the test chamber. Throughout the system, remotely controllable switches are interposed at appropriate points to permit automatic switching of various system components as directed by the test software. Shown in the center of the diagram are the required power amplifiers, to which can be added an extender for generating signals in the range of 18 to 40 GHz. At the extreme right side of the diagram are the various transducers for generating fields and the various sensors for calibrating the resulting levels.

6.6.2 System Operation for Radiated Susceptibility Testing

System software is designed to guide the operator through the required tests without confusion, but with sufficient error checking to prevent incorrect entries. Figure 6.9 shows a typical software flow chart for susceptibility testing. Interaction between the operator and the computer begins with a program calling for entry by the operator of all parameters pertinent to the testing to be performed, including the levels of field strength to be generated. Once the

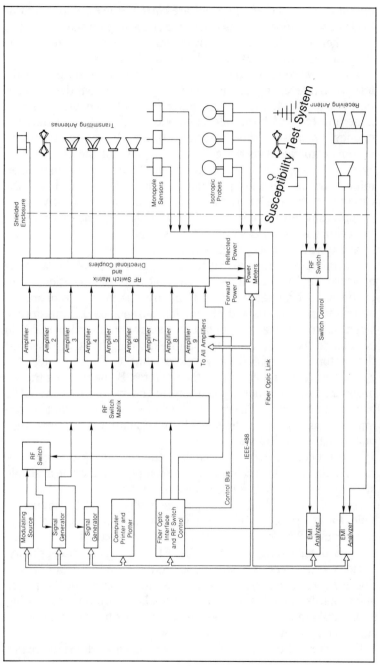

Figure 6.8—Functional Block Diagram of Computer-Automated EMI Susceptibility Test System

6.31

operator concurs that all entries are correct, the executive routine loads in other subprograms which access the appropriate transducer and other correction factors, calculate the signal levels required and then instruct the operator in details of the test setup.

The software then proceeds to the field calibration part of the test. With a receiving antenna or field sensor placed at the proposed location of the EUT, the computer instructs the proper signal generator to furnish the calculated output at the desired start frequency. The system then uses the output of the receiving antenna or sensor to calculate the closed-loop "gain" of the transmitting system. This process is then repeated until the system gain is determined for all desired frequencies. The software includes the capability to perform this calibration automatically at a preprogrammed set of frequencies. Once the sequence is complete, the calibration data is stored on a disk and available for later use in actual radiated susceptibility testing.

The operator is then instructed to remove the receiving antenna or sensor and to substitute the EUT at the same location. After ensuring that all safety precautions are observed, the operating system then proceeds with the testing. As soon as the appropriate signal source is tuned to the start frequency and the calculated field is radiated, both its frequency and field strength are displayed at the bottom of the CRT. Before proceeding to the next step, the system waits for a response by the operator. By depressing the appropriate key, the operator can inform the system that the EUT has passed or failed. The system then allows the operator to determine the susceptibility threshold by manipulating a cursor to raise or lower the level of the radiated field.

This process is iterated at each of the remaining test frequencies. Again, all data is collected by the computer and made available at the end of the test for storage and analysis.

For assistance in finding frequencies at which the EUT is susceptible, the operator can also select a slow, automatic search mode of operation. This scan is sufficiently slow to allow operator interaction in determining whether the EUT exhibits susceptibility. Various scan speed considerations are discussed in detail in Section 9.4.6 (Chapter 9). The system permits control of the power on/off status of each amplifier from the keyboard and monitoring of all vital amplifier conditions. Also available to the operator are cursor-controlled manual frequency scans.

The fiber optic link coupled sensors shown at the right center

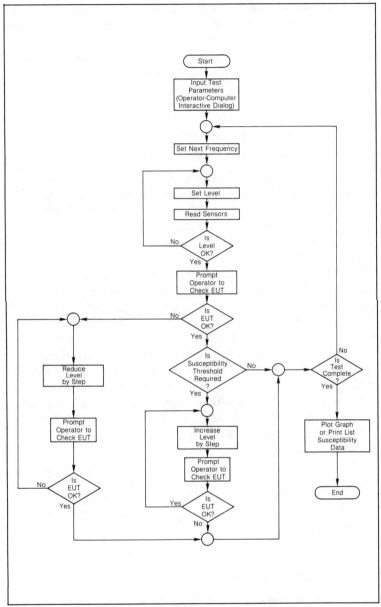

Figure 6.9—Typical Software Flow Chart for Susceptibility Testing

of Fig. 6.8 can be used to provide real-time information to the computer and the operator regarding the field strength actually being generated. However, this data must be used with due consideration for discrepancies in field strength between the locations of the EUT and the sensor, such as those caused by reflections from the walls of the shielded enclosure and from the EUT itself.[4, 5]

6.6.3 System Operation for Conducted Susceptibility Testing

For testing conducted EMI susceptibility, the test signal sources are controlled by the computer to feed known levels of signals onto power and signal lines and into various ports of the EUT. The levels applied are measured by a computer-controlled EMI analyzer or power meter and then conveyed to the computer via the IEEE-488 bus.

For the more automated tests, once the setup is established, the computer will step the signal source and the EMI analyzer through the desired frequency range while the operator monitors the EUT. The EMI analyzer is used to provide a measure of the test level to the computer so that it can be leveled at each frequency. If no susceptible EUT responses are found, the computer simply provides a record of the test details, showing the frequencies and levels at which the EUT was not susceptible. If a susceptible response is found, the operator stops the programmed sequence and causes the computer to adjust the test signal level until the threshold of susceptibility is determined. The resulting information is then recorded by the computer.

This approach to conducted susceptibility testing uses the computer for those tasks to which it is best suited but permits operator intervention as often as needed. As compared to completely manual susceptibility testing, the chance of human error is reduced significantly.

6.6.4 Data Display and Analysis

Once the measurements are completed, the system provides several options for output of the collected date. As is the case for emission measurements, the data can be presented in either graphic or tabulated form. For the graphic readout, the operator can view the performance of the EUT against the specification limits with a significant amount of annotated data, including the EUT model and serial numbers, the test mode, the report number and the date. Presentations in tabular form include complete listings of failure points and threshold levels.

All data can also be stored on a disk for recall and analysis. Display formats can be modified and expanded to facilitate analysis of the recalled data. A moving cursor can also be used to track the displayed data and determine the frequency and amplitude of any selected response.

6.6.5 Computer Monitoring of the EUT

In a computer-automated system, the signals indicative of EUT performance degradation can be routed onto the IEEE-488 interface bus either directly via fiber optic or high-impedance transmission lines, or indirectly via cable connections to EUT performance monitors, external controllers, external circuitry, simulated loads or peripherals which are located outside the test chamber. The direct method requires telemetry links which are not part of the EUT, while the indirect method requires proper filtering of any leads which penetrate the test chamber walls. This protects equipment outside the test chamber from any RF energy they convey from the test chamber.[2, 6]

Once the onset of a degradation is noted by the computer, it can initiate various preprogrammed operations such as shutting down the appropriate power amplifier, sequencing the EUT to other modes of operation or dwelling on particular frequencies to evaluate further how they affect the EUT.

6.7 References

1. Bronaugh, E.L., "Scan Speed Limits in Automated EMI Measurements," *Proceedings of Fifth International Conference on EMC*, pp. 293-299 (London: Institute of Electronic and Radio Engineers, 1986).
2. Heirman, D.N., "Automated Immunity Measurements," *Proceedings of the Sixth Symposium and Technical Exhibition on Electromagnetic Compatibility*, pp. 7-10 (Zurich: Association of Swiss Electrotechnicians, 1985).

3. SAE J1507, Information Report on "Anechoic Test Facility/Radiated Susceptibility, 20 MHz to 18 GHz Electromagnetic Field," (Warrendale, PA: Society of Automotive Engineers).

4. Bronaugh, E.L., and McGinnis, W.H., "Whole-Vehicle Electromagnetic Susceptibility Tests in Open-Area Test Sites: Applying SAE J1338," SAE Paper No. 830606, from 1983 International Congress and Exhibition, republished in *SAE Transactions*, Vol. 92 (Warrendale, PA: Society of Automotive Engineers, 1983).

5. Bronaugh, E.L., "Highlights of Forthcoming SAE J1507 and a Practical Realization of Its Procedures for Radiated Susceptibility Testing of Automotive Systems," *Proceedings of the 1985 IEEE International Symposium on EMC*, (New York: IEEE, 1985).

6. Rose, M.L., Jr.; Bronaugh, E.L.; and Rethman, H.W., "Multiple Isolated Probe Electromagnetic Field Measuring System," *Proceedings of the 1985 IEEE International Symposium on EMC*, pp. 143-150 (New York: IEEE, 1980).

Chapter 7

Test Facilities and Enclosures for EMI Testing

This chapter considers the electromagnetic and physical environments in which EMI testing is performed. A number of basic approaches can be taken to establish the EMI test environment:

1. **Open-Area Test Site.** The test area can be made as transparent as possible to electromagnetic radiations, with little or no effort made to establish any shielding between the EUT and the ambient environment. The ideal example of this approach is the open-area test site which is preferably sited to take advantage of the natural shielding of its surrounding terrain, but which otherwise is physically and electromagnetically open. Because the open-area site has the least effect on test results, it is frequently used as a standard to resolve discrepancies observed among other test environments.

2. **Sheltered Open-Area Test Site.** The test area can be enclosed by a shelter which affords protection against the natural elements but is constructed of wood, plastic or some other electromagnetically transparent, nonmetallic material. The resulting degree of transparency is usually conditional, based on the materials used and the possible presence of precipitation and other contaminants.

3. **Basic Shielded Enclosure.** The test area can be enclosed by a metallic structure which provides shielding against electromagnetic radiated energy escaping or entering but includes little or no provision for suppressing reflections within the structure. The usefulness of such enclosures is usually limited to conducted EMI testing or radiated testing in which the distance between the EUT and the radiating or receiving transducer is short relative to the enclosure dimensions. This type of shielded enclosure is commonly used for radiated emissions testing at 1 m spacing in accordance with MIL-STD-461/462.

4. **Shielded Anechoic Chamber.** The test area can be enclosed by a metallic structure which provides shielding against electromagnetic radiated energy escaping or entering but which also incorporates absorbing material on its inner walls to reduce the effects of reflections within the structure. Thus, the performance of a well-designed shielded anechoic chamber approaches that of an ideal open-area site or free space.

5. **Shielded Test Cell.** The test area can be enclosed by a metallic structure which provides shielding but which also uses the reflectivity and other characteristics of the structure to control the distribution of electromagnetic energy in the vicinity of the EUT. Transverse electromagnetic (TEM) cells, reverberation enclosures and mode-tuned chambers are examples of test structures which provide shielding but which also participate in the distribution or collection of the EMI test energy.

All of these will be discussed in some detail in the following sections. Also considered are some hybrid facilities and structures which incorporate characteristics of two or more of these basic types.

7.1 Open-Area EMI Test Sites

Open-area test site measurements are preferred for much EMI testing, e.g., to determine FCC compliance, because they are most amenable to theoretical analysis and because they can be more readily correlated to actual operating conditions of the EUT. As already noted in the introductory section above, because they have little effect on test results, open-area sites are used to resolve ambiguities and discrepancies in data derived from other types of sites. Although open-area sites are used for both emission and susceptibility testing, the following discussions will be based on the emission application. Any special considerations pertinent to susceptibility testing will be duly noted.

7.1.1 Design Considerations

7.1.1.1 Site Dimensions

The primary factor in determining the size of the open-area test site is the measurement distance to be used between the EUT and the pickup transducer. Most standards and regulations specify distances of 3, 10 or 30 m, but some call for distances of 100 or 300 m. The most common situation is when the EUT is sufficiently small to be rotated 360°, either manually or by use of a turntable. Here, the obstruction-free area for the site can be most efficiently shaped like an ellipse, with the EUT at one focus and the test antenna at the other. As illustrated in Fig. 7.1, if the distance, F, between the foci is the maximum measurement distance to be used, the major axis is twice that distance, and the minor axis is

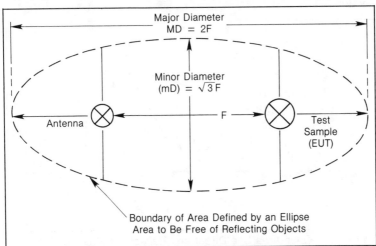

Figure 7.1—Obstruction-Free Area for Open-Area Test Site

7.3

that distance multiplied by the $\sqrt{3}$. Within this area, the terrain should be as flat as possible and free of any obstructions such as bushes, trees or metal objects which could reflect a portion of the radiated energy.[1, 2]

7.1.1.2 Reflections

As shown in Fig. 7.2, there must be two and only two paths for the EMI emission to follow in getting from the EUT to the test antenna: one is the direct path between the antennas, and the other is the major reflection off the ground plane lying between them. Arrival of energy at the test antenna via any other path will invalidate the test results. Thus, there must be no metal fence around the test area nor any other presence such as a vehicle or a wall at the border of the ellipse which could produce a significant reflection. To assure that multiple reflections from objects beyond the periphery of the obstruction-free area do not combine to produce measurement errors, especially with smaller sites, it is good siting practice to assure that major objects such as buildings are at least eight times the measurement distance away from the site. For larger sites, this proximity of major objects is not so important; thus, a 3 m site could not be surrounded by a parking lot with numerous reflecting vehicles, but a 30 m site probably could tolerate such surroundings. Methods for testing the validity of a site are covered in Section 7.1.2.

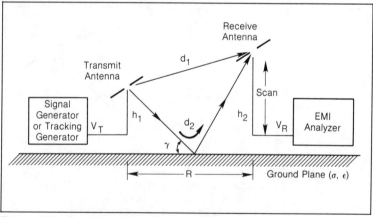

Figure 7.2—Open-Area Site Direct and Reflected Paths

7.1.1.3 Ground Plane

Although the exact ground plane requirements are determined largely by the size of the site and the type of EUT to be tested, the quality and size of the ground plane always exert a major influence on open-area site performance. For testing computer-type equipment or other EUTs that are mounted near the ground plane, on a 3 m or 10 m site, the ground plane definitely should be metal. However, for the same sites, if the EUT is a device normally mounted at least 2 m above the ground, the metal plane may not be necessary if the conductivity of the earth is good. Such a plane is never needed on a 30 m or larger site if the earth conductivity is good.

Exactly what constitutes good earth conductivity is an open question. The earth definitely should embrace no buried metal or other debris that would disturb its homogeneity. Also, in accordance with CCIR Recommendation 527, it should be moist with a relative dielectric constant between 15 and 30, a relative permeability of unity and a conductivity between 0.001 and 0.15 siemens per meter. For 3 m and 10 m sites, the safest course of action is to choose a metal ground plane; otherwise, site performance could change perceptibly from month to month as a function of the relative levels of ground moisture.

The size and smoothness of the ground plane are also subjects which have been studied with the goal of establishing suitable criteria. Recommendations range from 1 up to 20 Fresnel zones for minimum size. They also call for smoothness in accordance with the Rayleigh criteria.[1] However, more recent practical experience has shown that a 7 × 7 m metallic ground plane is adequate for a 3 m site for use at 30 MHz, despite the fact that axes of the first Fresnel ellipse imply a 10 × 9.5 m ground plane; the smaller dimensions are consistent with the dimensions of 6 × 9 m as recommended by IEC Publication 106.

For a 3 m site used up to 1,000 MHz, with the EUT 1 m above ground and the test antenna scanned between heights of 1 and 4 m, the Rayleigh criterion for smoothness allows a maximum roughness of 4.5 cm. However, practical experiences seems to show that this criterion might also be tighter than necessary.[2]

The metal ground plane typically used is either placed directly on the surface of the earth or physically raised slightly above it by a hard stand. Although the ground plane may be a solid sheet of metal, it is more often a mesh or screen. A nonmagnetic metal such as aluminum is preferred, but galvanized steel such as **hardware cloth** is frequently used. The metal plane should be on top of the earth surface with no intervening dielectric and, in particular, no poor dielectric such as asphalt or a similar material. Also, no large cavities such as workrooms should be placed under the ground plane. When these recommendations are followed, the metal ground plane couples quite tightly with the earth at the EMI test frequencies of interest. This makes the techniques used for grounding the EUT and test equipment less critical.

However, when a work space is located beneath the ground plane, details of grounding both the EUT and the test equipment become much more critical. Chapter 9 presents guidelines to be followed to minimize grounding problems at open-area sites.

7.1.2 Site Characterization

Site characterization is needed to ensure that EMI measurements made on various open-area test sites can be properly compared. Until a given site is carefully tested and characterized as falling within allowable tolerances for attenuation of radiated signals over the frequency range of intended usage, any measurements taken on it must remain suspect. In addition, each open-area site should be calibrated at least annually.

The basis for site characterization is shown in Fig. 7.2.[3-5] With the identical transmit and receive antennas spaced at the appropriate distance, i.e., 3, 10 or 30 m, the site attenuation, A, is the ratio of the voltage into the transmit antenna, V_T, divided by the voltage delivered into the EMI analyzer or spectrum analyzer by the receive antenna, V_R:

$$A = V_T/V_R \qquad (7.1)$$

or in dB:

$$A = V_T - V_R \qquad (7.2)$$

where,

V_T and V_R are both expressed in terms of dBμV

As developed by Smith[3], it is more meaningful to express the theoretical attenuation in the following terms:

$$A = \frac{279.1 \ AF_R AF_T}{f_m E_{max}} \qquad (7.3)$$

or expressed in dB terms:

$$A = -20 \log f_m + 48.9 + AF_R + AF_T - E_{max} \qquad (7.4)$$

where,

f_m = measurement frequency in MHz

AF_T = antenna factor of the receiving antenna in dB(1/m)

AF_R = antenna factor of the transmitting antenna in dB(1/m)

E_{max} = maximum field strength in dBμV/m intercepted by the receive antenna in response to a transmitted power of 1 pW from the transmit antenna

It is assumed above that both antennas are theoretical half-wave dipoles, and the receive dipole is varied in elevation between two selected heights.

Height limits of 1 and 4 m are generally used for both 3 m and 10 m separation distances between the transmit and receive antennas, while a range from 2 to 6 m has been specified by the FCC for the 30 m distance. However, a precise range of height variation is not vital to the following discussion.

A more useful characterization, **normalized site attenuation (NSA),** is developed by subtracting the antenna factors from Eq. 7.5:

$$NSA = -20 \log f_m + 48.9 - E_{max} \qquad (7.5)$$

where,

NSA = normalized site attenuation in dB

The NSA parameter is obviously of great value because the NSA for any open-area site can be measured and compared to a single theoretical curve for its respective measurement geometry. However, it is very important that the antenna factors be accurate because, to obtain the NSA, they must be subtracted from site attenuation as actually measured. Reference 4 summarizes many aspects of work conducted by Subcommittee One of ANSI Accredited Standards Committee C63. It includes the NSA values at 24 discrete frequencies for the most widely used antenna separations and heights, and both horizontal and vertical polarizations. If automated systems are used to measure the NSA, the results can be compared to plotted curves connecting these tabulated values.

It has been shown that site attenuation measurements using vertical polarization are necessary because they tend to disclose anomalies not apparent from horizontally polarized measurements.[6] Vertical polarization site attenuation measurements display an inherently greater sensitivity to ground plane anomalies, buried metal and surrounding objects which can affect EMI measurements.[7]

7.1.2.1 Measuring the NSA

As given by Heirman,[4] Eq. 7.5 is easier to use for actual measurement of NSA if it is expressed in terms of the transmitted and received voltage levels rather than as field strength produced by 1 pW into the transmit antenna:

$$NSA = V_T - V_R - AF_T - AF_R - (C_T + C_R) - \Delta F_{TOT} \quad (7.6)$$

where,

NSA = normalized site attenuation in dB

C_T and C_R = transmit and receive cable losses, respectively, (which need not be known if the following recommended substitution procedure is used)

ΔF_{TOT} = a correction for mutual coupling of the antennas which applies only for horizontally-polarized dipoles spaced 3 m apart (as given in Ref. 4) and which ranges between −1.9 and +2.7 dB

The recommended substitution procedure calls for two measurements of V_R, the voltage into the EMI or spectrum analyzer. The first reading is taken with the two coaxial cables disconnected from their antennas and connected to each other via an adaptor. The second reading is taken as the maximum obtained with the cables reconnected to their respective antennas and the receive antennas scanned over the prescribed range of height. It is important that the signal source voltage, V_T, be constant for the two readings.

If the first reading of V_R is called V(direct) and the second V(site), Eq. 7.6 can be rewritten as:

$$NSA = V(direct) - V(site) - AF_T - AF_R - \Delta F_{TOT} \qquad (7.7)$$

In Eq. (7.7), V(direct) − V(site) represents the basic definition of site attenuation given in Eq. (7.1), assuming V(direct) as reduced by the cable losses is V_T and V(site) is V_R.

Note that V(direct) has taken into account the losses in both cables and has thus eliminated the need to measure them separately. The final term, ΔF_{TOT}, is available in Reference 4 as mentioned above. This same reference directs the reader to excellent sources for accurately determining the two antenna factors. The importance of determining these factors accurately cannot be emphasized too strongly, since any errors carry over into the measured NSA and all EMI measurements using these factors.

Since the antenna factors are defined in a 50 Ω system, a 10 dB attenuator should be inserted at the receive end of the receive antenna cable to avoid possible mismatch errors. Correspondingly, a similar attenuator is recommended at the input terminals of the transmit antenna.

7.1.3 Sheltered Test Sites

Protective covers can be constructed over the operating area of an open site to protect equipment and personnel against the weather. Such covers must be nonconductive under all conditions to avoid the introduction of serious discrepancies in test results. Although a few nails or bolts not longer than 5 cm would probably not cause problems, the cumulative effect of dozens of such elements would be significant and dictates the general rule that all fasteners and supports should be nonconductive. The outside surface of any sheltering cover must be kept clean, since any accumulation of dust or other debris would probably affect the measurements. Also, if the outside surface can become wet during rainfall, undesirable reflections will result. Regardless of the direction from which they originate, any reflections which are not present without sheltering can deteriorate performance and should be avoided. Reference 8 covers sheltered open-area sites in some detail.

7.2 Shielded Enclosures

Shielded enclosures serve two basic purposes:

1. To shield sensitive EMI emission test setups against high-level ambient electromagnetic fields
2. To shield the ambient electromagnetic environment against high-level emissions which are generated to test EMI susceptibility

There are many specification requirements for both applications which require the attenuation of the enclosure to be at least 100 dB. In addition, shielded enclosures have many other uses, including the protection of personnel against high-power emissions, the containment of energy from high-power industrial RF heating sources and the protection of sensitive equipment, such as biomedical instruments and computers, against high-level ambient fields.

7.2.1 Types of Construction

The shape of a shielded enclosure is generally that of a rectangular parallelepiped, both to conform to the structure of most buildings and for physical convenience in construction and use. Shielded enclosures have been built in a wide range of sizes, up to at least five stories in height, and have been adapted to a wide range of fixed and mobile installations. The remainder of this section considers some pertinent details of enclosure construction and examines how to use such enclosures to achieve optimum results. Anechoic shielded enclosures, which evolve when an enclosure's inner walls are properly lined with RF absorbing material, are the subject of Section 7.3.

The basic material of the shielded enclosure is either steel or copper. Steel, in the form of galvanized sheets, is now more commonly used than copper, which can be applied either in the form of sheets or fine mesh screening. For equal cost and comparable construction, steel generally provides performance comparable to copper at all frequencies for electric fields. Below about 150 kHz, its greater permeability makes steel more effective for magnetic shielding.

Special precautions are sometimes needed to prevent very powerful magnetic fields from saturating the high-permeability steel. A laminated construction comprising a layer of copper bonded to a layer of steel is especially helpful; the layer of copper facing the high-strength field source reduces the field reaching the steel to a level that is no longer sufficient to saturate it.[9]

Figure 7.3a illustrates the three most common types of construction for shielded enclosures which are capable of being demounted and moved to a new location. Figure 7.3b shows construction of the same three types of enclosures for permanent installation at a given location.

Of the three demountable constructions shown in the top half of Fig. 7.3, the single-shield type is seldom used because its cost is not sufficiently lower than that of the double-shielded types to justify its lower performance. Both of the double-shielded demountable types have their proponents, and neither is clearly superior to the other as long as they both use the same total thickness of

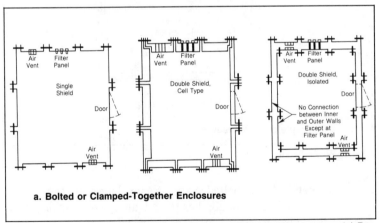

a. Bolted or Clamped-Together Enclosures

Figure 7.3—Constructions of Three Types of Shielded Enclosures (a) Demountable and (b) Permanent Installations

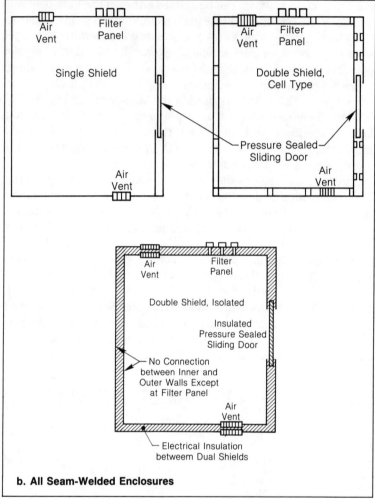

b. All Seam-Welded Enclosures

Figure 7.3—(continued)

ᴖne same metal. Where bolted seams are used for both, the double-shielded, isolated construction has the advantage of providing a second opportunity to clamp the seams closed.

Of the three permanent-installation constructions shown in the lower half of Fig. 7.3, the single-shield type is potentially superior, provided that its seams are properly welded, because electromagnetic leaks are virtually eliminated and there are no possible intra-wall resonances with which to contend. However, it is difficult to weld the seams without developing voids which are not visually apparent but which allow leakage.

Double-shielded enclosures often use a sandwich panel with two steel sheets bonded to a 19 mm (0.75") plywood core. The separate panels are not butted together but are clamped at each edge by special continuous channels and stripping. Figure 7.4 shows the methods of joining panels both along the sides of the room and at the corners. The channel and strap are pulled together every few inches by machine screws.

An alternative to this sandwich-type enclosure is a single solid-

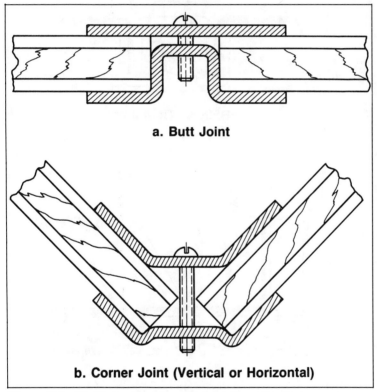

a. Butt Joint

b. Corner Joint (Vertical or Horizontal)

Figure 7.4—Methods of Joining Sandwich-Type Panels

wall type in which the shield material is rolled steel and which includes the U-channels and U-tensioners shown in Fig. 7.5. Plated steel is used for all fittings, bolts, screws and spline nuts used to fasten the framing members together. Many variations in construction are used by various manufacturers.

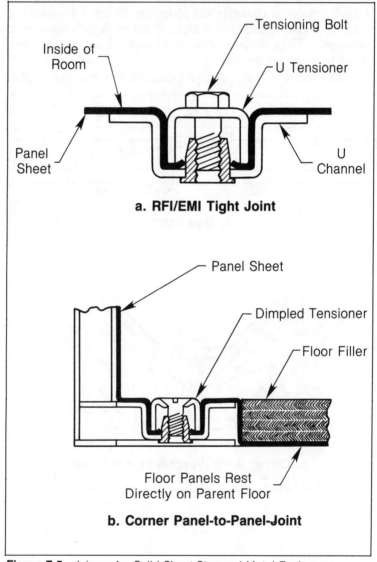

a. RFI/EMI Tight Joint

b. Corner Panel-to-Panel-Joint

Figure 7.5—Joiners for Solid Sheet-Stressed Metal Enclosures

Shielded enclosures require periodic maintenance to retain their original design characteristics. The most vulnerable areas are the door and the various joints and seams. The enclosure manufacturer usually gives a torque rating on the fasteners which are used to join the panels tightly. Except for the doors, no maintenance is required on all-welded enclosures since no bolts are used for fastening. Finger-stock gasketing along the edge of the door must be kept in good condition. If fingers are damaged or broken off, a new section of fingers may be soldered or bonded in position as a replacement. Such fingers ensure a good bond between the enclosure and the door by providing a wiping motion for a short distance along the door frame. Except for the pneumatic door, which does not use finger stock, the door frame must always be kept smooth and clean to maintain good gasketing action.

One version of the pneumatic-sealed door uses a set of pressurized air bags to force the door edges against a mating flange. Figure 7.6 shows an improved version of a more conventional arrangement which uses two rows of metallic finger stock or hidden rows to effect a good seal between the door and the frame. Regardless of design, all shielded enclosure doors remain vulnerable to leakage and should be checked frequently for proper operation.

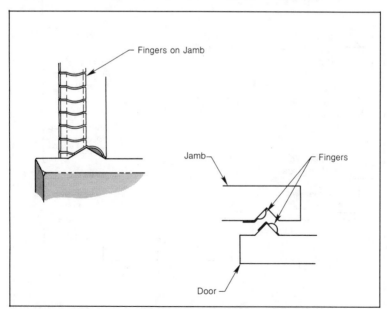

Figure 7.6—Contact Fingers of Enclosure Door and Jamb

7.2.2 Apertures and Penetrations

Illustrated in Fig. 7.7 are some of the many discontinuities, or apertures, which can compromise the performance of a shielded enclosure.

Other than the access door, the most prominent aperture is usually that for the entry of the power service and its associated filtering. The basic requirement for shielded enclosure filters is that they provide a certain minimum amount of attenuation over the entire

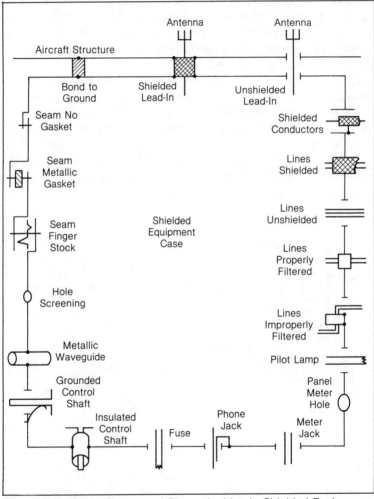

Figure 7.7—Some Sources of Discontinuities in Shielded Enclosures

operating range of the enclosure, which is typically 10 kHz to at least 10 GHz. The exact amount of attenuation required in the filters is determined by the particular situation. It is usually adequate if it approaches the dB level of shielding effectiveness for the enclosure itself. Sometimes the filter assembly must be placed in a magnetically-shielded box to avoid compromising the attenuation of the enclosure at lower frequencies. Filters are usually installed outside the enclosure, with the filtered line entering the enclosure through pipe nipples. In some installations, it is necessary to cascade filters, with one on each side of the enclosure wall.

The design of the enclosure must also provide for lighting, heating and air conditioning. Lighting should be of the incandescent type to avoid the RF noise associated with ionization. However, special fluorescent fixtures with built-in filters, shields and conductive cover windows are available for use in activities peripheral to the actual testing.

Existing facilities for heating and air conditioning usually can be adapted to service the shielded enclosure. Forced-air ducting usually can be extended from existing entry and exhaust ducts to circulate air through the enclosure, using honeycomb vents which are designed to preserve shielding integrity. However, these vents are vulnerable to leakage and should be checked often to confirm that their mechanical integrity is intact.

Additional penetrations of the enclosure walls are often needed to provide other services. Gas, water and compressed air may be furnished through steel or copper piping which is dimensioned to act as a waveguide beyond cutoff. As long as the pipe is joined to the enclosure wall using a clean, tight bond, the shielding effectiveness of the enclosure need not be compromised.

A similar method is used to bring coaxial lines through the enclosure wall. Special fittings are available which are similar to a threaded pipe nipple, except that suitable coaxial fittings are used. However, coaxial cables feeding such fittings from outside the enclosure can still reduce the shielding effectiveness of the enclosure by providing a conducted path for high-level ambient emissions which penetrate their shields. The use of triaxial or quadraxial cables can minimize this possibility.

7.2.3 Enclosure Performance and Checkout

Properly engineered and installed shielded rooms of the modular clamp-together type are designed to conform to the shielding requirements of MIL-STD-285 for USAF Class I Shielding[10] or to NSA Spec. 65-6.[11] Shown in Table 7.1 are some typical levels of performance realized for the three basic types of enclosures.

Table 7.1—Summary of Typical Performance of Shielded Enclosures

Enclosure Type	Wall Type	Material	H-Fields		E-Fields and Plane Waves	
			60 Hz	15 kHz	1 GHz	10 GHz
Double Electrically Isolated	Screen	Copper	2-3 dB	68 dB	120 dB	77 dB
		Bronze	0 dB	40 dB	110 dB	57 dB
		Galvanized	—	50 dB	50 dB	—
	Solid	24 Ga. Steel	15 dB	80 dB	120 dB	90 dB
		Cu and Steel	20 dB	90 dB	120 dB	120 dB
Cell Type	Screen	Copper	—	50 dB	80 dB	—
	Solid	24 Ga. Steel	—	80 dB	120 dB	100 dB
		Copper	—	50 dB	100 dB	100 dB
Single Shield	Screen	Copper	2 dB	50 dB	60 dB	60 dB
	Solid	24 Ga. Steel	—	48 dB	90 dB	—
		16 Ga. Copper	—	34 dB	120 dB	120 dB

Once the installation of a new enclosure is complete, it is usually tested in accordance MIL-STD-285, NSA 65-6 or IEEE Std 299[12] to determine whether it satisfies its procurement specifications. Because such testing is usually performed in the near fields of both the radiating and receiving test antennas at frequencies below UHF, it is essential the specified procedures be followed rigorously and that the tests be thoroughly documented.

Testing of the enclosure should be repeated periodically to verify that its attenuation characteristics are unchanged. It is appropriate to treat the shielded enclosure as an item of laboratory inventory that is subject to periodic scheduled calibration. Retesting should occur at least every second year. Interim spot checks may be desirable in conjunction with special EMI test programs or in the event that degradation of enclosure performance is suspected for any reason.

7.2.4 Size Requirements

Although cost considerations dictate that the size of the shielded enclosure be kept to a minimum, it must be large enough to contain the EUT and allow additional space for antennas and other accessory devices. As discussed in Chapter 8, when radiative transducers are used a minimum spacing must be allowed between the transducer and the walls and ceilings of the enclosure to achieve repeatable measurements.

The internal height of the enclosure must be sufficient to allow use of a 1 m (41") vertical rod antenna as required for testing to military standards. About 1 m of clearance is required both above and below the vertically oriented rod to avoid detuning effects, which implies a minimum height for the enclosure of about 3 m. Both the width and length of the structure should be at least this great to accommodate larger EUTs which must be placed on the floor of the enclosure. The minimum width becomes 4.5 m if the EUT is to be measured from both its front and back while maintaining 1 m spacing from the enclosure wall.

If radiating transducers are to be placed on opposite sides of the EUT, as required for some susceptibility tests, the enclosure length should be at least 5 m. However, a length of 6 m would be ideal to allow adequate access for test personnel and to accommodate some test benches. These factors imply a minimum enclosure size of about 3 × 5 × 6 m in height, width and length, respectively; however, because of economic and spatial limitations, the most popular enclosure size is only 2.4 × 3.7 × 5.5 m, which is too small for some applications.

A desirable but nonessential shielded enclosure feature is an anteroom. As shown in Fig. 7.8, this is a small contiguous enclosure that is used to house items such as test instrumentation and accessories. The use of the anteroom provides isolation for such instrumentation from the EUT as well as from the outside electromagnetic environment. For susceptibility testing, signal sources and amplifiers are placed outside of both enclosures, with the EUT kept in the main enclosure. In many cases, these sources and amplifiers are installed in an additional shielded anteroom, as shown in Fig. 9.4 (Chapter 9).

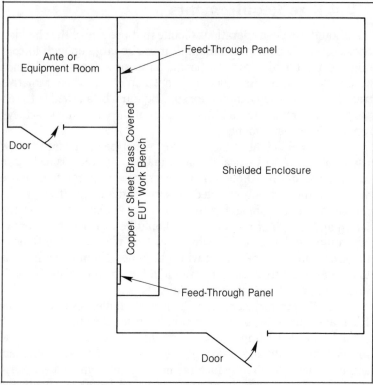

Figure 7.8—Enclosure Arrangement with Anteroom

7.2.5 Reflection and Proximity Problems within Shielded Enclosures

The accuracy of radiated measurements within a shielded enclosure can be severely affected by:

1. Reflections of energy from its metal walls
2. The proximity of transducers to the walls
3. Resonances within the enclosure

Larger enclosures present less of a problem in this respect than do smaller ones. These effects are considered in detail in Chapter 8, while use of a hooded antenna and other methods to reduce them are discussed in Chapter 9.

7.2.6 Semi-Shielded Enclosures

EMI test situations arise in which some degree of shielding is required, but a high-performance shielded enclosure such as discussed thus far in this section is not available. In such cases, a lower level of shielding performance is adequate. Two possible alternatives to a permanent enclosure are shown in Figs. 7.9 and 7.10. These structures can provide up to 70 dB of shielding to electric fields and plane waves below 30 MHz, and up to 40 dB shielding effectiveness at 1 GHz when built using close-mesh screening. Attenuation at 1 GHz is about 30 dB less if chicken wire is used.

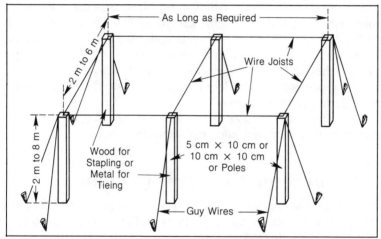

Figure 7.9—Above-Ground Guyed Structure to Support Screening Wire

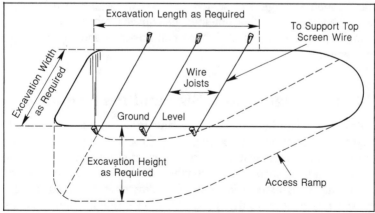

Figure 7.10—Below-Ground Excavation to Support Screening Wire

The wooden vertical supports pictured in Fig. 7.9 have either a rectangular or round cross-sectional area of at least 50 cm^2 and can range in height from 2 to 8 m as required. They need be set into the ground only a few centimeters to prevent slippage and are secured with horizontal and diagonal guy wires and joists as illustrated. The screen or chicken wire is stapled to the vertical supports to provide the four walls and ceiling of the enclosure, while the screening for the floor can be laid directly on the ground. Mating corners of the screening are secured together by interlacing or tieing together at intervals of about 8 cm.

Construction of the below-ground structure shown in Fig. 7.10 is simpler in that the only frame to be added consists of the wire joists for support of the ceiling screening. The earth is excavated to the desired depth to form a rectangular parallelepiped with an approach ramp at one end for entry and exit. Screening can be applied to the walls, and floor if shielding is not adequate without it. A joist-supported wooden floor if desirable to avoid problems from mud during rainy weather.

Basic structures such as these can be augmented with various refinements and turned into semipermanent facilities.

7.3 Anechoic EMI Test Chambers

Anechoic test chambers for EMI testing are metallic structures that provide electromagnetic shielding and protection against the elements. They also incorporate absorbing material on their inner walls to suppress the effects of reflections within the structure. For the frequency range over which its internal performance is sufficiently anechoic, the ideal shielded anechoic chamber possesses the principal advantages of both the open-area site and the shielded enclosure.

7.3.1 Configuration, Size and Performance

Anechoic chambers for EMI testing range in size from small boxes to installations larger than 15 × 15 × 40 m. For a given application, the chamber must be of sufficient size to encompass the EUT in a quiet zone or volume in which the level of reflected energy is typically 30 to 60 dB below that of the direct ray of desired energy. However, as little as 10 dB of round-trip reflection loss may be adequate for some EMI test applications. The quiet zone must be at a distance from the transmitting antenna which satisfies far-field criteria for both the amplitude and phase distributions of the illuminating field. The receiving antenna must be sufficiently separated from the anechoic material to avoid loading effects on its impedance.

Anechoic chambers have been constructed in a number of configurations to match specific applications. Although the conventional rectangular-box configuration is generally most useful, a funnel-shaped chamber can provide superior low-frequency performance at less expense than a comparable rectangular chamber. However, at higher frequencies, the funnel type requires more careful design and setup to achieve equally good field distribution and freedom from cross-polarization and ellipticity effects. For maximum economy, it is important to match the design of the anechoic chamber to the intended task and not to specify greater absorption than actually needed. Also, absorbing materials must be chosen carefully, since the reflectivity ratings of most materials do not apply for mounting on a shielding surface.

A very large low-frequency, funnel-shaped chamber is illustrated in the plan view drawing of Fig. 7.11.* This chamber is 38 m (125 ft) in length and 12 m (40 ft) square at its large end. The inner surfaces are covered with Eccosorb® Type HPY pyramidal absorber ranging from a thickness of 230 mm (9") near the tip of the funnel to 4.6 m (15 ft) on the back wall. A 4.6 × 4.6 × 6.1 m (15 × 15 × 20 ft) quiet zone in the large end of the chamber offers reflectivity of −40 dB at 100 MHz and −45 dB or better at 220 MHz and higher frequencies to at least X-band. The 9.1 m (30 ft) conical tip of the funnel is especially designed to provide maximum freedom from the effects of changing polarization. The axial ratio of the chamber, measured in the quiet zone with a spinning linearly polarized transmitting antenna at the funnel tip, is 0.2 to 1.5 dB over the frequency range from 100 MHz to 10 GHz.

---

*Note: The chamber was built to English units of measurement, from which metric equivalents were derived.

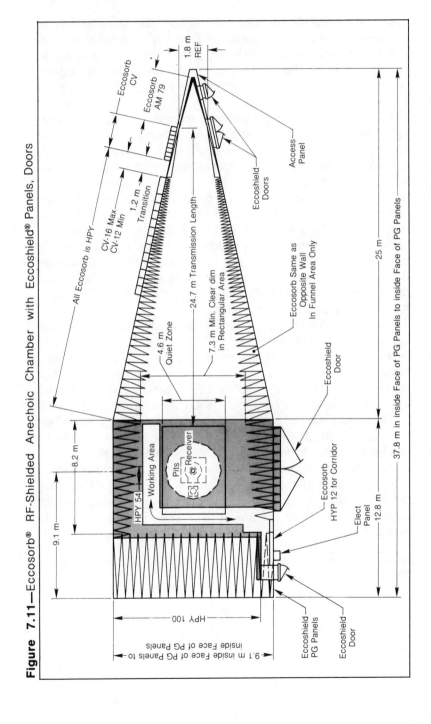

Figure 7.11—Eccosorb® RF-Shielded Anechoic Chamber with Eccoshield® Panels, Doors

7.3.2 Absorber Materials and Configurations

The two general categories of absorbing material utilized in anechoic chambers are lossy dielectric and ferrite. Both types function by converting into heat a high percentage of the electromagnetic energy that impinges on them. To achieve maximum extraction of electromagnetic energy from an impinging wavefront, the absorber should be designed to present an impedance that is as close as possible to that of the medium in which the energy is being propagated. However, the dielectric or magnetic materials possessing the proper loss characteristics to dissipate the energy within a reasonable volume usually have such low intrinsic impedances that excessive reflection would occur at any large plane interfaces between such materials and the air of the enclosure. Two basic design techniques are utilized to overcome this incompatibility and permit maximum penetration of impinging energy into the material:

1. The materials are shaped into pyramids, cones, wedges or other shapes so that the effective impedance per unit depth of the absorber decreases gradually from that of free space at the point of interface to its minimum value at its mounting surface.
2. Tiles or sheets of the materials are manufactured in three or more layers of different composition which present impedances ranging from maximum at the impinging surface to minimum at the mounting surface.

The absorbers used to cover large areas such as exist within shielded enclosures usually are of the lossy dielectric type and are pyramidal or conical in shape to ensure diffuse scattering of the small amount of energy which they reflect rather than absorb. The choice of dielectric materials over magnetic materials, which have some superior properties, is determined by considerations based on their lighter weight and lower cost.

The lossy dielectric materials used are usually open-cell foams of polyurethane composition which are impregnated with a carbon-latex solution. Both the basic foam and the impregnating solution can be made effectively fire-retardant, which is a very desirable feature. The foams are fabricated into cones or pyramids which range in height from a few inches to many feet, depending on the lowest frequency at which they are to be effective. Pyramids 52 mm (2") in height exhibit reflectivities ranging from about −30 dB at

5 GHz to −45 to −50 dB at 15 GHz and higher. Pyramids 1.8 m (6 ft) in height provide reflectivities ranging from −20 dB at 75 MHz to −45 to −50 dB at 3 GHz and higher. Pyramidal absorbers at least 4.6 m (15 ft) in height have been used in anechoic chambers.

A number of excellent special absorber materials are available for special applications such as operation at high temperatures or in very high power densities. An example is Eccosorb Type NZ®, which is a fully sintered ceramic tile. It provides −15 dB reflectivity up through the UHF range in a completely waterproof material which is capable of operating up to at least 371°C (700°F).

7.3.3 Other Types of Absorbing Chambers

Two possible alternatives to the absorber-lined type of anechoic chamber are the coke-lined enclosure and the underground chamber. The coke-lined chamber has the potential advantage of low cost but is not available as an engineered and repeatable system.

The underground low-Q chamber has been more widely used. It consists simply of an underground room or tunnel which is sufficiently deep to provide adequate isolation from the electromagnetic environment. One such installation evaluated by Crawford involved walls of solid granite having a relative permittivity of about 6.[13] His investigation indicated that measurement errors of 40 dB, which are possible in conventional shielded enclosures, can be reduced to less than 8 dB over the frequency range of 20 to 1,000 MHz. Similar results can probably also be achieved in limestone caves and salt mines. Use of underground chambers is less satisfactory at frequencies below 20 MHz because of insufficient shielding from the ambient electromagnetic environment unless the distance from the source of interference transmission is great enough to reduce sufficiently its field strength and/or angle of incidence to the surface above the chamber.

7.4 Shielded Cells for EMI Testing

Shielded cells for EMI testing enclose the test area in a metallic structure which provides shielding, but they also utilize the inner reflectivity and dimensions of the structure to control the distribution of electromagnetic energy in the vicinity of the EUT. The TEM cell is one example of this type of test structure. It provides a shielding interface against the electromagnetic environment and also participates in the generation or collection of the EMI test energy.

7.4.1 TEM Cells

The TEM cell can be considered to be an extrapolation of the tri-plate line, which is similar to the other TEM field producers discussed in Section 5.2.2. A tri-plate line is a balanced parallel-plate line with a ground plane or plate on each side of a center plate. These lines are normally used at frequencies below a few megahertz to avoid higher-order modes and radiation of energy from the plates. Although used only for electric-field testing, both electric and magnetic fields exist between the plates.

Fringe fields from the tri-plate line can be confined by placing the line in an enclosure or by making it into a TEM cell as illustrated in Fig. 7.12 from the referenced NBS paper.[13] The TEM cell is essentially a tri-plate transmission line with the sides closed in to produce a shielded interface with the electromagnetic environment. An RF absorber may be placed inside the cell to suppress multimoding and thus extend its upper useful frequency.

Similar to the conversion of a shielded enclosure into a TEM long-wire chamber, as discussed Section 5.2.2.3, an existing shielded enclosure can be converted into a TEM cell using techniques described in Ref. 14. As with the parallel-plate and strip-line antennas described in Section 5.2 for susceptibility testing, the test fields are established between the plates as fed from a generator at one end with the other end terminated. For radiated emission testing, the EUT is placed between the plates. Any emissions radiated from it are coupled to detectors connected at one end of the terminated transmission line.

An important characteristic of these TEM lines is that the TEM fields established between their plates simulate planar far fields in open space. The major difference between the TEM cell and the TEM field producers discussed in Section 5.2 is that the cell is shielded and operates as a 50 Ω transmission line, while the other devices are not shielded (except for the long-wire chamber) and usually operate at transmission line impedances of at least 100 to 200 Ω. However, the 50 Ω transmission line impedance presented by the TEM cell should not be confused with the wave impedance for the TEM mode within the cell itself, which is 120π Ω.

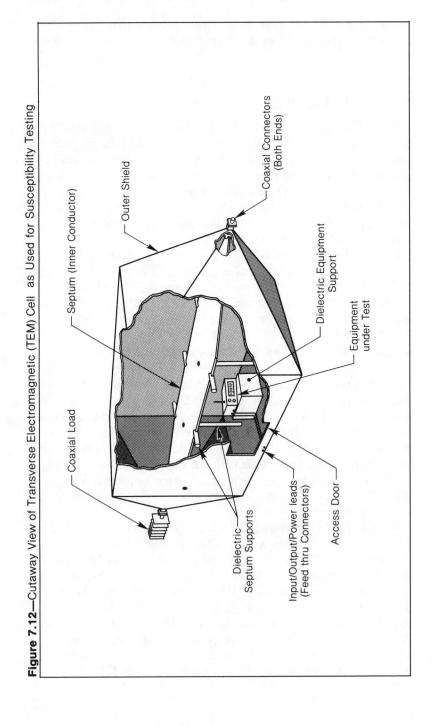

Figure 7.12—Cutaway View of Transverse Electromagnetic (TEM) Cell as Used for Susceptibility Testing

7.4.2 Reverberating and Mode-Tuned Enclosures

Closely related are three additional types of enclosures used for EMI testing: the reverberating enclosure,[15, 16] the reverberating TEM cell, and the mode-tuned enclosure.[17] These enclosures and techniques make use of multimoded, randomly polarized fields for susceptibility or radiated emission testing of the EUT. In the reverberating case, one or two large reflecting surfaces (vanes) are installed in the enclosure or TEM cell and rotated to cause spatial and temporal perturbations in the field within the enclosure. This is shown in Fig. 7.13. The field and its modes are effectively stirred around the EUT and are amplitude modulated at rate deter-

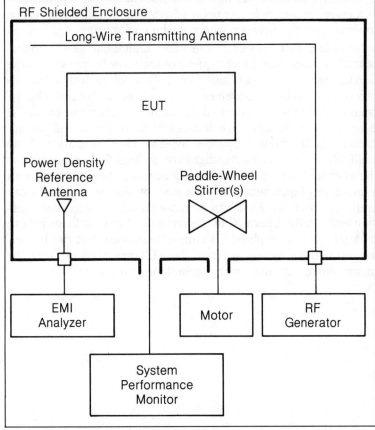

Figure 7.13—Measurement System Using Reverberating Enclosure

The mode-tuned enclosure is similar to the reverberating enclosure in that a large reflecting surface is used. However, instead of rotating this surface continuously, it is stepped in increments of motion to produce a maximum reading at the receive antenna as shown in Fig. 7.14. A sampling procedure then can be used to redistribute the energy in the vicinity of the EUT and to record it as a function of the position of the reflecting surface.

mined by the rotational velocities of the reflecting surfaces. If the resultant field is sampled and averaged to remove the rotational components, the measured field will be uniform to within about 1 dB, on a time-averaged basis. This is conditional on the measurement not being made too close to the wall of the enclosure. Such an enclosure is calibrated by determining a coefficient based on its Q. Once this factor is determined, a single measurement of the field at a given frequency at any point within the enclosure will suffice to determine the field anywhere in the enclosure.[13]

According to Crawford,[13] the main limitations of the mode-stirred or mode-tuned techniques are their low-frequency restriction (caused by the lack of sufficient high-order modes) and the inability to correlate measurements made in such a shielded, closely-coupled environment to actual operating conditions of the EUT. Also, these techniques are inherently narrowband and do not preserve polarization properties for EMI characterization of the EUT. However, strong advantages accrue from these same factors: the system is so sensitive that strong fields can be established with a minimum of generator power (for susceptibility testing) and weak emissions from the EUT can be more readily detected (for emission testing). Also, because of the variation of the test fields in both polarization and amplitude, a simple, worst-case test can be performed without having to rotate the EUT and raise or lower the measurement antenna or change antenna positions.

Figure 7.14—Radiated Susceptibility Test System Using Mode-Tuned Enclosure

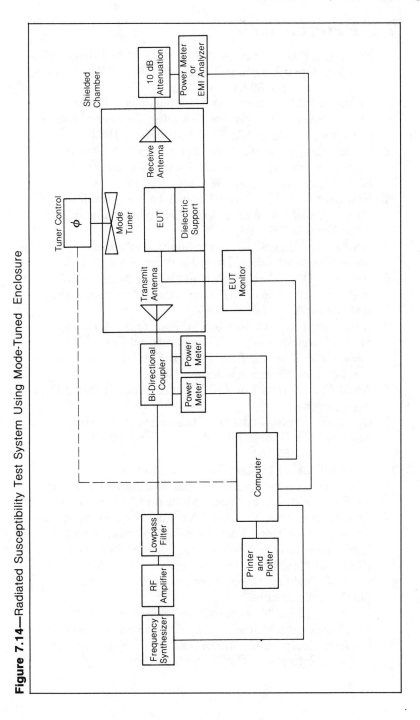

7.5 References

1. Bronaugh, E.L., "A Review of the Proposed Addition to ANSI C63.4 on Open-Area Sites," *EMC Technology*, Vol. 1, No. 4, October 1982, pp. 60-65.
2. Bronaugh, E.L., "Open-Site Electromagnetic Emission Measurements," *Interference Technology Engineers' Master* (Plymouth Meeting, PA: R&B Enterprises, 1983).
3. Smith, A.A., Jr., et al, "Calculation of Site Attenuation from Antenna Factors," *IEEE Transactions on EMC*, EMC-25, No. 3, August 1982, pp. 301-316.
4. Heirman, D.N., "Definitive Open Area Site Qualifications," *Proceedings of the IEEE International Symposium on EMC*, (New York: IEEE, 1987).
5. "Open Area Test Sites," Draft Addition to American National Standards C63.4, Draft 15, dated August 1985.
6. Heirman, D.N., "Vertical Attenuation—A Necessity," *Proceedings of the 1986 IEEE International Symposium on EMC* (New York: IEEE, 1986).
7. Bronaugh, E.L., "Comparison of Four Open Area Test Sites," *Proceedings of the 7th International Zurich Symposium and Technical Exhibition on EMC* (Zurich: Association of Swiss Electrotechnicians, 1987).
8. ANSI C63.X1 (Draft of ANSI Standard on Sheltered Open-Area Sites).
9. Ott, H.W., "Noise Reduction Techniques in Electronic Systems" (New York: John Wiley & Sons, 1976), pp. 140-141 and 159-164.
10. MIL-STD-285, "Military Standard Attenuation Measurements for Enclosures, Electromagnetic Shielding, for Electronic Test Purposes, Method of," 25 June 1956.
11. Specification NSA No. 65-6, "National Security Specification for RF Shielded Enclosures for Communications Equipment: General Specification," 30 October 1964.
12. IEEE Std 299-1969, "Recommended Practice for Measurement of Shielding Effectiveness, High Performance Shielding Enclosures."
13. Crawford, M.L., "Comparison and Selection of Techniques for Measuring EM Radiated Emissions and Susceptibility of Large Equipment," *International EMC Symposium Proceedings*, Rotterdam, The Netherlands, 1979.

14. Crawford, M.L., and Thomas, C.L., "Converting a Rectangular Shielded Enclosure into a TEM Transmission Cell for EMI Measurements," *Proceedings of the IEEE International Symposium on EMC* (New York: IEEE, 1977).

15. Corona, P., et al., "Use of a Reverberating Enclosure for Measurement of Radiated Power in the Microwave Range," *IEEE Transactions on EMC*, Vol. EMC-18, pp. 54-59, May 1976.

16. Bean, J.L., and Hall, R.A., "Electromagnetic Susceptibility Measurements Using a Mode-Stirred Chamber," *Proceedings of the 1978 IEEE International Symposium on EMC* (New York: IEEE, 1978).

17. Cummings, J.R., "Translational Electromagnetic Environment Chamber: A New Method for Measuring Radiated Susceptibility and Emission," Proceedings of the 1975 IEEE National Symposium on EMC (New York: IEEE, 1975).

Chapter 8

Errors in EMI Testing

This chapter discusses errors in EMI testing. Covered are errors that originate in the test instrumentation and its sources of calibration as well as in the test setup and measurement procedures. The first section is an overview which discusses whether errors are random or systematic; it concludes with a summary showing several dozen points at which errors arise in the various phases of EMI testing. Various techniques for calculating or estimating error magnitude are discussed throughout the chapter, as well as methods for mitigating their impact. Errors due to human mistakes are not included in the analyses.

The magnitude of the errors for some EMI test situations can exceed 40 dB, which emphasizes the extreme importance of carefully analyzing and minimizing errors whenever EMI testing is performed. This caveat becomes especially significant when considered in the context of the potential legal and economic consequences from erroneous test results. Incorrect measurements can lead to an overdesign of a product to achieve a higher degree of EMC than actually needed. This can be as costly as underdesigning a product because erroneous results falsely indicate that the necessary degree of EMC has been attained.

Errors in EMC testing are functions of many variables, not all of which are readily definable. Because of this lack of definition, statistical methods commonly are used for this process: μ to designate the **average** error and σ to designate the **variability** around μ. Assuming that a normal or gaussian error distribution prevails, the principal contributions of error might be the following, each of which entails a number of uncertainties in its own subset:

σ_e = standard deviation of a scintillating electromagnetic ambient environment

σ_m = standard deviation due to EMI performance measurement errors

σ_s = standard deviation associated with selecting an emission or susceptibility specification limit margin

σ_i = standard deviation associated with the variables of an equipment or system site installation

For independent phenomena and assuming log-normal distribution, the total standard deviation, σ_t, of the above is:

$$\sigma_t = (\sigma_e^2 + \sigma_m^2 + \sigma_s^2 + \sigma_i^2)^{1/2} \qquad (8.1)$$

As an example of applying Eq. (8.1), if each of the four errors contributed a standard deviation of 6 dB, then the total deviation would be 12 dB. If this and associated equipment in its environment were expected to perform with a probability, P, of 90 percent ($P = 1.28\,\sigma$) certainty of no EMI, a 15 dB (12 dB × 1.28) margin of protection would be required above a deterministic prediction ($\mu = 0$). For a 98 percent probability ($P = 2.05\,\sigma$) of no EMI, a margin of 25 dB (12 dB × 2.05) protection is needed. If there were no measurement error [$\sigma_m = 0$ instead of 6 dB in Eq. (8.1)], this 25 dB margin would be reduced to 21 dB, which is not a significant reduction. However, if the measurement error had been larger than the other errors, say $\sigma_m = 12$ dB, then the corresponding σ_t would be 16 dB. The total margin for a 98 percent probability of no EMI (i.e., that a condition of EMC exists) would have been 33 dB (16 dB × 2.05), which is an enormous and costly design margin.

The foregoing serves to illustrate the importance of performing an error analysis on:

1. The EMI prediction process
2. The electromagnetic ambient environment
3. The EMI performance measurement instrumentation and test procedures

Since items 1 and 2 are treated in other volumes of this handbook series, the remainder of this chapter concentrates on the errors associated with the EMI measurement instrumentation and test procedures.

8.1 Overview of the Measurement Error Problem

As a preface to discussing the various forms of measurement error and the impact on overall test results, it is appropriate to review a few fundamentals of measurement and statistics. First, each of the two basic types of error (systematic and random) will be discussed briefly.

8.1.1 Systematic Errors

Systematic errors are those which add a bias to the true value in one direction; i.e., they make a measurement read too high or too low most of the time or for most of the population sample. They contribute a shift in the mean value (probable value) and may also add an uncertainty. An example of a systematic error occurs when radiated emission measurements are made inside a small shielded enclosure (2.4 m H × 3.7 m W × 6.1 m L). The presence of the walls and ceiling of the enclosure serve to detune the measurement antenna so that electric field strength from the EUT reads too low. Below about 30 MHz, reflections off the walls and ceiling all combine sufficiently out of phase with the direct emission to produce readings which are lower than the value which would be measured in free space.

Another example of a systematic or bias type of measurement results from failure to match the polarization of an EMI radiated emission being intercepted. The antenna and its associated EMI analyzer can never indicate more than the true value (for matched polarization) and might (for cross polarization) read more than 20 dB less than that value. Since the measured values are always equal to or less than the true value, the distribution is not gaussian. However, for random polarizations an equivalent log-normal distribution over a limited range would be $\mu = -6$ dB and $\sigma \approx 6.1$ dB. Note that in this case the result is both a systematic error ($\mu = -6$ dB) as well as a random error ($\sigma = 6.1$ dB).

Another type of error can be either systematic and random or random only, depending on the conditions. It does not necessarily shift the mean value but can cause an asymmetrical probability distribution. This type of error is exemplified by the effects of either VSWR mismatch or antenna pattern formation due to the direct path and reflection from the ground. The effects of antenna pattern formation can cause no more than a 6 dB increase in level, by adding in phase, while VSWR from antenna-to-transmission line and transmission line-to-EMI analyzer mismatches can cause an increased indication of more than 9 dB in extreme cases. Each can result in deep nulls of 20 dB or more. Again, while not a log-normal distribution, an approximate $\mu \approx 0$ and $\sigma = 4$ dB results over a limited range provided the phasing can take on all values with an equal probability. However, if the phasing is fixed, μ then becomes a systematic error.

For proper treatment, systematic errors must be identified as such and separated from any random error contributions. Then the systematic errors must be broken down into either a positive or negative shift of their mean departure, μ, from true value. The equivalent of an associated standard deviation with respect to this mean shift is then treated separately as illustrated previously for the polarization-matching situation.

8.1.2 Random Errors

Random errors are those that are independent of other errors and produce additive effects due to a number of independent random causes. Additionally, an appreciable number of these random causes produce effects of nearly maximum variance. This is known as the **Central Limit Theorem**. The errors are additive as an rms deviation from the mean or average value:

Mean Value:

$$\mu = \frac{1}{n} \sum_{i=1}^{n} \mu_i \tag{8.2}$$

Standard Deviation:

$$\sigma = \left[\frac{1}{n-1} \sum_{i=1}^{n} (\mu - \mu_i)^2 \right]^{1/2} \tag{8.3}$$

where,

$1/(n-1)$ is correct for small samples, i.e., approx. $\leqslant 50$

From population samples, the mean value of a particular error has a corresponding standard deviation described by Eq. (8.3). It may be calculated from a set of measurements or estimated. Its probability density may follow a normal (gaussian) distribution, a log-normal distribution, Poisson, binomial, chi-square, t, F or another distribution function. The total standard deviation associated with a set of independent errors, however, was given in Eq. (8.1), which is now expressed in the form:

$$\sigma_t = \left(\sum_{i=1}^{n} \sigma_i^2 \right)^{1/2} \tag{8.4}$$

in which a log-normal distribution is assumed or approximated.

The log-normal distribution is shown in Fig. 8.1. The mean value, μ, is located at the 50 percent probability point on the abscissa. The probability distribution is located about the mean to give a $\mu + \sigma$ of 84.1 percent and a $\mu - \sigma$ of 100 percent − 84.1 percent = 15.9 percent. Thus, 84.1 percent − 15.9 percent = 68.3 percent of the situations fall within $\mu \pm \sigma$, and 100 percent − 68.3 percent = 31.7 percent fall outside. These facts are detailed in Table 8.1.

The log-normal distribution is normalized by multiples of σ, the standard deviation, above and below μ, the mean value (or in the present case, the mean error). Any measured or expected deviation must be normalized to the distribution by dividing it by σ to

$$\mu = \frac{1}{n} \sum_{i=1}^{n} \mu_i$$

$$\sigma = \left[\frac{1}{n-1} \sum_{i=1}^{n} (\mu - \mu_i)^2 \right]^{1/2}$$

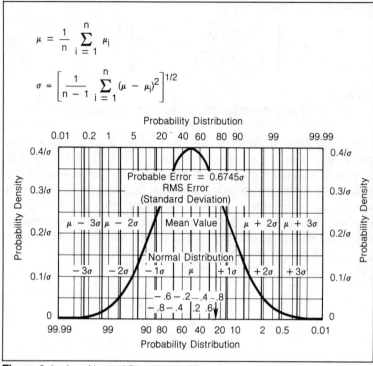

Figure 8.1—Log Normal Distribution Showing Location of $\mu \pm \sigma$ and Other Values

find k, the multiple or normalizing factor. Table 8.1 contains a tabulation of values of k (in the $k\sigma$ columns) versus intervals of $k\sigma$ above and below the mean ($\mu + k\sigma$ and $\mu - k\sigma$, in percent) and the two probability values that the deviation is "inside" the interval or that it is "outside" the interval. The first interval listed is for k = 0.00, which causes the interval to be zero with the probability of 0 percent that the deviation is "within" the interval and 100 percent that the deviation is "without," or "outside" the interval.

Illustrative Example 8.1

Assume that the standard deviation associated with a batch of RF attenuators in the 40 dB position is $\sigma = 0.8$ dB. Assuming log-normal distribution, calculate the probability that the attenuator will have an error in excess of 2 dB. Also calculate the probable error.

8.6

Table 8.1—Probability Errors Based on Normal Distribution

kσ	μ+kσ	μ−kσ	Inside Probab.	Outside Probab.	kσ	μ+kσ	μ−kσ	Inside Probab.	Outside Probab.
0.00	50.0%	50.0%	0%	100%	2.00	97.72%	2.28%	94.45%	4.55%
0.05	52.0	48.0	4.0	96.0	2.05	97.98	2.02	95.96	4.04
0.10	54.0	46.0	8.0	92.0	2.10	98.21	1.79	96.43	3.57
0.15	56.0	44.0	11.9	88.1	2.15	98.42	1.58	96.84	3.16
0.20	57.9	42.1	15.9	84.1	2.20	98.61	1.39	97.22	2.78
0.25	59.9	40.1	19.7	80.3	2.25	98.78	1.22	97.56	2.44
0.30	61.8	38.2	23.6	76.4	2.30	98.93	1.07	97.86	2.14
0.35	63.7	36.3	27.4	72.6	2.326	99.00	1.00	98.00	2.00
0.40	65.5	34.5	31.1	68.9	2.35	99.06	0.94	98.12	1.88
0.45	67.4	32.6	34.7	65.3	2.40	99.18	0.82	98.36	1.64
0.50	69.1	30.9	38.3	61.7	2.45	99.29	0.71	98.57	1.43
0.55	70.9	29.1	41.8	58.2	2.50	99.38	0.62	98.76	1.24
0.60	72.6	27.4	45.1	54.9	2.55	99.46	0.54	98.92	1.08
0.65	74.2	25.8	48.4	51.6	2.576	99.50	0.50	99.00	1.00
0.675*	75.0	25.0	50.0	50.0	2.60	99.53	0.47	99.07	0.93
0.70	75.8	24.2	51.6	48.4	2.65	99.60	0.40	99.20	0.80
0.75	77.3	22.7	54.7	45.3	2.70	99.65	0.35	99.31	0.69
0.80	78.8	21.2	57.6	42.4	2.75	99.70	0.30	99.40	0.60
0.85	80.2	19.8	60.5	39.5	2.80	99.74	0.26	99.49	0.51
0.90	81.6	18.4	63.2	36.8	2.85	99.78	0.22	99.56	0.44
0.95	82.9	17.1	65.8	34.2	2.90	99.81	0.19	99.63	0.37
1.00	84.1	15.9	68.3	31.7	2.95	99.84	0.16	99.68	0.32
1.05	85.3	14.7	70.6	29.4	3.00	99.87	0.13	99.73	0.27
1.10	86.4	13.6	72.9	27.1	3.05	99.89	0.11	99.77	0.23
1.15	87.5	12.5	75.0	25.0	3.090	99.90	0.10	99.80	0.22
1.20	88.5	11.5	77.0	23.0	3.10	99.90	0.10	99.81	0.19
1.25	89.4	10.6	78.9	21.1	3.15	99.92	0.08	99.84	0.16
1.282	90.0	10.0	80.0	20.0	3.20	99.93	0.07	99.86	0.14
1.30	90.3	9.7	80.6	19.4	3.25	99.94	0.06	99.88	0.12
1.35	91.1	8.9	82.3	17.7	3.291	99.95	0.05	99.90	0.10
1.40	91.9	8.1	83.8	16.2	3.30	99.95	0.05	99.91	0.09
1.45	92.6	7.4	85.3	14.7	3.35	99.96	0.04	99.92	0.08
1.50	93.3	6.7	86.6	13.4	3.40	99.97	0.03	99.93	0.07
1.55	93.9	6.1	87.9	12.1	3.45	99.97	0.03	99.94	0.06
1.60	94.5	5.5	89.0	11.0	3.50	99.98	0.02	99.95	0.05
1.645	95.0	5.0	90.0	10.0	3.55	99.981	0.019	99.961	0.039
1.65	95.1	4.9	90.1	9.9	3.60	99.984	0.016	99.968	0.032
1.70	95.5	4.5	91.1	8.9	3.65	99.987	0.013	99.974	0.026
1.75	96.0	4.0	92.0	8.0	3.70	99.989	0.011	99.978	0.022
1.80	96.4	3.6	92.8	7.2	3.75	99.991	0.009	99.982	0.018
1.85	96.8	3.2	93.6	6.4	3.80	99.993	0.007	99.986	0.014
1.90	97.1	2.9	94.3	5.7	3.85	99.994	0.006	99.988	0.012
1.95	97.4	2.6	94.9	5.1	3.89	99.995	0.005	99.990	0.010

The probable error corresponds to kσ = 0.675 where 50% of situations fall inside (within) and 50% fall outside (without).

A 2 dB level corresponds to 2.0 dB/0.8 = 2.5 σ. Looking at the "kσ" column in Table 8.1 (the value of k being 2.5 for this example), the probability that 2.5 σ (or 2 dB) will be exceeded is 1.24 percent. Note that this is made up of a 0.62 percent probability that the level is below $\mu - 2.5\sigma$ and a 0.62 percent probability that the level is above $\mu + 2.5\sigma$. The probable error is 0.675 σ, thus PE = 0.675 × 0.8 = 0.54 dB.

Illustrative Example 8.2

Assume that the standard deviation associated with the antenna factor of a conical log-spiral antenna is $\sigma = 2$ dB and that of the attenuation of a 10 m cable at UHF is 1.5 dB. Assuming further no antenna loading or reflections by the enclosure walls or other error effects, calculate that error which has a 10 percent probability of being exceeded.

From Eq. (8.4), $\sigma = (2\text{ dB} + 1.5\text{ dB}) = 2.5$ dB. From Table 8.1, the 10 percent probability corresponds to 1.645 $\sigma = 1.645 \times 2.5$ dB = ±4.1 dB. Thus, there exists a 10 percent probability that the combination antenna and cable will yield an error in measurements exceeding 4.1 dB.

Many of the random errors pertinent to EMI testing do not fit a log-normal distribution. However, as discussed in later sections of this chapter, they may be approximated by such a distribution over a limited range, approximately from $\mu - \sigma$ to $\mu + \sigma$. The compelling argument for doing this is the simplicity of the mathematics in calculating the total error. However, it must be remembered that calculation of 2σ or 3σ points has no validity, as exemplified by Illustrative Example 8.1. Furthermore, the data bases for many random variables do not exist for other than a few population samples. Thus, what takes place beyond the $\mu \pm 1\sigma$ regions is unknown. Whether the distribution is log-normal or otherwise is also unknown.

8.1.3 Combined Systematic and Random Errors

From the foregoing, it is apparent that measurement errors must be identified in terms of their individual systematic or random contributions, or both. The systematic errors will have their mean bias components added algebraically and their associated standard deviations, within certain restrictions, added on an rms basis. The standard deviations associated with systematic errors, if any, then will be rms-added with those of the random errors.

Illustrative Example 8.3

Assume that the tabulation below summarizes a few errors associated with a semiautomatic radiated-emission test process which is recording the transients from a test sample on an X–Y plotter. Calculate (1) the probability that the measurement could be too low by 20 dB from the true value and (2) the probability that the true value was exceeded.

The combined systematic and random errors are $\mu = -13$ dB and $\sigma = \sqrt{(4.9)^2 + (2.7)^2} = 5.6$ dB. The systematic error with respect to a 20 dB too low measurement is 20 dB – 13 dB = 7 dB above a –20 dB low margin. This corresponds to a 7 dB/5.6 dB = 1.25 σ point below μ. From Table 8.1, 1.25 σ = corresponds to a $\mu - 1.25 \sigma = -20$ dB situation with a 10 percent probability of occurrence. Thus, a 20 dB or lower value of measured electric field strength from the true value has a 10 percent probability of existing. Also, it is 50 percent probable that the measured value is 13 dB too low (i.e., $\mu = -13$ dB). The probability that the true value was exceeded in measurement is 13 dB/5.6 dB = 2.32 σ and $\mu + 2.32 \sigma = 0$. From Table 8.1, this has about a one percent probability of occurrence. However, it should be noted that sufficient population samples usually do not exist to support deviations exceeding 1 σ. Furthermore, it may not be known that a log-normal distribution is a good model for probabilities smaller than $\mu - \sigma$ and greater than $\mu + \sigma$.

Tabulation of Errors for Illustrative Example 8.3

Type of Error	Systematic μ	Systematic σ	Random σ
Antenna	—	—	2 dB
Wall/Ceiling Detuning	−5 dB	3 dB	—
Coax Cable Loss	—	—	1.5 dB
Wall/Ceiling Reflections	−4 dB	2 dB	—
VSWR Receiver and Antenna Mismatch	−1 dB	3 dB	—
Peak Detector/X–Y Plotter	−3 dB	1.5 dB	—
Substitution Impulse Generator	—	—	1 dB
Total Errors	−13 dB	4.9 dB	2.7 dB

In the above example it is interesting to note that it is more probable that the measurement is 20 dB below true value than that it exceeds true value (10 percent to 1 percent, respectively). This partially explains why EMI measurements often lack good reproducibility and why test samples frequently appear to perform better than they really do. As explained in subsequent sections, some EMI measurements may have errors exceeding 40 dB for certain situations. Thus, the importance of performing an error analysis is evident.

8.1.4 A Summary of Measurement Errors

Figure 8.2 and Table 8.2 summarize more than 40 EMI measurement errors identified and discussed in subsequent sections of this chapter. Between 10 and 30 of these errors may apply to any particular measurement. In the following sections, each error will be identified as systematic or random and will be accorded a **default** value for use when specific data are not available.

Table 8.2—Principal Errors in EMI Measurements

Instrument Errors	
Antennas	**Sensor-Receiver Couplers**
Antenna Factor	Transfer or Insertion Loss
Near-Field Correction	Input/Output VSWR
Polarization	Lead-in/Out Cable
Antenna Gradient	Attenuation Loss
Lead-in Line Loss	Saturation
VSWR	**Receiver Predetector**
Antenna Surroundings	Input VSWR
Reflections, Walls/Ceiling	RF Attenuator
Loading, Walls/Ceiling	Linearity (NB & BB)
Resonance, Standing Waves	Spurious Response
Current Probes and LISNs	Saturation
Transfer Impedance	Gain Stability
Active Inverse Amplifier	**Receiver Post-Detector**
Power Line Impedance	CW versus Pulsed CW Level
Saturation	Peak Detector-Single Transient
Insertion Loss	Gain Stability
VSWR	NB and BB Dynamic Range

Calibration Errors	
IG/Signal Generator Level	Impulse Bandwidth
IG/Signal Generator VSWR	Coherent versus Noncoherent BB
Lead-in Line Difference	Gain Stability

Test Setup and Procedure Errors	
Modes of Operation	Probability of Intercept
Gradient Errors	Test Sample Bonding
Test Sample Faces	Test Sample Layout
Current Probe Position	Parallel Plate VSWR
Signal Generator Modulation	

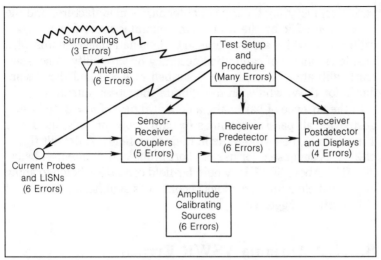

Figure 8.2—Summary of EMI Test Measurement Errors

Perhaps the principal value of this chapter is that it exposes the naivete with which some EMI standards and specifications require measurements to be accurate to within limits as precise as ±2 dB. It would be much more meaningful to require that the test plan include an error analysis for each series of measurements which justifies the maximum feasible accuracy for each measurement.

8.2 Instrumentation Errors

This section discusses measurement errors associated with EMI test instrumentation as listed in the top section of Table 8.2. A discussion of calibration errors is presented in Section 8.3, and test setup and procedure errors are reviewed in Section 8.4.

8.2.1 Antenna Errors

8.2.1.1 Antenna Factors

The antenna factor for receiving antennas, as covered in Section 2.5.5, is subject to errors from manufacturing variations, calibration or aging and abuse. It may not be feasible to quantify error data from these causes because they are functions of so many variables, including the type of antenna, its manufacturer and the care accorded it by the user. Some manufacturers provide good calibrations which are traceable to various national standards, plus usable estimates of calibration accuracy or variability. Also, standard calibration methods are described in ANSI and IEEE standards for those who wish to calibrate their own antennas.

In the absence of hard data, a default figure of σ = 3 dB is suggested for all passive antennas (usually loops or rods) used at a 1 m distance, below 30 MHz in their near fields. A default figure of 2 dB is suggested for use of short-probe active antennas below 30 MHz. Above 30 MHz, where far-field conditions begin to apply and near-field gain corrections become less significant, an error of σ = 2 dB is suggested.

8.2.1.2 Antenna VSWR Errors

Errors from impedance mismatch between the antenna and the cable which connects it to the EMI analyzer can be significant and are more readily quantified than the errors of the preceding section. However, the effects of antenna output VSWR interact with EMI analyzer input VSWR. These are discussed in Section 8.2.5.1 along with EMI analyzer input mismatch errors.

8.2.1.3 Antenna Polarization Mismatch Errors

The reduction of signal pickup due to mismatch between the polarization of a measuring antenna and that of an arriving radiated emission from an EUT is, in dB:

$$\text{Error} = 20 \log \cos \ominus \qquad (8.5)$$

where,

$\ominus$ = the angle between the two polarizations

It can be seen from Eq. (8.5) that the measurement error is systematic and is always negative or equal to zero. When $\ominus$ is near 90°, large negative numbers can exist. In actual practice, however, a cross-polarized situation rarely results in a measured EMI signal reduction exceeding 20 dB. This is due to a lack of polarization purity, disturbance of the field by the measuring antenna and other factors.

The shape of the polarization coupling probability distribution is also asymmetrical. Polarization at a 45° diagonal to an unknown arriving horizontal or vertical polarization will result in a −3 dB systematic error. When a log-normal distribution is fitted to an unknown linearly polarized source, the systematic mean value, $\mu = -6$ dB and the standard deviation, $\sigma = 6.1$ dB. The problem in using this approximation is again apparent because $\mu + \sigma = +0.1$ dB, which is a greater value than for matched polarization (error = 0 dB).

8.2.1.4 Summary of Antenna Errors

The following is a tabulation of default values that may be used in lieu of better data when analyzing measurement errors on antennas used for MIL-STD-462 radiated emission tests at a 1 m distance:

Error Source	Mean Value, μ	Standard Deviation, σ
Antenna Factor (excl. VSWR)		
Below 30 MHz	0 dB	3 dB
Above 30 MHz	0 dB	2 dB
Antenna Polarization	−6 dB	6.1 dB*

*For Unknown Source

8.2.2 Antenna-Enclosure Errors

Discussions of radiated emissions thus far in this chapter have been based on measurements in the open with no significant reflections from nearby objects. This condition obviously does not exist within a shielded enclosure, where significant reflections can be expected from the walls and the ceiling. This section discusses the measurement errors that result from the coherent combination of these reflections with the direct emissions from the EUT as they appear at the test antenna. It also covers the antenna detuning effect from mutual coupling between it and its images in the walls of the shielded enclosure.

8.2.2.1 Antenna Detuning from Proximity to Walls and Ceilings

When a shielded enclosure is used as the EMI test environment, internal reflections can cause antenna calibration problems. The location of various objects within the enclosure, which typically is dictated by practical and logistical considerations, can result in error-producing proximities to the metal walls and ceiling of the enclosure.

When a radiating source or receptor is located near the walls or ceiling, it can be affected by mutual impedance coupled into it from its images. Figure 8.3 shows a 1 m rod in a free-space condition, while Fig. 8.4 shows the same antenna as influenced by the enclosure. In the free-space condition, the electric field is symmetrical about the axis of the rod and extends from the rod to the ground plane. Within the enclosure, however, with its panels at or near the same potential as the antenna ground plane, there is now considerable distortion of the electric field. This results in a variation of the radiated or measured field from its true open-field value as a result of additional **virtual** grounds which vary the reference for the antenna rod. This variation increases as one moves the antenna closer to the enclosure panels.

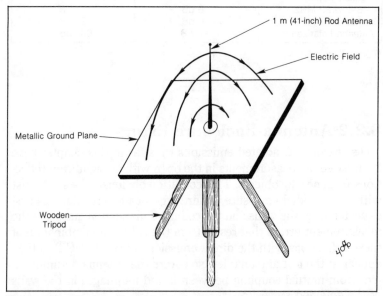

Figure 8.3—Electric-Field Lines of a Typical 1 m (41-inch) Rod Antenna in Free-Space Conditions

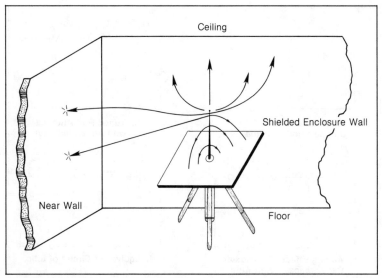

Figure 8.4—Electric-Field Redistribution (Detuning) of Antenna when Placed in a Shielded Enclosure

Another way to observe the effect of the proximity of the enclosure panels begins with the recognition that an untuned rod antenna appears as a capacitance from the rod to its ground plane reference. As shown in Fig 8.5a, this capacitance, typically 10 pF for 1 m rods, is in series with a signal source that induces the open-circuit voltage in the antenna. Practical designs for EMI test applications add an inductor to series resonate with the capacitance. This results in the equivalent circuit shown in Fig. 8.5b, which includes the residual resistance of the inductor, R_{ind}.*

---

*In some designs, a parallel-resonant step-down transformer is used to broadly resonate with the rod capacitance to provide an approximate match to both the antenna and the EMI analyzer. The effects described are the same.

However, when the antenna is placed in a metal enclosure, an additional capacitance, C_{encl}, is added between the rod and ground. This detunes the antenna output circuit as shown in Fig. 8.5c. As a result of this detuning, the antenna now has a higher source impedance. As a consequence of the greater ratio of voltage division with the 50 Ω input impedance of the EMI analyzer (see Fig. 8.5d), the antenna is less efficient than before. Thus, the proximity of

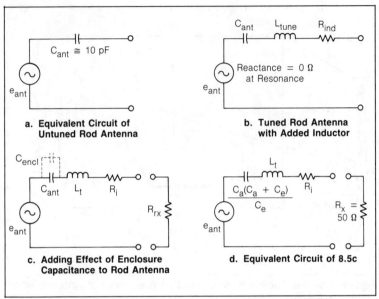

Figure 8.5—Effect of Proximity of Enclosure Wall on Equivalent Circuit of Rod Antenna

shielded enclosure panels to a rod antenna is seen to result in erroneous measurements with a systematic error on the low side.

Another example of the detuning effect is shown in Fig. 8.6. This illustrates the impedance of a tuned dipole in a shielded enclosure versus that in an open area. The sharp peak in the magnitude of the impedance is at the fundamental cavity resonance of the shielded enclosure. The shielded enclosure resonance phenomenon and the errors it causes are discussed in Section 8.2.2.2.

An approximate default value for the antenna detuning error for commonly used antennas in a shielded enclosure is a systematic error of $\mu = -5$ dB with $\sigma = 3$ dB. The error from this effect can be minimized in three ways:

1. For the rod antenna, provide a continuous ground plane between the antenna and the EUT using a wide, highly conductive plate between the counterpoise of the antenna and the copper-topped table upon which the EUT is mounted. For floor-standing EUTs, mount the rod antenna with its counterpoise as nearly flush with the floor as possible, and bond the counterpoise to the floor between the antenna and EUT with a wide, highly conductive plate. Several military standards require these

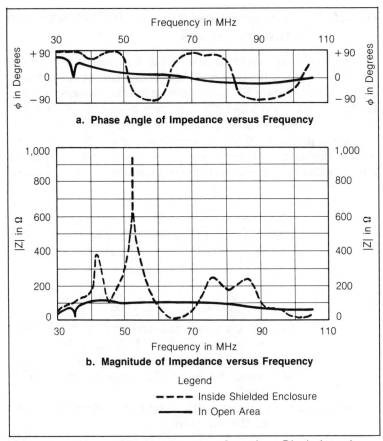

Figure 8.6—Shielded Enclosure versus Open-Area Dipole Impedance

measures, but they are often ignored.

2. For all types of antennas, keep the antenna as far from the reflective surfaces of the shielded enclosure as possible to reduce its coupling to its images. Maximize the distance to the nearest reflective surface as compared to the distance to the EUT—the larger the shielded enclosure, the better.

3. The preferred approach is to use an active antenna with element(s) much shorter than the distances to the reflecting surfaces of the shielded enclosure. This minimizes any mutual impedance (coupling) with its images. The small, active antenna can be improved further by bringing its output signal to the EMI analyzer via a nonconductive transmission line such as a fiber optic link.

8.2.2.2 Enclosure Resonance, Reflections and Standing Waves

The shielded enclosure can also act as a resonant cavity at frequencies for which the electric field becomes zero at one of the inside surfaces. Figure 8.7 shows the coordinate system of a rectangular prism upon which the boundary-value problem is based. The electric field becomes zero at one of the planes, where x = 0 or x = a (the sides of the rectangle); where y = 0 or y = b (the ends of the rectangle); and where z = 0 or z = c (the bottom and top, respectively). The natural resonant frequencies of a cavity are:

$$f = 150 \sqrt{\left(\frac{k}{W}\right)^2 + \left(\frac{m}{L}\right)^2 + \left(\frac{n}{H}\right)^2} \qquad (8.6)$$

where,

f = resonant frequency in MHz

k, m and m = integer numbers corresponding to the resonance modes (0, 1, 2, ...,) with the condition that not more than one of the three integers may equal zero for any resonance mode

W, L and H = interior width, length and height in meters of the enclosure

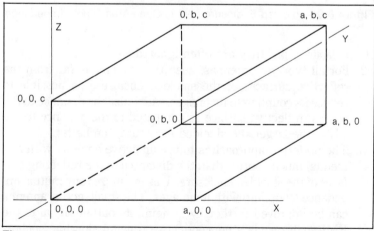

Figure 8.7—Boundary Value Representation of a Shielded Enclosure

Figure 8.8 shows a plot of Eq. (8.6) for a common size of shielded enclosure whose dimensions are 3.6 m W × 5.4 m L × 2.4 m H (12 × 18 × 8 ft). The lowest, or fundamental, resonant frequency for this enclosure is for the transverse electric 110 (TE_{110}) mode at 49 MHz. As shown in Fig. 8.8, resonance can exist at many frequencies within such an enclosure. The total number of modes is approximately $1.7 \times 10^{-7} f^3_H$ per cubic meter (f_H in megahertz), in the above case 26 modes. Thus, it is apparent that, although the enclosure shields the test setup against the electromagnetic environment external to the room, this advantage is obtained at the cost of interior resonances that can significantly alter many test results above its lowest resonant frequency.

At frequencies below the first cavity resonance of the shielded enclosure (the TE_{110} mode), the reflections from the walls, floor and ceiling of the room combine to give about −3 dB of coupling between the EUT and the test antenna compared to open-field values. The variations in this number are in the range of ±1 dB at frequencies below about 63 percent of the first cavity resonance. For default values, use $\mu = -3$ dB and $\sigma = 1$ dB.

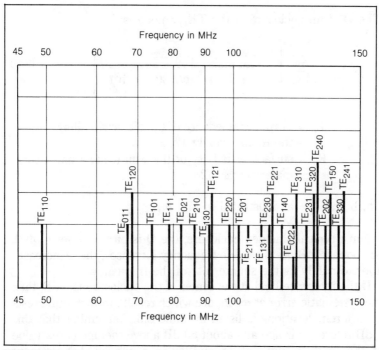

Figure 8.8—Resonant Frequencies of a 3.6 m W × 5.4 m L × 2.4 m H (12 × 18' × 8') Shielded Enclosure

Starting at a frequency just below the first cavity resonance, dramatic changes occur in both the field patterns and the field strengths in the shielded enclosure as the frequency of the emission is increased. At resonances for the dominant TE_{110} mode, the relative electric field strength is a maximum at the middle of the enclosure and decreases toward the walls, but not the ceiling, to yield:

$$\mu = Q \sin \Theta_x \sin \Theta_y \qquad (8.7)$$

where,

$Q = \omega$ (Energy Stored)/Average Power Lost
$\Theta_x = \pi x/a$
$\Theta_y = \pi y/b$
a and b = as illustrated in Fig. 8.7

In dB:

$$\mu = 20 (\log Q + \log \sin \Theta_x + \log \sin \Theta_y) \qquad (8.8)$$

The Q of an enclosure at the TE_{110} mode is:

$$Q = \frac{Z_0}{4R_s} \left[\frac{(a^2 + b^2)^{3/2}}{a^3 + b^3 + (ab/2c)(a^2 + b^2)} \right] \qquad (8.9)$$

Z_0 = intrinsic impedance of the dielectric filling the room, usually 120π
R_s = surface resistivity of the wall (ceiling and floor) material, $\sqrt{\omega \, \mu/2\sigma}$

a, b and c = as illustrated in Fig. 8.7

For a typical shielded enclosure, the Q is on the order of 400, or about 52 dB. As the mode frequency increases, the Q increases approximately as the square root of the frequency.

If the reference field at the center of the enclosure is 0 dB, then the systematic error at resonance which results from making tests at different locations is listed in Table 8.3. Remember that this 0 dB reference is actually about 50 dB above the open-area value of the field strength of an emitter in a similar measurement geometry.

Table 8.3—Systematic Errors in Making Electric-Field Measurements at the TE Resonant Frequency of Shielded Enclosure

Percent of Dimension		Error
x/a	y/b	μ
50	50	50 dB
25 or 75	50	47 dB
50	25 or 75	47 dB
25 or 75	25 or 75	44 dB

The systematic errors listed in Table 8.3 take on entirely different values for other resonant modes. For example, for the TE_{120}, as well as the TE_{210} and TE_{220} modes, the electric field is smallest at the center (theoretically zero) and increases rapidly with displacement away from the center:

$$\mu_i = Q \sin 2\Theta_x \sin \Theta_y, \qquad \text{for } TE_{210} \text{ mode} \qquad (8.10)$$
$$= Q \sin \Theta_x \sin 2\Theta_y, \qquad \text{for } TE_{120} \text{ mode}$$
$$= Q \sin 2\Theta_x \sin 2\Theta_y, \qquad \text{for } TE_{220} \text{ mode}$$

For the dB equivalent:

$$\mu_i = 20 \, (\log Q + \log \sin 2\Theta_x + \log \sin 2\Theta_y) \qquad (8.11)$$

Equation (8.11) implies a null in the center, giving a value of $\mu_i = -\infty$. In reality, of course, such drastic variations do not exist for several reasons: no actual antenna is a point source, the modes within the enclosure cavity are distorted by the presence of equipment and work benches and the power losses in the walls and objects in the enclosure remove energy from the modes due to induced currents, thus reducing both their positive and negative excursions. A graph of the responses in an empty shielded enclosure versus an occupied one appears in Fig. 8.9.[1]

From an inspection of the graph, it may be seen that the average error is near 0 dB over the lowest several modes but with large variations. As the higher-order modes are encountered, the average error is higher but with smaller excursions. This is because the antenna increasingly integrates the gradient of the resulting field strength pattern distributions. At much higher frequencies, not shown on the graph, the average error again becomes less, but its variability remains about the same as for the mid range. This is because the physically smaller antennas are relatively farther from the reflec-

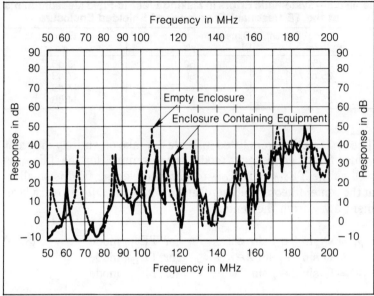

Figure 8.9—Resonance Effects on Field Strength wtihin a Shielded Enclosure

ting surfaces in the enclosure and thus have less image mutual impedance effects, plus integration of many of the mode maxima and minima. Default values for the systematic error and its variation are shown in the following tabulation where f_0 is the lowest resonance of the enclosure.

Frequency Range	μ in dB	σ in dB
0.63 f_0 to 3 f_0	−1.5	28
3.0 f_0 to 5.4 f_0	+13	17
5.4 f_0 to 1 GHz	+3.5	17
1 GHZ and above	+2	6

In the frequency range above 1 GHz, unidirectional antennas are used. This reduces the mode coupling to the antenna. Also, since these antennas are relatively small compared to a typical enclosure size, their characteristics are distorted very little. The best way to reduce the error effects of shielded enclosure resonances is to reduce the Q of the enclosure cavity with absorber materials such as those discussed in Sections 7.3.2 and 7.3.3. This approach can range from the addition of small amounts of strategically placed absorber to full anechoic treatment. Other error-reducing approaches include the use of isolated antennas below about 500 MHz[1,2] and hooded antennas above 200 MHz up to about 1 GHz.[3]

8.2.3 Current Probe and LISN Errors

8.2.3.1 Current Probe Errors

Current probes, which were discussed in Section 2.4.2 (Chapter 2) and Section 4.1.1 (Chapter 4), are subject to errors from:

1. Variations in the manufacturing process
2. Variations in the original calibration
3. Variations due to aging and use
4. Variations due to changes in VSWR with frequency

Errors due to factors 1 and 2 are largely unpredictable, but some manufacturers calibrate the probes quite accurately, and a few even supply calibration uncertainty data. Probe output VSWR data, however, are seldom provided since the probe itself is not expected to match the 50 Ω transmission line but, rather, is properly calibrated for operation into a 50 Ω load.

The magnitude of errors from factors 2, 3 and 4 can be greatly reduced by recalibrating the probe over its intended range of use in accordance with the procedure covered in Section 4.1.1. Such recalibration is especially warranted if there is suspicion that the probe has been subjected to potentially saturating high levels of current. Instances have been cited in which current probes were found to be in error by amounts ranging from 6 to 25 dB, with the latter number probably caused by a reduction of toroidal core permeability as a consequence of such saturation.[4]

In the absence of recalibration or other specific data, a default figure of $\sigma = 2$ dB is suggested.

8.2.3.2 LISN Errors

As is the case for current probes, representative errors for LISNs are largely unknown. In the absence of empirical data, a default figure of $\sigma = 2$ dB is suggested, provided that the LISN is used over its recommended range, and its current rating is not exceeded.

If the LISN is operated at lower frequencies for which a 50 Ω impedance is required, and its input impedance, Z, is less than 50 Ω, then the systematic error of μ becomes:

$$\mu = 20 \log (Z/50) \tag{8.12}$$

This is based on the assumption that the EUT presents a constant current source (the impedance of the EUT as a source is much greater than Z) so that the voltage developed is proportional to Z.

It is important to note that application of Eq. (8.12) to determine the systematic error, μ, is based on the assumption that a 50 Ω input impedance to the LISN is specified for the frequency of measurement. Some EMI test documents call for LISN measurements at frequencies for which the specified LISN presents a lower impedance than 50 Ω. In such situations, where the lower input impedance of the LISN is deliberately accepted by the controlling document, no correction for a lower impedance is appropriate.

8.2.4 Sensor-Receiver Coupler Errors

Devices inserted between the field sensor and the receiver (for emissions measurements) and between the radiating transducer and the signal source (for susceptibility measurements) are prolific sources of potential errors. The following tabulation suggests default errors for a number of such devices which are applicable to the listed MIL-STD-462 methods and other similar EMI test methods.

Coupler/Device Identification	Test Method	Suggested Error, σ
Directional Coupler	CE06	0.5 dB
RF Rejection Network	CE06/RE03	1.0 dB
Insertion Transformer	CS01	0.5 dB
Insertion Audio Oscillator	CS01	0.5 dB
Insertion Capacitor	CS02	0.5 dB
Insertion Signal Generator	CS02/CS07	0.5 dB
Three-Port Network	CS03/CS05/CS07	0.5 dB
Two Signal Generators	CS03/CS05	1.0 dB
Insertion Spike Generator	CS06/RS02	1.0 dB
Insertion Impulse Generator	CS07	1.0 dB
Calibration Resistor	CS06/RE01/RS01	0.3 dB
Antenna Switch Block Below 200 MHz	RE02	0.5 dB
Antenna Switch Block Above 200 MHz	RE02	1.0 dB
Associated Cables and Connectors Below 200 MHz	All	0.5 dB
Associated Cables and Connectors Above 200 MHz	All	1.0 dB

8.2.5 EMI Analyzer Predetector Errors

8.2.5.1 Input Mismatch Errors

VSWR errors from impedance mismatch at the RF input terminals of the EMI analyzer or other receiver being used for measurement are affected by interactions with mismatches at the outputs of antennas, probes, LISNs and other transducers. When the VSWR, r_s, of an antenna or other transducer is combined with the VSWR, r_a, of a receiver or EMI analyzer, the combination is phase coherent and will not combine in accordance with Eq. (8.4). The combination will vary from a minimum VSWR equal to the quotient of the two VSWRs to a maximum VSWR equal to the product of the two VSWRs. The quotient is always taken in the sense that it is equal to or greater than one.

These values have no direct effect on the losses and errors in the lines due to the mismatches. However, the load VSWR directly affects the excess cable loss in the transducer-to-analyzer (lead-in) cable. The effect is most pronounced when the cable loss is low under matched conditions. When the matched cable loss is greater than 3 or 4 dB, the effective line VSWR is reduced, and the excess loss is a smaller fraction of the total. Also, the excess loss tends to increase more slowly with increasing matched line loss. The excess cable loss, E, in dB, due to VSWR is:

$$E = 10 \log [1 + (10^{0.1A} - 1) (r^2 + 1)/2r] - A \quad (8.13)$$

where,

$\quad\quad\quad r = r_a$, the load VSWR
$\quad\quad\quad A = $ loss in dB when the line is matched

The excess loss, E, is a negative systematic error in the measured level of EMI. A default value for typical lines used in EMI measurements is $\mu = -0.6$ dB and $\sigma = 0.2$ dB.

The errors produced by the interactions between mismatches at the transducer output and EMI analyzer input are systematic in that they represent an ohmic power loss due to higher voltages and currents on the line because of the VSWRs, plus a random error due to the variation of the EMI analyzer input impedance from 50 Ω. The power loss term depends on how the transducer is calibrated. The least power loss error results when the transducer is calibrated (using a reliable method) into a 50 Ω load. The greatest error results when the transducer "calibration" or performance is assumed or calculated from ideal theory. An example of this is a tuned dipole or horn antenna which is assumed to have ideal free-space gain and impedance.

The physical situation may be visualized from an inspection of Fig. 8.10. The situation depicted in Fig. 8.10 has the power produced by the transducer or source traveling down the transmission line to the load. At the load, the mismatch causes some of the power to be reflected toward the source. The rest of the power is transmitted onto the load, where it is dissipated. These relationships are shown as P_r/P_i and P_t/P_i, respectively. The elements of the model are further subscripted as being associated with the source or the load with an "S" or an "L," respectively. When the power reflected

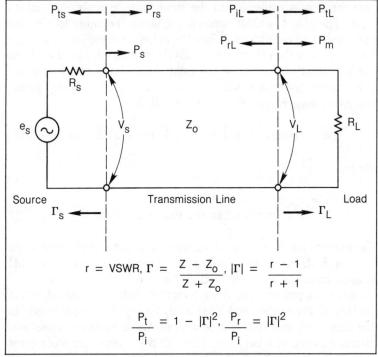

$$r = \text{VSWR}, \ \Gamma = \frac{Z - Z_0}{Z + Z_0}, \ |\Gamma| = \frac{r - 1}{r + 1}$$

$$\frac{P_t}{P_i} = 1 - |\Gamma|^2, \ \frac{P_r}{P_i} = |\Gamma|^2$$

Figure 8.10—VSWR and Power Relationships in the Transducer—Transmission Line—EMI Analyzer Circuit

by the line-load mismatch reaches the line-source junction, any mismatch there causes part of the power to be reflected again toward the load. This process continues until all the power is dissipated in the load, the source or the lossy elements of the transmission line.

It is apparent that once the power is injected on the line, more is transferred to the load if the load VSWR is low and if the source VSWR is high. If the source VSWR were unity, then any power reflected by the load would flow back into the source and be lost. For example, if the source is an antenna perfectly matched to the line, any power reflected to it by the load would be reradiated and thus not available for measurement.

For transducers which are calibrated by measurements in a 50 Ω system, i.e., into a load of 50 Ω, the following equation gives the ratio of measured power to power supplied by the transducer:

$$\frac{P_m}{P_s} = \frac{1 - |\Gamma_L|^2}{1 - |\Gamma_s|\,|\Gamma_L|^2} \qquad (8.14)$$

For transducers in which the performance is calculated from ideal parameters, the ratio P_m/P_s is given by Eq. (8.15). In this case, e_s and R_s are either known or calculated, and V_s or P_s is calculated. Frequently, R_s is assumed to be nominally equal to Z_{o1}.

$$\frac{P_m}{P_s} = \frac{(1 - |\Gamma_s|)^2(1 - |\Gamma_s|)^2}{1 - |\Gamma_a|^2|\Gamma_L|^2} \qquad (8.15)$$

The source output power is given by (see Fig. 8.10):

$$P_s = e^2/4R_s \text{ and } \Gamma_s = \frac{R_s - Z_o}{R_s + Z_o}$$

Since the load does not necessarily match the line, an uncertainty is added to the mismatch loss. This would not be the case if the EMI analyzer were a calorimeter so that it could measure the actual power delivered to it, but since the EMI analyzer can only measure the two-terminal voltage at its input, the uncertainty exists. The uncertainty factor is:

$$\frac{V_L}{V_s} = \sqrt{\frac{R_L}{Z_o}} = \sqrt{\frac{1 \pm |\Gamma_L|}{1 \mp |\Gamma_L|}} \qquad (8.16)$$

The mismatch loss error in dB from either of Eqs. (8.14) or (8.15) is given by:

$$E_p = 10 \, \log(P_m/P_s) \qquad (8.17)$$

The uncertainty error from Eq. (8.16) in dB is:

$$E_v = 20 \, \log \, (V_L/V_s) = +10 \, \log \, \frac{1 \pm |\Gamma_L|}{1 \mp |\Gamma_L|} \qquad (8.18)$$

The total error and uncertainty, in dB, are:

$$E_t = E_p + E_v = 10 \, \log \, (P_m/P_s) + 20 \, \log \, (V_L/V_a) \qquad (8.19)$$

or,

$$E_t = 10 \, \log \, P_m/P_s + 10 \, \log \, \frac{1 \pm |\Gamma_L|}{1 \pm |\Gamma_L|} \qquad (8.20)$$

Note that Eq. (8.20) has the form $\mu + k\sigma$.

The following list of ranges of VSWR in the various frequency ranges for EMI analyzers and for transducers such as LISNs, current probes and antennas comes from an analysis of manufacturers' data and actual experience.

Ranges of VSWR

Frequency Range in Hz	Transducer VSWR, Typical Maximum		EMI Analyzer VSWR, Typical Maximum	
20 to 50 k	3 to 20	> 30	1 to 1.05	1.15
50 k to 5 M	3 to 10	20	1.1 to 2	3
5 M to 30 M	1.5 to 4	10	1.5 to 3	4
30 M to 200 M	2 to 7	10	1.5 to 3	4
200 M to 3 G	1.2 to 1.8	4	1.3 to 2	3
3 G to 18 G	1.15 to 1.3	3	1.2 to 2	3

Using combinations of several typical and maximum values of transducer VSWR and several typical and maximum values of EMI analyzer VSWR, a statistical analysis gives average mismatch errors and uncertainties as shown in the following tabulation. Note that these are systematic errors.

Mismatch Errors

Frequency Range in Hz	Calibrated Sensors		Uncalibrated Sensors	
	μ	σ	μ	σ
20 to 5 M	−0.5 dB	1.3 dB	−3.3 dB	2 dB
5 M to 30 M	−0.9 dB	3.6 dB	−2.9 dB	4 dB
30 M to 200 M	−0.9 dB	3.6 dB	−2.9 dB	3.9 dB
200 M to 3 G	−0.6 dB	1.4 dB	−1.1 dB	1.6 dB
3 G to 18 G	−0.6 dB	1.4 dB	−1.1 dB	1.6 dB
Average	−0.7 dB	2.5 dB	−2.5 dB	2.8 dB

Provided that the resulting loss can be tolerated, the error resulting from high VSWR can be reduced by inserting a matched buffer pad at the antenna output terminals or between the antenna lead-in cable and the EMI analyzer. If possible, it is better to use the first input attenuator step in the EMI analyzer if it functions at the very input, ahead of any reactive circuits. This puts the buffer pad within the calibration loop of the instrument so that any variations in its attenuation are included in the amplitude calibration of the instrument. If the first input attenuator step is not in front of the first reactive circuits, a pad may be added at the input connector on the analyzer. Figure 8.11 shows the resulting VSWR after addition of the matched fixed attenuator pad versus the VSWR before the pad is added. Since it is common for some EMI antennas for the VHF-UHF range to exhibit VSWRs of about 3.5 near the band edges, it is desirable to reduce this to VSWR no greater than 2. It is apparent from Fig. 8.11 that this can be accomplished with a 3 dB pad.

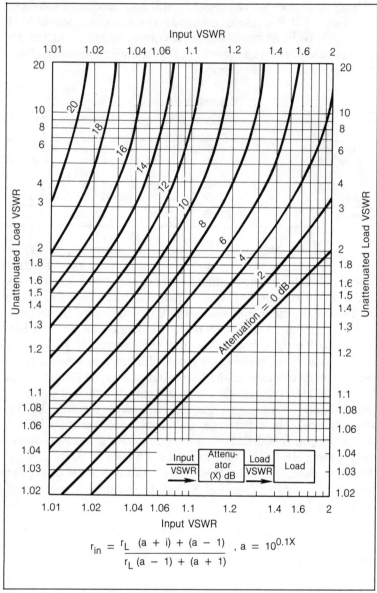

Figure 8.11—VSWR Reduction by the Insertion of Matched Buffer Pads

Illustrative Example 8.4

This example is based on the following tabulated error values, which are default values developed in the preceding paragraphs.

Type of Error	Error in dB	
	μ	σ
Antenna Factor	0	2
Shielded Enclosure Antenna Detuning	-5	3
Shielded Enclosure Reflection (below 63% f_0)	-3	1
Coaxial Cable Matched Loss	0	0.2A*
VSWR Analyzer/Transducer Mismatch		
Calibrated Sources	-0.7	2.5
Uncalibrated Sources	-2.5	2.8
Coaxial Cable Mismatched Excess Loss	-0.6	0.2
Substitution Impulse Generator	0	1

*A is the line loss in dB

Assume that a biconical antenna is used to make radiated emission measurements in the open field in the 20 to 200 MHz frequency range and that a 10 m (30 ft) length of RG-8 cable is used to connect it to the EMI analyzer. Calculate the probable error and also the probability that an indicated 6 dB margin within specification limits is actually being exceeded.

A default figure of $\sigma = 2$ dB is used for the antenna factor independent of VSWR considerations (see above table). The biconical antenna exhibits a relatively poor VSWR, especially at the low end of its coverage range. An average value of error, $\mu = -0.7$ dB and $\sigma = 2.5$ dB (see above table) is assumed. The cable loss is 0.2 dB at 21 MHz; the error is $\sigma = \underline{0.2 \times 0.2} \approx \underline{0.04}$ dB. The total error is $\mu = -0.7$ dB and $\sigma = \sqrt{(2^2 + 2.5^2 + 0.04^2)} = 3.2$ dB. The probable error (PE) from Table 8.1 is PE $= \mu \pm 0.675\ \sigma = -0.7 \pm 0.675 \times 3.2 = -0.7 \pm 2.2$ dB.

In units of σ, the indicated 6 dB specification limit margin = (6 dB $-$ 0.7 dB)/2.2 dB = 2.41 σ. From Table 8.1, it is 0.8 percent probable that the specification limit is exceeded.

If instead of an open-field site the measurements are made in a typical size shielded enclosure where $f_0 = 50$ MHz, the answer is quite different. It is now necessary to add antenna detuning error $\mu = -5$ dB, $\sigma = 3$ dB and reflection error $\mu = -3$ dB, $\sigma = 1$ dB.

The total error is now $\mu = -8.7$ dB and $\sigma = 4.5$ dB. The PE = -8.7 ± 3.0 dB. The indicated 6 dB margin is now $(6 - 8.7)/3.0 = -0.9$ σ. The minus sign interchanges the columns $\mu + k\sigma$ and $\mu - k\sigma$ in Table 8.1, so it is now almost 82 percent probable that the limit is exceeded!

8.2.5.2 RF Attenuator Errors

Effects from mismatch of the built-in RF attenuator of an EMI analyzer or other receiver are presumed to be included in V_r of the previous section. Thus, the entire error, σ_{attn}, is assumed to result from the calibration insertion loss of the attenuator, A. In the absence of measured data, the following default value for the standard deviation of the attenuator error is suggested:

$$\sigma_{attn} \approx 0.01A \qquad (8.21)$$

Nominal attenuation values of 20 dB yield σ of about 0.2 dB.

8.2.5.3 Impulse Bandwidth of the EMI Analyzer

Various techniques described in Section 3.5.2 provide a high degree of accuracy for measuring the impulse bandwidth, B_i, of an EMI analyzer or other receiver. However, there is unavoidable variation of B_i with the tuned frequency and the level at which it is measured. As a result, the degree of accuracy is dependent on the proximity of the measured signal in frequency and amplitude to those at which the calibration was performed. In the absence of measured data, a default value of $\sigma = 0.7$ dB is suggested.

8.2.6 EMI Analyzer Postdetector and Display Errors

The recent popularity of inertia-free readout media (such as hard-copy printouts of displays from storage-type CRTs or data after computer processing) has decreased the relative importance of postdetector display errors. Such errors are primarily associated with the measurement of transients when X-Y plotters are used to record the test results. In accordance with procedures described in Section 6.2.1, the plotter is precalibrated using a broadband source such as an impulse generator. When a single-shot pulse or transient is being measured, it becomes likely that the plotter will indicate a response smaller than the true value. Although the errors associated with this effect should be measured and used to correct the data, when this is not feasible the values in Table 8.4, based on typical measurements, are suggested as default values.

Table 8.4—Combination Receiver and X-Y Plotter Errors on Transients

Bandwidth (B_3)	μ Error	σ Error
≤ 10 kHz	0 dB	0 dB
30 kHz	−2 dB	1 dB
100 kHz	−5 dB	2 dB
300 kHz	−8 dB	3 dB
1,000 kHz	−12 dB	4 dB

The modeling for Table 8.4 is roughly as follows:

$$\mu = \sqrt{B_p/B_a}$$

where B_a and B_p are the EMI analyzer and X-Y plotter half-power (−3 dB) bandwidths (B_3), respectively.

In terms of dB:

$$\mu = 10 \log \sqrt{B_p/B_a} = 5(\log B_p - \log B_a)$$

Since typical X-Y plotters have B ≈ 10 kHz, for B_a in kHz:

$$\mu = 5 (1 - \log B_a)$$

or,

$$\mu = -5(\log B_a) + 5 \tag{8.23}$$

To assure a 99 percent probability that all values lie below 0, $k\sigma$ from Table 8.1 is 2.576 and $\mu/k = \sigma$ The model for σ in dB is then:

$$\sigma \approx 5 (1 - \log B_a)/2.576$$

$$\approx 2 \log B_a - 2 \tag{8.24}$$

If a high-quality EMI analyzer meeting the specifications of ANSI C63.2 with peak-hold/dump is used, this error can be eliminated by proper adjustment of the instrument.

8.3 Calibration Errors

This section discusses the calibration errors listed in Table 8.2.

8.3.1 Impulse Generator Level Errors

8.3.1.1 IG Flatness

Impulse generator flatness in terms of dBμV/MHz is best determined by the methods indicated in Section 3.5.2. In lieu of actual measurements, however, a default value of $\sigma = 0.5$ dB is suggested.

8.3.1.2 IG VSWR

Corresponding to a VSWR $\approx$ 1.1, a default value of $\sigma = 0.4$ dB is suggested.

8.3.1.3 IG Attenuator

A suggested default value for IG attenuators based on use of 2 percent precision resistors is $\sigma = 0.2$ dB.

8.3.1.4 Combined Error for IG Factors

The resulting total when all three IG factors are combined using Eq. (8.4) is an overall random error, $\sigma = 0.7$ dB.

8.3.2 Signal Generator Level Errors

Errors involving the signal generator in a setup will vary greatly with a number of parameters, including calibration technique, RF attenuator and VSWR. In lieu of actual measurements, a default value of $\sigma = 1$ dB is suggested. High-quality calibration generators and attenuators will produce much better results.

8.3.3 Lead-In Line Difference Errors

This calibration error results from the difference between the transducer-to-EMI-analyzer RF line length when an internal IG is used. It is a consequence of the fact that the IG is injected at the receiver and not at the sensor end of the input cable. Additionally, the IG is injected in one arm of an internal coaxial switch while the sensor is injected through another arm. The variation is a function of line length, coaxial-switch VSWR and the frequency of measurement. If actual data are not available, the following default values may be assigned:

$$\sigma = (0.4 \text{ dB} + 0.01\alpha) \text{ below 1 GHz for VSWR} = 1.1$$
$$\sigma = (0.8 \text{ dB} + 0.01\alpha) \text{ above 1 GHz for VSWR} = 1.2$$

where,

$$\alpha = \text{sensor input cable attenuation}$$
$$\text{VSWR} = \text{coaxial switch VSWR}$$

8.3.4 Impulse Bandwidth Errors

Errors in impulse bandwidth of the EMI analyzer or receiver versus frequency of measurement and signal level were discussed in Section 8.2.5.3 where a default value of $\sigma = 0.7$ dB was suggested.

8.3.5 Coherent and Noncoherent Sources

The error discussed here results from treating a noncoherent (or random) signal as coherent, e.g., by substituting an IG signal when measuring it. As identified in Section 2.3.4.8, the error from this effect is:

$$\mu = 10 \ \log(1 \ \text{MHz/BW})$$

and,

$$\sigma = \text{Summation of calibration errors, from Eq. (8.1)}$$

Examples of noncoherent sources to which such an error could apply are corona, gas discharge, white noise, bandwidth-limited white noise and noise diodes. For such sources, this type of error can become enormous as the bandwidth becomes small. This serves to emphasize the extreme importance of not using a coherent broad-band source, such as an IG, to calibrate a measurement of non-coherent broadband noise. Do not use IG substitution to measure noise unless you are certain that its type is broadband coherent!

8.3.6 Gain Stability

Errors associated with precalibration gain stability are a function of many variables involving the complete EMI test system and the time between calibrations. These errors may vary from much less than 1 dB to 10 dB or more. It is suggested that a default figure of $\sigma = 1$ dB be used when the actual errors are unknown.

8.3.7 Composite Example: Instrument and Calibration Errors

To illustrate instrument and calibration errors, compute the probable error ($\mu \pm 0.675 \sigma$) associated with performing a current probe measurement on a transient waveform using an EMI analyzer with a 50 kHz bandwidth tuned to 10 MHz.

Source of Error	Systematic Error μ	Systematic Error σ	Random σ	Reference Section
Current Probe			2 dB	8.2.3.1
EMI Analyzer VSWR	−0.7 dB	2.5 dB		8.2.5.1
RF Attenuator (20 dB)			0.2 dB	8.2.5.2
EMI Analyzer Impulse Bandwidth			0.7 dB	8.2.5.3
Peak Detector & X-Y Plotter	−3.5 dB	1.4 dB		8.2.6
IG Level			0.7 dB	8.3.1
Lead-in Line 6 m (20 ft) cable			0.4 dB	8.3.3

Total error from Eq. (8.4): $\mu \pm \sigma = -4.2$ dB ± 3.7 dB. In terms of the probable and random errors, this value becomes:

$$\mu \pm 0.675 \sigma = -4.2 \text{ dB} \pm 2.5 \text{ dB}$$

Thus, it is 50 percent probable that the measurement will read between 1.7 dB and 6.7 dB below actual value.

8.4 Test Setup and Procedure Errors

Listed in the lower section of Table 8.2 are the principal errors associated with the test setup and procedures. Unlike the preceding sections of this chapter, it is not feasible to characterize and quantify most of these errors in the form of explicit tables and equations since they are dependent on the specific setup and procedures employed. Chapter 9 includes useful information on this subject and implicitly covers such errors.

The two exceptions which can be analyzed concern gradient errors, as described in the next two sections.

8.4.1 Test Sample Distance Gradient Errors

When the EUT is large, significant errors in radiated emission or susceptibility test results may occur because much of the EUT is farther than the prescribed distance away from the test antenna. This effect is illustrated in Fig. 8.12 for a multimodule EUT to be tested at a prescribed measurement distance of 1 m. Although the following discussion deals with emission testing, it is apparent that the susceptibility situation is completely analogous.

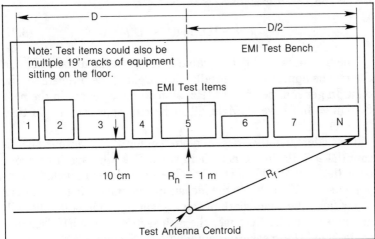

Figure 8.12—Multimodule Test Setup Illustrating Field Gradient Error

If it is assumed that all parts of the EUT are radiating equally, it is clear that the highest field strengths at any measurement point will appear from the closest parts of the EUT. The error in field strength from any part of the EUT relative to that of the nearest part follows the radiation law criterion:

$$\mu(\text{error}) = 20 \log (R_n/R_f)^n \qquad (8.25)$$

where,

R_n = nearest distance = 1 m
R_f = more distant source = $\sqrt{R_n^2 + D^2/4}$ (8.26)
n = radiation law criteria (assumes dimensions of EUT modules are much smaller than λ):
n = 1 when both sources are in the far field ($R \gg \lambda/2\pi$)
n = 2 when R_n is in the near field and R_f is in the far field ($\lambda/2\pi$ = crossover criterion)
n = 3 when both sources are in the near field ($R \ll \lambda/2\pi$)

When R_n = 1 m, as for most MIL-STD-462 situations, the error in Eq. (8.25) becomes:

$$\mu = -10n \log(1 + D^2/4) \qquad (8.27)$$

The n term is readily calculable in terms of the distance D, and the results appear on the inside left margin of the ordinate in Fig. 8.13. In general, below 10 MHz, all test items appear in the near field (n = 3). Above 48 MHz, all such items appear in the far field (n = 1).

It is evident that the error, as plotted in Fig. 8.13, becomes significant ($|\mu| \geqslant 3$ dB) in the near field when $D \geqslant 1$ m, and it becomes large ($|\mu| \geqslant 10$ dB) when $D > 2$ m. The error does not include components which are due to the measuring antenna being in the near or far field, the beamwidth of the measuring antenna failing to illuminate the entire EUT (see the next section) or the EUT loading or detuning the measuring antenna (see Section 8.2.2).

To reduce the errors to acceptable levels, it may be necessary to sample the EUT from additional vantage points. Figure 8.13 shows as the right ordinate the maximum distance allowable between such

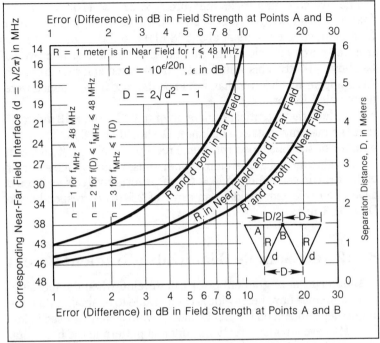

Figure 8.13—Electric-Field Gradient Error in Radiated Measurements

sampling locations. This may be modified when the EUT modules are all larger than $\lambda/2$. The criteria for n in Eq. (8.25) become:

n = 1 when both sources are in the far field ($R \gg \lambda/2\pi$)

n = 0.5 when R_n is in the near field and R_f is in the far field

n = 0 when both R_n and R_f are in the near field ($R < \lambda/2\pi$)

Illustrative Example 8.5

Radiated emission measurements are to be made from 10 kHz to 30 MHz on a five-bay, 19" rack (O.D. measures 22" each) computer cabinet including peripherals. Determine the potential error due to a single-station measurement at the center of the middle (third) rack and calculate the minimum number of station measurements required to reduce the test item gradient error to 2 dB.

8.39

The five adjoining racks measure $5 \times 22" = 110" = 2.79$ m. Figure 8.13 shows that at D = 2.79 m, the near/far field crossover for a point source occurs at about 28 MHz, and the potential error from a source emission near the far edge of the test item would be about −14 dB. This would make the radiated emission from the EUT appear much lower than would be the case if the antenna were illuminated uniformly.

To reduce the potential gradient error to 2 dB, Fig. 8.13 indicates that the maximum station distance, D, should be 0.8 m. Thus, the number of stations (spectrum runs) required is N = 2.79 m/0.8 m = 3.5. This means a minimum of four runs, which yields an error of 1.5 dB corresponding to D = 0.7 m. Alternatively, N = 3 could have been selected, yielding an error of 2.5 dB corresponding to D = 0.93 m.

8.4.2 Test Sample Beamwidth Gradient Errors

Another form of gradient error can develop when the measurement antennas have beamwidths comparable to or smaller than the angle they subtend on the EUT. Rod, or whip, antennas used below 30 MHz have an omnidirectional antenna pattern in the horizontal plane and thus do not manifest this type of error. The dipole family of antennas, including the biconical from 30 to 200 MHz, also appears free of the problem, provided the EUT is less than D = 2 m long (see Fig. 8.11) and R_n = 1 m. For this condition, the angle of subtense is 2 arctan $(R_n D/2) = 90°$.

Thus the 3 dB beamwidth of a dipole is 90°, and the error at the edge of the EUT is 3 dB. However, from Fig. 8.13, the gradient error at D/2 is also 3 dB for the far field, and the total error would be 6 dB. Consequently, it appears that the one-beamwidth criterion is too crude, leading to the suggestion of a better criterion discussed below.

Many EMI test antennas used above 200 MHz exhibit forward directional gain in excess of that of a dipole (G = 1.6 = 2 dB). Some representative antennas and their gains, which were discussed in Section 4.3.1, are listed in Table 8.5.

Table 8.5—Gain and Beamwidth Characteristics of Representative EMI Antennas Used above 200 MHz

Frequency Range	Antenna Type	Maximum Gain	Minimum Beamwidth
200 - 1,000 MHz	Conical Log Spiral	4.5 dB	70°
200 - 1,000 MHz	Double-Ridged Guide	13 dB	35°
1 - 10 GHz	Conical Log Spiral	6 dB	60°
1 - 10 GHz	Double-Ridged Guide	12 dB	40°

Figure 8.14 shows the maximum allowable antenna gain that can be tolerated for testing at 1 m using the 3 dB beamwidth illumination criterion. It is apparent that the log conical spiral antenna can be used above 200 MHz, since its gain never exceeds 10 dB. While the double-ridged guide horn antenna gain does exceed 10 dB, this occurs at a frequency that still allows conformance to Fig. 8.14. The figure indicates that the 3 dB beamwidth of this antenna will just encompass a dual-bay rack or console at a gain of 12 dB and still be in the far field. This is also roughly confirmed by Table 8.5, where $R_n D/2 = \tan \theta /2 = \tan 17.5° = 0.32$, or $D = 0.64$ m for $R_n = 1$ m. Other aspects of this source of measurement error are discussed in Ref. 5.

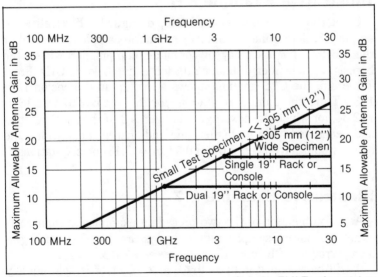

Figure 8.14—Maximum Allowable Antenna Gain for EMI Testing at 1 m

Table 8.6 shows the measurement error from edge illumination of a test item from other than antenna boresight conditions in the far field. This table suggests that a good criterion would be to use 65 percent of the antenna beamwidth and thus keep edge gradient illumination errors to 1 dB.

Table 8.6—Antenna Off-Boresight Error and Corresponding EUT Dimensions for R = 1 meter

Percent of Antenna Beamwidth	Gradient Error in dB	Maximum EUT Dimensions in cm*				
		Biconical 30-300 MHz	CLS ≤ 1 GHz	CLS ≥ 1 GHz	DRG ≤ 1 GHz	DRG ≥1 GHz
0	0	0	0	0	0	0
51	−0.5	85	64	55	31	36
65	−1	112	84	71	40	46
76	−1.5	136	100	84	47	54
84	−2	155	113	94	52	60
100	−3	200	140	115	63	73
114	−4	250	167	136	73	84
127	−5	310	196	157	82	95

* $D = 2R_n \tan \theta/2$

Illustrative Example 8.6

Using the same equipment and setup discussed in Illustrative Example 8.5, determine the number of station samples required for the 2.67 m, five-rack bay of computer equipment to keep the boresight gradient error under 2 dB for testing below 1 GHz. From Table 8.6, the CLS antenna allows a maximum dimension D of 113 . Thus, the number of stations for the test is 2.67 m/1.13 m = 2.36, for which the next higher integer is 3. If the DRG antenna had been used, with its higher gain and sharper beamwidth, the result would have been 2.67 m/0.52 m = 5.13, or six stations.

Illustrative Example 8.7

As a combination of the two preceding examples, compute the number of station samples required to assure that the overall gradient error of both types does not exceed 2 dB.

It will be assumed initially that the 2 dB error is split equally between the two types. Figure 8.13 indicates that a CLS antenna (all in the far field above 200 MHz) requires a station distance of D = 1 m. Thus, N = 2.67 m/1 m = 2.67, or three stations. Table 8.6 indicates that a CLS antenna will require N = 2.67 m/0.84 m

= 3.18, or four stations. It can be shown that, by reallocating the 2 dB error, three stations will suffice. For further reading on this topic, see Ref. 5.

8.5 References

1. Bronaugh, E.L., and Kerns, D.R., "A New Isolated Antenna System for Electromagnetic Emissions Measurements in Shielded Enclosures," *Proceedings of the 1978 IEEE International Symposium on Electromagnetic Compatibility* (New York: IEEE, 1978), pp. 137-142.
2. Van Steenberg, G.; Bronaugh, E.L.; Darilek, G.T.; and Dolle, W.C., "An Isolated Antenna System for Shielded Enclosure Measurements, 20-200 MHz," *Proceedings of the 1971 IEEE International Symposium on EMC* (New York: IEEE, 1971), pp. 198-202.
3. Free, W.R., et. al., "Electromagnetic Interference Measurement Methods—Shielded Enclosure," Georgia Institute of Technology, Quarterly Report 1, Contract DA28-043 AMC-02381(E), January 1967.
4. White, D.R.J., EMC Handbook Vol. 2, *EMI Test Methods and Procedures* (Gainesville, VA: Interference Control Technologies, Inc., 1980).
5. Bronaugh, E.L., "Antennas for EMI Measurement, Parts 1 and 2," *RF Design*, Vol. 9, Nos. 11 and 12.

8.6 Bibliography

Matheson, Robert J., "Instrumentation Problems Encountered Making Man-Made Electromagnetic Noise Measurements for Predicting Communications System Performance," *IEEE Transactions on EMC*, Vol. EMC-12, No. 4, November 1970, pp. 151-158.

Paolini, E., et. al., "Practical Accuracy of Ordinary Field Meters," *Proceedings of the 1972 IEEE Symposium on EMC* (New York: IEEE, 1972), pp. 77-85.

Stuckey, C.W., and Toler, J.C., "Statistical Determination of Electromagnetic Compatibility," *IEEE Transactions on EMC*, Vol. EMC-9, No. 2, September 1967, pp. 27-34.

Stuckey, C.W., et. al., "Statistical Description of Near Zone Spurious Emissions," Georgia Institute of Technology, Final Technical Report, Contract AF 33(615)-3329, AFAL, Wright-Patterson AFB, Ohio.

Toler, J.C., and Stuckey, C.W., "The Power Distribution Measurement Technique—A Method for Measuring Radiated Fields From Equipment Cases," 20th Meeting of the SAE EMC Committee, Wright-Patterson AFB, Ohio, May 1967.

Weinschel, B.O., et. al., "Precision Coaxial VSWR Measurements by Coupled Sliding-Load Technique," *IEEE Transactions on Instrumentation and Measurement*, Vol. IM-13, December 1964, pp. 292-300.

Chapter 9

Preparation for EMI Testing

This chapter covers the additional points pertinent to EMI testing that were not covered in the eight preceding chapters. Included here are specifics on the conditions of the test area, placement of the EUT and its cables, operation, stimulation and loading of the EUT, sampling practices for maximum efficiency in measurements and principles for formulating the most effective accumulation and presentation of the required data. The basic function of this chapter is to establish a common background against which to present the specific EMI test methods and procedures of the remaining chapters.

The chapter begins by considering the various aspects of the electromagnetic environment in which the testing is performed and examines how the EUT and its associated equipment are deployed to assure that the testing is efficient and repeatable. Attention is then focused on the subject of data acquisition and sampling practices which assure an accurate EMC assessment of the EUT. Test plans and test reports that organize the test procedures and resulting EMI data into efficient sequences and documentation are then examined. Finally, there is a discussion of recommended practices for performing and documenting the calibration of the EMI test equipment.

Because of the drastic differences between military and non-military testing with regard to their test environments and EUT layouts, separate parts of the chapter are devoted to military testing as exemplified by MIL-STD-462 methods. Other parts are directed toward nonmilitary testing as exemplified by FCC requirements. First, however, attention is given to the various considerations affecting electromagnetic environments and test layouts which are common to both military and nonmilitary environments.

9.1 Test Environment, Test Equipment and EUT Deployment

9.1.1 Testing in the Presence of Ambient Emissions

Performing an accurate measurement of a radiated or conducted emission in the presence of an ambient signal or noise which falls within the bandpass of the EMI analyzer is a problem encountered with both shielded rooms and open-area sites. Whenever the ambient emission is strong enough to affect the measurement of a test emission, its contribution usually can be removed by a mathematical process. The process to be applied depends on the type of ambient emission which is influencing the reading.

9.1.1.1 Noncoherent Broadband Ambient

The graph in Fig. 9.1 can be used to determine the level of the measured signal, V_t, under the following conditions:[1]

1. The EMI signal to be measured, V_t, is analyzable as a narrowband signal.
2. The ambient noise, V_a, is predominantly random (noncoherent broadband).
3. The total measurement of the signal and noise together, V_o, is within 10 dB of that for the noise alone. The size of this difference in dB, ΔX, is a vital part of the calculation process and is represented as the horizontal axis of Fig. 9.1.

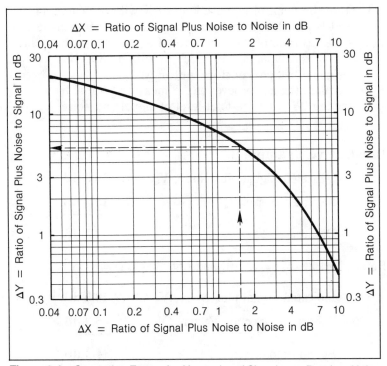

Figure 9.1—Correction Factor for Narrowband Signal near Random Noise Level (Note: This figure is a low-resolution model of the original Electro-Metrics graph. The more elaborate version is available from that company. Courtesy of Electro-Metrics)

The process for using the graph is as follows:

1. Determine ΔX in dB by reading the dBμV level of V_o, the total of signal plus noise, and subtracting from it the dBμV level of the noise alone, V_a, as measured with the EUT turned off.
2. Provided that ΔX does not exceed 10 dB, enter the graph at ΔX on the horizontal scale and proceed vertically to the curve.

3. From the point of intersection of ΔX with the curve, proceed left to the vertical axis and note the level. This level is the dB ratio of the total level of signal and noise to the level of the signal alone, which ratio in dB will be designated as **correction factor** ΔY.
4. Calculate the actual level of the measured signal by subtracting ΔY from the total level of signal and noise, V_o.

Illustrative Example 9.1

Indicated Signal plus Noise, V_o	19.5 dB
Indicated Noise, V_a	18.0 dB
Difference, ΔX	1.5 dB

Enter chart at ΔX = 1.5 dB and find that ΔY = 5.3 dB

Indicated Signal plus Noise, V_o	19.5 dB
Subtract Correction Factor, ΔY	5.3 dB
Actual Signal, V_t	14.2 dB

9.1.1.2 Relating Noisy Measurements to Specification Levels

Figure 9.2 is useful for comparing the actual signal level to the specified limit. Again, all of the conditions of Section 9.1.1.1 apply to both the signal and the ambient noise. In this graph, the five straight-line curves are for five levels of ΔX, the difference between the indicated EMI analyzer readings with the EUT on and off. The X-axis is the difference, in dB, between the indication for ambient noise alone and the specification limit, V_s, as referred to the input terminals of the EMI analyzer. Shown as the Y-axis is the amount, in dB, by which the test voltage, V_t, exceeds (+) or satisfies (−) the specification limit, V_s. It is seen that a signal can always be measured at or somewhat below the ambient level. For example, Fig. 9.2 shows that a signal can be measured 12 dB below limits for ΔX = 1 dB when the ambient is 6 dB below specification limits.

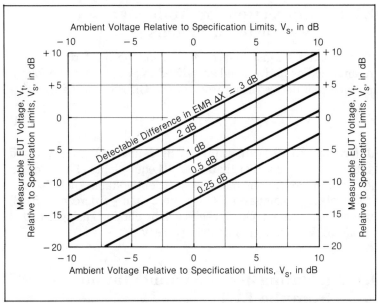

Figure 9.2—Detectable Signal in the Presence of Ambient Emissions Relative to Specification Limits

For situations where it is not feasible to turn the EUT on and off (e.g., automatic testing), a value of V_a not to exceed $0.5\ V_s$ is normally used. (The ambient is kept at least 6 dB below the specification limit.) From Eq. (9.1), when $V_a = V_t = 0.5\ V_s$, the meter reading will be 3 dB below specification limits. Alternatively, V_a may be read by tuning slightly away from the EUT emission, provided that the EUT emission is narrowband.

Reducing the ambient from sources external to the test site to a satisfactory level does not alone assure that the overall ambient, which includes contributions from the complete setup with everything operational except the EUT, is satisfactorily low. Therefore, it should be determined and documented in the test plan that the above criterion of ambient at least 6 dB below specification limits (with noted exceptions) is satisfied for the operational setup before each series of EMI tests is performed.

9.1.1.3 Correction for Ambient Narrowband Signals

When both the signal to be measured and the interfering ambient are analyzed as narrowband as defined in Section 2.3, the following equation, derived from work of the CISPR, can be used:[2]

$$V_t^{1.1} = V_o^{1.1} - V_a^{1.1} \tag{9.1}$$

All terms in Eq. (9.1) are as previously defined but are expressed as units of voltage rather than their dB equivalents. The frequencies of both emanations must be sufficiently stable such that the EMI analyzer readings do not vary more than ± 6 percent (0.5 dB) during measurement. Good results will be obtained using Eq. (9.1) as long as V_a is not greater than twice V_t.

9.1.2 Isolating Test Instrumentation from the EUT

When performing conducted emission tests using a voltage probe, current probe or LISN, it is imperative that crosstalk and fortuitous conducting paths be minimized. Inputs along the intended path of coupling from the sensor into the EMI analyzer must exceed by a sizeable margin any "sneak-path" or "backdoor" entries, including those over the sensor-to-EMI analyzer coaxial cable and the EMI analyzer power leads. Three measures may be taken to accomplish the necessary isolation:

1. The use of separate ac phases and filters for the EUT and test instrumentation
2. The use of an isolation transformer
3. Avoidance of pickup by measurement cables

9.1.2.1 Use of Separate AC Phases for Isolation

The EUT and the test instrumentation should derive their power from separate phases of the ac power mains. One phase of a three-phase, four-wire (Y-type) source is usually used for purposes such as lighting and housekeeping. A second phase is used for test instrumentation, and the third phase is used to power the EUT. When testing is performed in a shielded enclosure, this practice utilizes the power line filters of the shielded enclosure to provide added isolation between the EUT and the EMI test instrumentation. Filtering the power mains in nonshielded test areas is somewhat less effective but usually is worthwhile.

9.1.2.2 Use of Isolation Transformers

Two types of isolation transformer are available for connecting the EMI analyzer to its ac power source through an isolation transformer: shielded and nonshielded. Breaking the path to chassis power ground at this point prevents the possible circulation of ground currents via the loop that would otherwise be formed from (1) EMI analyzer chassis to (2) ac neutral to (3) the EUT to (4) the ground plane and back to (1) the EMI analyzer chassis.

Because of the sensitivity of the EMI analyzer, magnetic coupling into the loop could be significant. However, unless the isolation transformer is shielded, it is not likely to afford much protection against ground currents at frequencies higher than the audio range. An isolation transformer incorporating Faraday shielding can be connected between the EMI analyzer and the ac mains to provide both inductive and capacitive decoupling or RF isolation.

Transformer isolation of the EMI analyzer creates a shock hazard to personnel in the event of a power short to its chassis. Thus, in accordance with the National Electrical Code, the EMI analyzer chassis must be bonded to the enclosure wall or, if it is positioned on the test bench, to the benchtop ground plane. The EMI analyzer is always grounded to the ground plane of the test site or enclosure.

9.1.2.3 Solving Problems from Cable Pickup

During a test procedure, it is common to observe that operator contact with the coaxial cable which runs between the pickup transducer and the EMI analyzer alters the meter reading. Such sensitivity of the cable indicates that it is intercepting and conveying to the EMI analyzer a phase-coherent sample of the same radiated signal as being furnished from the transducer; the amplitude of the resultant signal at the EMI analyzer input terminals is affected by the operator contact.

This effect can be mitigated by the following practices:

1. Use of a triaxial cable such that the center coax functions as the carrier of the intended signal and the outer sheath acts as a Faraday shield. The outer shield is grounded at the EMI analyzer coaxial connector end and left ungrounded (floating) at the transducer end. Although this single-point grounding keeps common-mode currents off the inner coaxial line, its effectiveness is reduced when the length of the line approaches a quarter wavelength (λ/4).

2. Placement over the coaxial cable at the EMI analyzer end of a 30 cm (12") length of suppressant tubing such as manufactured by Capcon, Inc. This technique converts to heat any undesired RF currents above about 15 MHz (3 dB point). It becomes especially effective above 100 MHz, at which it provides 30 dB attenuation. It offers about 100 dB of absorption loss at 1 GHz.

3. A combination of techniques 1 and 2 for maximum effectiveness over a broad range of frequencies. The lossy tubing is slipped over the triaxial cable at the EMI analyzer end, and the outer shield is grounded only at that same end.

9.1.3 EUT Loading and Excitation

9.1.3.1 EUT Loading

EUTs which are intended to operate with other units, but which are not part of them, must be suitably loaded. Such loads may be electrical, electronic, mechanical or electromechanical. Although the importance of this is underscored in susceptibility testing, where performance or degradation monitors are directly affected by such loading, it is also important in emission testing. An example is electrical or electronic loading of relay contacts which are designed to control loads external to the EUT. For EUTs designed for communication electronics applications, the RF I/O lines are terminated with shielded dummy loads as long as the transmitter power output does not exceed 5 kW.

Following are some guidelines to assist in determining whether the load should be real or simulated:

1. The Case for Using Real Loads

The use of real loads avoids wasted time and money spent trying to simulate loads, especially when an interconnecting cable contains many loads where each wire pair requires special attention. The task can become immense in terms of both time and money for a large harness with hundreds of wire pairs. Also, because of factors such as parasitics, there is always doubt as to the extent that the inductance, capacitance and resistance of the real loads have actually been simulated at higher frequencies. When one part of the EUT normally loads (or excites) another, simulation would be especially wasteful since both parts must be tested for EMI compliance anyway.

2. The Case for Using Simulated Loads

When the real load is not part of the EUT, it sometimes is not available. On the other hand, it might be available but exist as an unknown with regard to EMI characteristics. Finally, it might be known to emit a level of EMI which would make it impossible to measure that of the EUT accurately. Some mechanical loads can be so large and heavy that their use is not feasible.

3. Practical Case: A Combination

Since both cases 1 and 2 have points in their favor, a mix of them could provide the optimum solution to a particular situation. Perhaps the real multiwire harness would be used as the load, but only the few wires carrying a disturbing level of EMI would be simulated. Frequently, such a mix is required by realities such as tight schedules and the absence of one or more required items.

9.1.3.2 EUT Excitation

Many of the considerations discussed above relative to EUT loading apply equally well to EUT excitation. Some excitation sources function as both a load and a stimulator at the EUT input terminals.

When feasible, the EUT should be exercised by the same means as in its intended installation. For example, if a solenoid or relay is to be activated by a thyristor or SCR circuit, it should not be tested using a toggle switch to simulate that operation. Actual intended operating conditions should be duplicated as closely as possible.

9.1.4 EUT Mounting and Grounding

When the EUT is designed for mounting on a base with shock and vibration isolators, it should be tested in that manner. Any bonding straps furnished with the mounting base should be connected to the ground plane.

When an external lug, stud or connector pin is available for a ground connection on the EUT and is used for this function in normal installation, it is also used to ground the EUT for EMI testing. If installation details are not known, then any such terminal is not grounded.

9.1.5 Test Fixtures

Test or "breakout" fixtures such as shown in Fig. 9.3 may be used to gain access to a test load via a cable harness without disturbing the harness. A current probe may be snapped around any one of the individual wires or a voltage probe may be applied to an access terminal, as applicable.

9.1.6 Susceptibility Criteria

Fundamental to testing EMI susceptibility is the establishment of a criterion for identifying that the EUT has been adversely affected by the test energy conducted into it or radiated at it. Such susceptibility criteria frequently are difficult to obtain because deterioration in EUT performance is a matter of relative degree of malfunction. However, they must be established and included in an approved test plan before testing can begin.

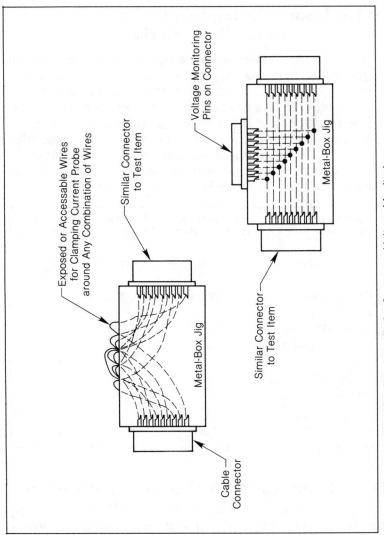

Figure 9.3—Cable Harness Breakout Jig for Current or Voltage Monitoring

9.1.6.1 Some Examples of Susceptibility Criteria

The following list illustrates some examples of malfunctions and performance degradations applicable to various equipments or subsystems, identifying their respective criteria for normal performance ("go" condition), the range over which the respective parameter is allowed to deteriorate during the testing and, finally, the degree of performance degradation which triggers a verdict of unacceptability ("no-go" condition). It is apparent that a thorough analysis of the EUT and its mission are needed to determine these thresholds accurately, and that they should be amply justified and documented.

Equipment or Subsystem	Go-Condition, No Malfunction	Allowable Degradation	No-Go Malfunction
Aircraft Navigation (DME)	$\leqslant 0.2$ mi	0.2 to 0.5 mi	>0.5 mi
Navigation Bearing Angle	$2°$	$2°$ to $5°$	>5°
Aircraft Control Surface Movement	<0.8 mm	0.8 to 3 mm	>3 mm
Digital Computer Bit Error Rate	$<10^{-6}$	10^{-6} to 10^{-5}	$>10^{-5}$
Voice Communication Word Intelligibility	>90%	75 to 90%	<75%
Engine Overheat Alarm Relay	No Alarm	No Alarm	Alarm

9.1.6.2 Susceptibility Criteria for Receivers

Although the assignment of specific threshold levels to susceptibility criteria for receivers is a function of their intended applications, it is typical to define such levels in terms of the **standard response** of the receiver. For several types of receivers they typically are as follows:

Receiver Type	Standard Response
AM and SSB Receivers	(S + N)/N = 10 dB
FM Receivers:	
Unmodulated CW	20 dB Quieting
Modulated	(S + N)/N = 10 dB
Pulsed Receivers	(S + N)/N = 10 dB

9.1.7 Modulation of Susceptibility Signals

When formulating a susceptibility test plan, the type of modulation for the test signal must be determined carefully. Some EUTs are more vulnerable to CW interference, while others are most susceptible to signals with specific types of modulation. In general, the choice of modulation type should be determined as that to which the EUT is most vulnerable. The various aspects of the problem can be most conveniently discussed by dividing the potential receptors into two types: **receivers** and **non-receivers.**

9.1.7.1 Modulation for Testing Receivers

Typical modulation practices for testing susceptibility of receivers are:

Receiver Type	Modulation Type
AM Receivers	50% with 1 kHz Tone
SSB Receivers	Unmodulated
FM Receivers	Unmodulated
Pulsed Receivers	Pulse Width $\approx 1.5/B_3$

Always choose the modulation to which the receiver is most likely to be susceptible.

9.1.7.2 Modulation for Testing Non-receiver EUTs

When the EUT contains one or more amplifiers or other sensitive devices which are not receivers, an analysis should be performed to determined the type of modulation to which it is most likely to be susceptible. For example, a digital data processor should be more or less immune to a CW RF source because the resulting demodulated dc level would be blocked by ac-coupled amplifier stages. Such a device is much more likely to be vulnerable to a signal modulated by pulses equal in width to that of the EUT data clock.

Another example is a limited-bandwidth amplifier (dc to 100 Hz) such as those used in medical equipment for monitoring vital signs. Although a CW test signal could be used, a lower susceptibility threshold might be produced by modulating it at a low frequency, such as 60 Hz from the power mains. Still a third example is another baseband device such as a phase-sensitive, or synchronous, detector. For this device, the lowest susceptibility threshold would be achieved by choosing the modulation frequency as equal to the reference frequency of the synchronous detector.

General guidelines for modulating susceptibility signals are listed below. They should be modified as necessary to comply with any governing documents and with the considerations just discussed.

Type of Equipment	Recommended Modulation
Non-receiver Video Amplifiers/Channels	90 to 100% pulse modulation with PW $= 2/B_3$ and pulse repetition rate $=$ bandwidth/1,000, where PW $=$ pulse width and $B_3 =$ video bandwidth
Digital Equipment	Pulse-modulate to simulate clock pulses
Non-tuned Equipment	Amplitude-modulate @ 50% with 1 kHz tone

9.1.8 Intermodulation and Spurious Responses in the Test Setup

When two signal generators are used simultaneously to feed test signals to the input of a receiver, the possibility exists that they will interact to influence the test results. Consequently, some test procedures properly require that tests be performed to determine whether the results are being affected by such interactions. Similarly, a separate test is performed for signal generator spurious emissions and EMI analyzer spurious responses. For any detected receiver response, the procedure to isolate the source is as follows:

1. Alternately reduce the output of each signal generator below the threshold of receiver (the EUT) sensitivity, by either switching it off or reducing its output level. If the receiver response remains when only one of the generators is off, it is either a harmonic or spurious response from the active generator or a spurious response from the receiver. If the response disappears, it is a product of intermodulation either in the signal generators or in the receiver.

2. After determining the levels for a standard response in the receiver (see Section 9.1.6.2), increase the outputs of both signal generators by 3 dB. Then switch in 3 dB of RF attenuation between the test setup and the EUT receiver and determine if the receiver output returns to its original indication. Receiver intermodulation products will vary nonlinearly with the amount of RF attenuation (i.e., show greater increments than the attenuator change), while any intermodulation products from the signal generators will vary by amounts closely equal to the attenuation increment.

Note that increments of increase in signal generator outputs and receiver input attenuation greater than 3 dB may be used for the tests, especially for a pulse-type receiver.

9.2 EMI Testing for Military Applications

9.2.1 Test Area Conditions

Covered in this section are several topics pertinent to the immediate EMI test area, including the test area contents, reflections from walls of the shielding enclosure, ambient electromagnetic levels, configuration of the test setup and methods for isolating the test instrumentation and its cabling from the EMI being measured.

9.2.1.1 Ambient Electromagnetic Levels

Ambient electromagnetic levels within the shielded enclosure should be measured at the time of the original enclosure installation. Thereafter, they should be remeasured every six months or so. In addition, a new set of measurements should always be taken immediately after any event which could be suspected of having compromised the integrity of either the enclosure or its bulkhead filters. Also, the known presence of a new emitting source which is capable of producing a significant level of field strength at the enclosure location is always cause for a new evaluation of the ambient situation within the enclosure. In any event, both the conducted and radiated levels inside the enclosure should be kept below some reference level which is lower than the limits of the specifications to which testing is performed.

9.2.1.2 Test Area Contents

To eliminate their possible influence on test results, all unnecessary items should be cleared out of the test area. This includes all test equipment which is not involved in the specific measurement, storage racks, chairs, desks and other furniture. Also, all personnel not actively involved in the test should be excluded from the enclosure. These actions will minimize antenna loading effects from nearby objects and changes in multiple reflections within the enclosure. Such variations occur with changes in the locations of personnel and objects. These precautions will also eliminate the possibility of inadvertently including emissions from equipment which is not a part of the test and will generally reduce potential distractions from extraneous activities.

The use of a shielded enclosure anteroom as shown in Fig. 9.4 makes the above recommendations easier to follow. Only the EUT, the receiving or radiating transducers and the necessary input/output cables are located in the main enclosure. Everything else, including items for EUT excitation and loading, test instrumentation and test personnel, are located in the anteroom. Although this arrangement significantly reduces the possibility of some emissions from the equipment located in the anteroom being coupled into the measurement, it may still be necessary to install bulkhead filters on some of the leads running from the anteroom into the main enclosure.

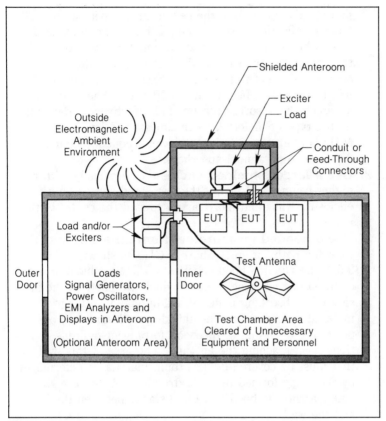

Figure 9.4—Shielded Enclosure with Optional Anterooms

9.2.1.3 Enclosure Wall Reflections

Section 8.2, on the subject of measurement errors, discussed radiated testing errors which result from reflections off the enclosure walls. There is no completely satisfactory solution to this problem short of making the enclosure entirely anechoic or moving the testing to an open-area site. However, the problem of reflections may be significantly mitigated by one or more of the following actions:

1. **Mount RF absorber material** on the enclosure wall behind the EUT and in line with the test antenna. Also,

9.17

mount this material on the ceiling in line with a one-bounce reflection between the EUT and the antenna. It should be noted that the absorber material will be transparent at or below 1 MHz, that it will offer a few decibels of effect in the 1 to 10 MHz range, and that it will begin to be effective above 10 MHz. The frequency at which the absorber reaches full effectiveness depends on the type of material, its thickness, and its shape; 200 MHz is often found to be the lower frequency bound for 0.6 m deep pyramidal absorbers.

2. **Use a larger shielded enclosure,** especially with a higher ceiling, and mount the test stand away from the enclosure walls and more nearly toward the center of the room.

3. **Use a hooded measurement antenna** to restrict the reflected paths of entry above 1 GHz as shown in Fig. 9.5.[3] The antenna hood consists of a metal shield or box, open on one end, the walls of which are lined on the inside with absorbing material. Additional absorbing material is required on the shielded enclosure wall opposite the open end of the hood to prevent multiple reflections from reaching the antenna. The area of this wall that must be covered by absorbing material is determined by the angle formed by the extremities of the receiving antenna and the hood and the distance between the hood and the wall.

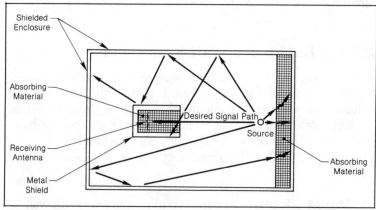

Figure 9.5—Use of Hooded Antenna to Decrease Shielded Enclosure Reflections

4. **Use an optically isolated active antenna system** that has very small elements and which is conductively isolated from its surroundings.[4] Since this type of antenna is electrically small, it can be used close to the EUT without perturbing its emission characteristics. Also, because of its small size and its lack of any metallic transmission line, coupling with the walls of the enclosure is reduced significantly. Use of these antennas can reduce errors due to wall reflections and coupling from more than 40 dB to less than 6 dB. These antennas can be used up to about 400 or 500 MHz.

9.2.1.4 Test Stand Characteristics

The purpose of the test stand in EMI shielded enclosure testing is to provide a convenient bench on which to place the EUT and some associated supporting or ancillary equipment. The minimum size of bench surface, or benchtop ground plane, is specified by MIL-STD-462 as 2.25 m^2 in area with a depth of at least 76 cm. Figure 9.6 shows a typical configuration with dimensions falling somewhat short of this specified size.

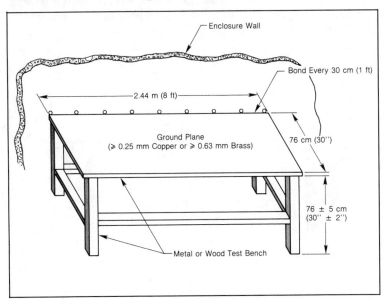

Figure 9.6—Typical Test Stand for EMI Measurements

Sometimes two or more test benches are used in a row to accommodate a multiple-box EUT and its interconnecting cables. Occasionally, when the shielded enclosure is large, the test bench may be a pedestal about 1 m square, as shown in Fig. 9.7. It is located in the middle of the enclosure so that antennas can be deployed around it to facilitate automatic measurements of radiated emissions. This configuration also reduces reflections from the wall behind the bench which could prove troublesome in the arrangement shown in Fig. 9.6. Antenna-to-antenna loading is relatively small because antenna center-to-center spacing exceeds 2 m. As a caveat, however, it should be noted that such deployment of antennas should not be used to test simultaneously the emissions from an EUT with a single face of maximum radiation. This is because, depending on the cable layout, the cable emissions might be shielded by the EUT at all but one measurement angle.

Since nearly all military test items are designed to be located on or near metal surfaces such as those of vehicles, decks, racks or consoles, it is appropriate that they be tested on a metal ground plane which is secured to the test bench. This ground plane is made of either sheet copper or brass to facilitate soldering of ground bonding straps or leads when necessary. Its minimum thickness is usually 0.25 mm (about 10 mil or 0.01" foil) for copper or 0.63 mm (about 25 mil or somewhat less than 1/32") for brass.

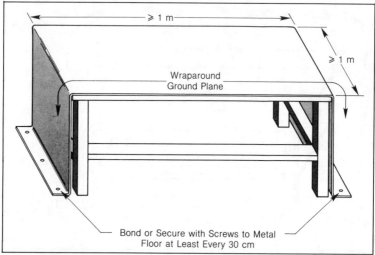

Figure 9.7—Test Stand for Larger Enclosures to Facilitate Automated Radiated Emission Testing

To assure continuity between the ground plane and the shielded enclosure, the two are bonded such that the dc resistance does not exceed 2.5 mΩ. Although MIL-STD-462 requires that the distance between adjacent grounding points not exceed 30 cm, it is not uncommon to make the bonding connection a continuous seam along the entire length of the bench. When two or more benches are butted together to create a longer working surface, their respective ground planes are bonded together at the interface. For test stands such as that shown in Fig. 9.7, the ground plane is usually extended down both sides of the stand and bonded to the floor at intervals along the entire width of the ground plane.

9.2.2 EUT Layout and Operation

To help assure repeatability of EMI test results, especially for radiated testing, the EUT must be deployed in a certain manner. MIL-STD-462 requires that the faces of the EUT be located 10 cm, ±2 cm, back from the front edge of the ground plane. When the EUT consists of multiple modules, their faces are aligned in a straight row (if the available length of the ground plane permits). If the configuration of the test bench and its ground plane is in the form of an "L," a horseshoe or some other shape to facilitate automated testing, the EUT modules still are arranged to follow that outline, with the faces 10 cm, ±2 cm, from the front edge of the ground plane. As explained in Section 9.4.4, additional faces of the EUT may have to be sampled for some situations.

9.2.2.1 Height and Location of Leads

For MIL-STD-462 radiated testing, the EUT cables and leads must be positioned approximately 5 cm above the test bench ground plane. The rationale for this requirement is that it encourages radiation from ground loop currents that would be suppressed by a closer proximity to the ground plane and thus cause the EMI problem to be understated. The same spacing above the ground plane must also be used for conducted emission testing to standardize the RF characteristics of the cables and leads. Thus, a 5 cm slab of styrofoam, wood studding or other nonconducting low-loss material is used as a ground-plane standoff for the test leads. The test leads are also to be located within 10 cm, ±2 cm, of the edge of the test bench ground plane.

9.2.2.2 Power Lead Length

The length of each power lead from the EUT to the 10 μF feed-through capacitor is limited to a maximum length of 1 m, per MIL-STD-462, if the lead is not a part of the EUT. The rationale for this restriction is that extra lead lengths act as built-in low-pass filters (due to series inductance and shunt capacitance) which can reduce conducted EMI emissions at higher frequencies. In addition, some functional installations for the EUT might require lead lengths even shorter than 1 m.

If interconnecting leads are part of a multiple-module EUT, and they are long with respect to the physical separation between the modules they interconnect, they must be arranged in a certain manner. A serpentine layout in which the cable is laid back and forth on itself is not permitted since this reduces the potential for both its radiated emissions and susceptibility. The approved practice, instead, is to lay out the cable(s) in a loop running down the front of the EUT, around its side, in the opposite direction around the back and other side, and then on top of the initial layer in the front. The rationale for this is to simulate a worst-case, rather than a best-case, EUT installation.

If cables or harnesses are not part of the EUT but are needed to make the EUT functional, then either of the following practices may be used:

1. Use 1 m of wiring as specified.
2. Cover the wiring with an inverted metal tray so that any radiation from the wiring will be shielded.
3. Route the wiring to a shelf below the metal-top test bench so that the bench ground plane shields the wiring.
4. Route the wiring through an enclosure bulkhead fitting to the anteroom, where it is coiled up and returned back to the test bench area.

9.2.2.3 Bonding the EUT

The provisions incorporated into the design of the EUT and details specified in its installation instructions should be used (1) to bond together the separate modules of a multiple-module EUT, (2) to bond the EUT to the ground plane or (3) both 1 and 2. Any bonding jumpers used should be as close as possible to those specified for functional installation of the EUT; in some cases, the jig fabricated for shock and vibration testing duplicates exactly the installation and can be used. EUTs designed for portable use and intended to be grounded through the third (green safety) wire should be grounded in that manner unless some special proposed installation indicates otherwise.

9.2.2.4 Impedance Matching

MIL-STD-462 states that, over the frequency range of concern in any given test, the VSWR of resistive dummy loads, attenuators, directional couplers, samplers, power dividers and like networks should not exceed 1.5:1 for transmitter loads and 1.3:1 for all others.

9.3 EMI Testing for Civilian Applications

This section discusses unique aspects of the test environment, test equipment, EUT deployment and EUT operation for EMI testing of products for nonmilitary applications. Many of the points of difference between the military and civilian categories of EMI testing stem from the basic requirement that nearly all nonmilitary testing of radiated EMI emissions be performed on open-area test sites (or their equivalents), while nearly all military EMI testing is to be performed in shielded enclosures. However, many of the precautions noted in the discussion of military-oriented testing, in Section 9.2, are equally valid for nonmilitary testing and should be observed unless they conflict with specific requirements as outlined below.

9.3.1 Open-Area Test Site Facilities

Requirements for the open-area test site (OATS) itself are discussed in Section 7.1 of Chapter 7, and additional pertinent details are contained in ANSI guidelines.[5] This is the primary source for the following recommendations on open-site facilities; other mandates will be noted only when their recommendations differ from those of Ref. 5.

9.3.1.1 Turntable

For convenience in measuring radiated emissions from, or susceptibility of, all sides of the EUT, a turntable is recommended. The
turntable or test stand should be built of a nonconducting material.
For EUTs that stand on the floor when installed, the turntable or
test stand should be metal covered and flush with the ground plane.
It may be necessary to bridge the gap between the periphery of
a turntable and the contiguous ground plane with some type of roll-
ing or rubbing flexible conductive gasket to achieve the proper **normalized site attenuation (NSA)** characteristic. It should be
noted, however, that some standards require a floor-standing EUT
to be insulated from the ground plane.

A nonmetallic turntable with the EUT-supporting surface 1 m
above the ground plane surface should be used for testing tabletop
EUTs. In this case, the ground plane should be continuous and the
turntable should be built of materials which do not adversely affect the NSA. For some applications, the turntable should have a
hole at its center which permits non-rotating feedthrough of control or power cables. In those instances in which not all modules
of the EUT will fit on the test stand or turntable, the excess modules
requiring least attention may be placed on nonconducting shelves
located under the top surface, but spaced the minimum feasible
distance from it. Instead of 1 m, some international EMI test standards call for a turntable height of 80 cm, which could result in
minor differences in measured results.

9.3.1.2 Services to the EUT

To the maximum extent possible, electrical service or mains wiring to the EUT should be run under the ground plane and preferably
at right angles to the measurement axis. All wires, cables and
plumbing to the turntable or other mounting stand for the EUT
preferably should also be run under the ground plane. When such
installation under the ground plane is not possible, the service to
the EUT should be run on top of, but flush with and bonded to,
the ground plane.

9.3.1.3 Installation of the Test Antenna Mast

The test antenna should be mounted on a nonconducting support which will allow the antenna to be varied in height above the ground plane between 1 and 4 m (for measurement distances of 10 m or less) and between 2 and 6 m (for measurement distances greater than 10 m).

For horizontally polarized antennas, to maintain antenna balance with respect to ground, the cable connecting the antenna balun to the test instrumentation should be run such that it is orthogonal to the axis of the antenna elements for all settings of antenna height. The cabling from the antenna should drop vertically to the ground plane approximately 1 m or more behind the antenna (away from the EUT), making a boom length of 1 m sufficient. From the point of initial contact with the ground plane, the shield of the cable should be bonded to the ground plane or, preferably, the cable should be soldered to a coaxial feed-through connector mounted on the ground plane and its run to the measurement instrumentation continued under the ground plane.

Cables that lie randomly on the ground or come closer than 1 m to any portion of the antenna elements should be avoided unless it can be shown that the effects on the site attenuation measurement are negligible. Although takeup reels and similar conveniences can be used, site attenuation measurements should be performed often enough to confirm that anomalies have not been introduced by the frequent cable flexing and connectors rotation which accompanies such use. The cable between the antenna and the EMI analyzer should be kept as short as possible to minimize transmission loss at higher frequencies.

For vertically polarized dipole-type antennas, the cabling to the EMI analyzer should be maintained in a horizontal aspect (i.e., parallel to the ground plane) for a distance of 1 m or more to the rear of the antenna (away from the EUT) before dropping to the ground plane. The reminder of the run to the EMI analyzer is treated the same as discussed above for the horizontally polarized antenna.

9.3.1.4 Deployment of the EMI Analyzer and Test Personnel

Both test personnel and test instrumentation must be located so as not to affect the EMI measurements by inadvertent scattering of radiated energy. If any doubt persists in this regard, it should be dispelled by a measurement of the NSA with both personnel and equipment positioned as they would be during actual testing. When standards require the presence of test personnel at the EUT for purposes such as cable manipulation to maximize radiated emissions, the scattering effect of such a presence can be determined by making another NSA measurement. In any case, the test site should be cleared of both personnel and equipment prior to the final measurement.

In addition to eliminating problems from scattering, an underground instrumentation room beneath the ground plane provides advantages in servicing the EUT. Another favorable location for test personnel and instrumentation is on a perpendicular to the test axis and outside of the obstruction-free area defined in Section 7.1.1.1. If the instrumentation room is located under the ground plane, precautions must be taken to assure that the ground plane is the true ground reference for all equipment involved and that it is an effective barrier for isolating the test setup from any possible emissions from the room below. The EUT and shields for the EUT cabling (if any), the antenna cable and the power line filters must be bonded to the ground plane.

9.3.1.5 Services to the EMI Analyzer

As discussed in Section 9.1.2.1, the electrical service to the EMI analyzer should be derived from a source which is isolated as much as feasible from that supplying the EUT; possible methods include use of separate phases of the ac supply and use of appropriate filters in each line. Electrical service to the EMI analyzer preferably should be run underground and should be separated to the maximum extent possible from the EUT and its electric service lines. When this ideal arrangement is not feasible, the service line should be kept flush, bonded to the ground plane and installed so that it is physically secure during testing.

9.3.1.6 Testing at User's Installation (In Situ Testing)

A ground plane need not be installed for testing at a user's installation unless it is to be a permanent part of the installation. If a ground plane is used, it must be bonded electrically to the ground of the building or the utility. Since results obtained when testing in situ are regarded as unique to the respective installation, efforts to standardize them, such as by using a LISN, are unnecessary.

For radiated emission measurements, in the absence of unique information to the contrary, the radial of maximum emission at the edge of the user's premises should be used as the point of measurement. In the event that this boundary point is less than 30 m from the EUT, the measurement should be made at 30 m distance along the radial. When measurements at the boundary or at 30 m are impractical, measurements may be made at distances less than 30 m from the EUT and then projected to the boundary distance or to 30 m, whichever is greater. Such projections are not recommended at frequencies below 30 MHz unless specific equivalence can be demonstrated.

9.3.2 Conducted EMI Testing in Shielded Enclosures

Although some requirements for conducted EMI testing of civilian products do not mandate the use of a shielded enclosure, such use is always recommended and preferred.

9.3.2.1 Layout for Conducted Power Line Measurements

Measurements made to determine the power line-to-ground EMI voltage or EMI current which is conducted from the EUT power input terminals require that the power source impedance be stabilized and standardized by connecting each side of the EUT power line to a LISN (see Section 4.2.1).

If the EUT is normally mounted on a desk or bench, it is placed on a nonconducting surface and spaced 40 cm from a grounded surface at least 2 m square in size, such as the floor or nearest wall of the enclosure, while maintaining a distance of at least 80 cm from any other conducting surface.

If the EUT is supplied without a flexible power cord, it is to be placed at a distance of 80 cm from the LISN, or from the mains outlet if a LISN cannot be used, and connected to the LISN or outlet by a lead not more than 1 m in length. If the EUT is supplied with a flexible power lead, the voltage or current is to be measured at the plug end of the lead. The length of lead in excess of the 80 cm needed to bridge the distance from the EUT to the LISN or mains outlet is to be folded back and forth in serpentine fashion so as to form a bundle not more than 40 cm in length as shown in Fig. 9.8. In all cases, the operator of the EMI analyzer is to be no closer than 1 m to the EUT.

If the EUT is normally operated with a ground connection, it is to be connected to ground at the LISN through the conductor provided.

9.3.2.2 Simulating Hand Effects

If the EUT is normally a hand-held device, the effects of the user's hand on the EMI emissions are to be simulated. This simulation consists of metal foil wrapped around the EUT in a specified fashion and connected to one terminal of an RC network. The network consists of a 200 pF capacitor in series with a 500 Ω resistor, with the other RC network terminal connected to ground. The following guidelines are applicable:

1. When the EUT case is entirely metallic, no foil is needed, and the capacitor of the RC network is connected directly to the body of the EUT.
2. When the EUT case is made entirely of insulating material, metal foil is to be wrapped around the handle(s) and also around any part of the main body of the EUT that the user might contact. All pieces of the foil are then connected to each other and to the capacitor terminal of the RC network.
3. When the EUT case is partly metal and partly insulating material, and it has insulating handles, metal foil is to be wrapped around the handles and on the nonmetallic part of the body. The sections of foil are then connected to each other and to the capacitor terminal of the RC network.

Figure 9.8—Shielded Enclosure Test Configuration for Civilian Products

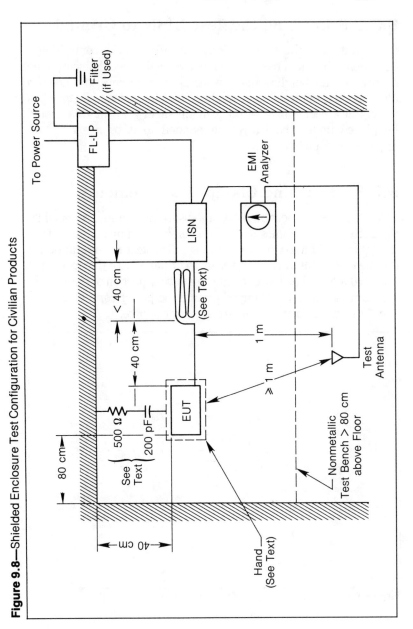

9.3.2.3 Bonding the Test LISN to Ground

In addition to the characteristics specified in the controlling document, the LISN used for conductive testing should incorporate a provision for bonding its housing to the reference ground. If a direct bond is not feasible, as might be true for concrete floors when testing at a user's installation, a metal sheet 2 m^2 in area should be placed under the LISN and bonded to it by a short, low-impedance connection.

9.3.3 Absorbing Clamp Measurements

As discussed in Section 4.4.1, an absorbing clamp developed by the CISPR is sometimes used in lieu of radiated measurements in the 30 to 1,000 MHz frequency range. The test configuration for the measurement of EMI power in accordance with this technique is shown in Fig. 9.9. The current transformer portion of the absorbing clamp assembly is clamped around the power cord which connects the EUT to the commercial power source.[6]

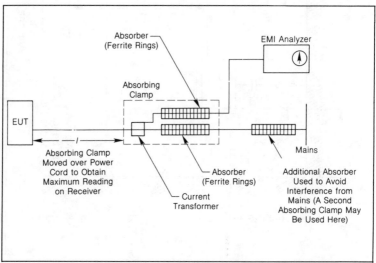

Figure 9.9—Absorbing Clamp Test Configuration

The EUT is placed on a nonmetallic table or, if it is a floor-standing unit, on the floor, and is located at least 40 cm from any other metallic object or surface. The power cord is positioned in a straight line so that the absorbing clamp can be moved along it to determine the maximum level of EMI. If the EUT is a floor-standing unit, the power cord should leave the EUT at an angle of less than 45° until it reaches a height of 40 cm above the floor.

9.4 Sampling Practices in EMI Testing

This section presents guidelines for sampling practices used in the EMI test procedures which are covered in the next four chapters. They are employed to assure a reasonable probability that an out-of-specification condition will be recorded. These guidelines will cover aspects of operation for both the EUT (e.g., its operating modes and frequencies) and the test procedures (e.g., current probe location, antenna location and polarization, number of EUT faces tested and frequencies of measurement).

9.4.1 Overview of the Sampling Problem

As an introduction to the nature of the sampling problem, it is pertinent to note the potential number of spectrum test runs that might have to be made if a "brute-force" approach were taken to assure that nothing was missed:

$$N_{CE} = M \times F \times I \times W \qquad (9.2)$$

$$N_{RE} = M \times F \times S \times E \times A \qquad (9.3)$$

where,

N_{CE} = maximum number of conducted emission (CE) spectrum test runs

N_{RE} = maximum number of radiated emission (RE) spectrum test runs

M = number of EUT operating modes

F = number of EUT operating frequencies selected, where applicable

  I = number of current probe locations along the test leads

 W = number of CE power leads to be tested

  = $4(\log_2 L - 1 + \Delta)$, where L = number of CE interconnecting leads in a single wire harness; Δ is chosen to make the total quantity in the parentheses the next higher integer

 A = number of test antenna positions for larger test samples

 S = number of test sample faces to be tested

 E = number of antenna polarizations to be used

For illustrative purposes, it is assumed that the following numbers are assigned to the above parameters: M = 5; I = 3; A = 1; E = 2; F = 6; W = 4; and S = 4. The numbers of CE and RE spectrum runs then become, respectively:

$$N_{CE} = 5 \times 6 \times 3 \times 4 = 360$$

$$N_{RE} = 5 \times 6 \times 4 \times 2 = 240$$

These numbers are impractically large and costly to execute. Simply to reduce the number of runs by arbitrarily reducing the numbers assigned to the sampling parameters is a poor solution to the problem, since the risk would be high that pertinent EMI data would be lost. The remainder of this section considers more carefully the assignment of appropriate numbers to these parameters.

9.4.2 EUT Modes of Operation

For EMI test purposes, each EUT mode is a unique combination of its operating settings or controls which results in a state of operation potentially accompanied by a unique set of EMI emission/susceptibility characteristics. Any determination of such modes prior to actual testing obviously implies an **a priori** judgment, based on the knowledge and experience of the EMI professional formulating the test plan.

9.4.2.1 On-Off Situations

One simple and basic parameter determining the EUT modes of operation is the position of on-off toggle switches. If the EUT has n = 15 such switches (one of which is the basic power on-off switch), the number of modes thus implied is $2n^{-1}$, or 4,098. However, consideration of the second half of the above definition of the EUT mode will probably lead to the conclusion that each unique combination of switch settings will not necessarily result in a unique set of EMI characteristics. For example, if one toggle switch controls whether the blower fan is on or off, it can reasonably be assumed that the EMI level is likely to be higher with this switch left in the "on" position. Thus, the problem is reduced by eliminating those operating modes which imply lower levels of EMI emissions or higher thresholds of susceptibility, such as a switch position that inserts 20 dB of RF attenuation into the front end of a receiver.

9.4.2.2 Controls with Multiple or Continuous Settings

The number of possible EUT operating modes can become arbitrarily high for settings of controls with multiple detents or continuous positions. An approach similar to that discussed in the preceding section is helpful in handling this situation and is best explained by two illustrative examples:

Illustrative Example 9.2: Minimum Actuation Rate

Suppose that the EUT has an event switch offering pulse repetition frequency (PRF) selection of 1, 10 and 100 pulses per minute (p/m). Further suppose that an emission test is to be performed using an automated measurement system with a scan rate, S, in units of MHz/s and a bandwidth, B, of 10 kHz. If the test plan allows a total time, T, of 50 s to scan the frequency range from 10 MHz

(f_L) to 200 MHz (f_H), and if at least three readings per octave are required, then to fulfill all conditions (refer to Section 2.2.4):

$$N_o = \log_2(f_H/f_L) \qquad (9.4)$$

$$= \log_2(200/10)$$

$$= 4.32$$

where,

$$N_o = \text{number of octaves}$$

f_L and f_H = lower and higher bounds of the frequency range, respectively

Note that $\log_2(x)$ can readily be calculated by a simple mathematical process:

$$\log_2(x) = (\log_{10} x)/\log_{10} 2$$

The total number of samples, N_s, is greater than or equal to $3N_o$, therefore:

$$N_s = 3 \times 4.32$$

$$\approx 13$$

Since the time allowed to scan the band is T = 50 s, the scan rate for a linear frequency scan, in MHz/s, is:

$$S_1 = (f_H - f_L)/T$$

$$= (200 - 10)/50 = 3.8$$

For a log-frequency scan, in octaves per second, the rate is:

$$S_2 = N_o/T$$

$$= 4.32/50$$

$$= 0.864$$

If the logarithmic frequency scan is assumed, the time in seconds, t, to scan one octave is:

$$t = 1/S_2 = T/N_o$$
$$= 50/4.32$$
$$= 11.6$$

During this time, t, at least three PRF strikes must occur to assure three samples per octave. Therefore, the minimum interval, $t_i = 1/PRF$, is:

$$t_i = t/3$$
$$= 11.6/3$$
$$= 3.86 \text{ seconds per pulse}$$
$$= 0.0644 \text{ minutes per pulse}$$

Thus,
$$PRF \geqslant 1/t_i = 15.6 \text{ p/min}$$

Of the available PRFs, only the 100 p/min rate satisfies this condition. As an alternative, increasing T to 78 s would permit use of the 10 p/min rate. Note that the bandwidth of the measurement system does not affect this solution. For convenience, the above relations may be summarized:

For a linear scan:

$$PRF \geqslant 180 \, (f_H - f_L)/Tf_L \qquad \text{p/min}$$

For a logarithmic scan:

$$PRF \geqslant (180/T) \log_2(f_H/f_L) \qquad \text{p/min}$$

Illustrative Example 9.3: Unity Probability of EMI Intercept

In this example, the test system and all other constraints are as given for Illustrative Example 9.2, but the EUT is an electronically scanned receiver with local oscillator (LO) radiation levels suspected to be significant at one or more unknown frequencies. It is further postulated that it is not feasible to have the EMI analyzer in the measurement system track the LO of the EUT. Thus, to minimize the scan time, the EUT receiver will be scanned at the maximum rate consistent with factors described below. How should the EUT receiver and the EMI analyzer be exercised and operated?

Since it is assumed that the scan rate of the EUT is much faster than that of the EMI analyzer, it is pertinent to apply Eq. (6.1) (see Section 6.1.2) to determine how rapidly (minimum time, t_m) the electronically scanned EUT can be allowed to sweep its entire 10 to 200 MHz range. Since the bandwidth of the EMI analyzer must intercept the EUT LO as it sweeps through, Eq. (6.1) applies for determining the minimum time in seconds, t_m, for the EUT to scan from 10 to 200 MHz:

$$t_m \geqslant \Delta F / B_i^2$$

$$= 190 \times 10^6 / 10^8$$

$$= 1.9$$

where,

B_i = impulse bandwidth

Δf = frequency segment being scanned

Looking next at how rapidly the EMI analyzer can be allowed to scan, if it were simply a matter of assuring interception of a fixed response at some unknown frequency in the 10 to 200 MHz range, the same formula could be applied and would yield the same result, namely 1.9 s. However, it is necessary to take into account the fact that, because of the limited scanning rate of the EUT, the LO signal to be measured sweeps through any given frequency only once every 1.9 s. Therefore, the EMI analyzer should scan sufficiently slowly so that in 1.9 s the center of its bandwidth window is not more than one bandwidth away from its previous position. Since there are $190 \times 10^6 / 10^4 = 19,000$ bandwidth windows, and 1.9 s must be allowed for each to intercept a potential signal, the total scanning time of the EMI analyzer is $19,000 \times 1.9 = 36,100$ s, or about 10 hours!

The minimum scanning time of the EMI receiver, thus, is the number of IF, or selectivity, windows, $\Delta F/B_i$, multiplied by the minimum scanning time of the EUT, $\Delta F/B_i^2$, or:

$$T \geqslant \Delta F^2/B_i^3 \qquad (9.5)$$

Equation (9.5) illustrates the importance of using the widest bandwidth consistent with adequate sensitivity in this type of application, since the scan time varies inversely as its cube. In the example immediately above, use of a 50 kHz bandwidth instead of 10 kHz, would have reduced the time by a factor of $(50^3/10^3) = 125$, or from 36,100 to 289 s. Thus, whenever large frequency segments must be scanned, it is most efficient to switch to successively higher bandwidths as frequencies increase.

9.4.3 Selection of Test Sample Operating Frequencies

Applicable military specifications typically state that EMI measurements are to be performed with the receiver or transmitter EUT tuned to not less than three frequencies per octave within each tuning band, tuning unit or range of fixed channels, as applicable. To be included in this selection of frequencies are those at 1.05 f_L and 0.95 f_H, where f_L is the lower frequency and f_H is the upper frequency of each tuning band, unit or range of channels.

When tuning segments are not defined in terms of bands, etc., the simplest method of choosing the specific frequencies is to use the formula given in Section 2.2.4:

$$f_n = f_o 2^{n/m}$$

where,

f_o = low-frequency end of the total range to be scanned

n = successive number of the frequency being calculated

m = number of desired frequencies per octave

For narrowband tests, the EUT is also to be tuned to any other frequencies which the test plan indicates to be potentially subject to undesired emissions or responses. For each chosen frequency setting of the EUT, either the EMI analyzer or the injected susceptibility source is to be scanned over the entire range as applicable to the specific EMI test.

As shown in Section 9.4.1, compliance with these requirements could result in a large number of test runs. For example, if the receiver EUT contained 8 tuning bands from 1 kHz to 10 GHz (7 decades or 23 octaves), at least 69 samples are indicated. This could increase the number of spectrum runs in the example of Section 9.4.1 from 240 or 360 to over 2,700. It would be necessary to adhere to the practices recommended in Section 9.4.1 to reduce the spectrum runs to a manageable number.

9.4.4 Wire Leads and Current Probe Position

Tests for conducted EMI emissions require that measurements be performed on ac and dc power leads as well as control and signal leads. Military testing further requires that the current probe be positioned along the respective lead to locate the point of maximum EMI response. It is apparent that slavish adherence to the letter of such practices could expand the testing task to unmanageable proportions. However, good engineering judgment must always be exercised to assure that the test is adequate.

9.4.4.1 Wire Lead Samplings

AC and DC Power Leads

Military EMI specifications typically require that all leads furnishing ac and dc power to the EUT be tested for conducted emissions and susceptibility, including neutral wires not grounded in the EUT. Thus, the number of EUT wires to be examined for conducted emissions is as shown below:

Leads	No. of Wires
Each DC Source (incl. 0 Vdc Line)	2
Single-Phase	2
Single-Phase, Two-Voltage	3
Two-Phase	3
Three-Phase, Delta Connected	3
Three-Phase, Wye Connected	4

The green wire, or safety ground line, is usually exempt from testing. Thus, a fairly complex EUT might have at least eight wires requiring test: 0 and +28 Vdc, neutral and 115 Vac, and 208 Vac (three-phase, four-wire).

Control and Signal Leads

Control and signal leads subject to conducted emission tests may be tested as groups, provided that certain procedures are followed. Although harnesses may contain hundreds of wires, group testing can reduce the number of spectrum runs to as few as two. However, if there is only a single wire pair in the harness which does not meet specification limits, the consequence can be as many spectrum runs, N_{CE}, as:

$$N_{CE} = 4(\log_2 L - 1 + \Delta) \tag{9.6}$$

where,

    L = total number of wires

    Δ = a positive number less than 1 to make the parenthetical term an integer

For example, for a harness containing 100 wires, Eq. (9.5) becomes:

$$N_{CE} = 4(\log_2 100 - 1 + \Delta)$$
$$= 4(6.64 - 1 + 0.36)$$
$$= 24 \text{ spectrum runs}$$

Thus, group testing of wires can result in only two spectrum runs, for no failures, and substantially reduce the number of spectrum runs when failures exist.

Military specifications usually allow control and signal leads within the same harness to be tested as a group provided that:

1. All control leads carrying unprocessed ac or dc power are treated as power leads and tested separately.
2. All matched pairs (high line and return line) of all wires are separated into two subgroups: outgoing and return. Coaxial lines, twisted pairs, shielded twisted pairs and similar integral combinations are exempt from this separation requirement but are divided approximately equally between the two subgroups.

3. Each subgroup is tested separately using a current probe. When emissions from a subgroup exceed the specification limit, that subgroup is further subdivided into approximately equal batches for further testing.
4. Step no. 3 is repeated until individual offending wires are identified and measured separately.

9.4.4.2 Current Probe Positioning

Test methods for conducted EMI testing of military products typically require that the current probe be moved along the tested lead until the maximum EMI response is found. This requirement greatly slows the measurement process and is in obvious conflict with test automation unless an acceptable sampling process is developed and adopted.

AC and DC Power Leads

The length of each power lead between the point of separation for testing and the 10 μF capacitor typically is set at 30 cm, ± 2 cm. The purpose in moving the current probe along the lead is to account for standing waves; however, at frequencies below 50 MHz, which is the highest usually specified for current-probe testing, the 30 cm length is only 0.05λ. Thus, any effect from standing waves is insignificant, and it is not necessary to change the current probe position.

Control and Signal Leads

For control and signal leads, the effect of standing waves is also insignificant at low frequencies; thus, the placement of the current probe on control and signal leads at low frequencies is not critical. However, for longer cables, the position of the probe can affect the measurement at higher frequencies since λ = 6 m at 50 MHz. In view of this factor, the following sampling procedure for current probe testing may be incorporated into the test plan:

1. For harness length smaller than 1.5 m (λ/4 at 50 MHz), make two spectrum scans, each with the current probe located at opposite ends of the cable, and use the higher value of EMI measured.

2. For harness length greater than 1.5 m, make four spectrum scans, the first two of which are as per no. 1 above. The third and fourth measurements are made at a distance of $\lambda/8$ and $3\lambda/8$, at the appropriate frequency, from the end with the higher reading. If such a measurement would be at a point beyond the end of the cable, it is, of course, irrelevant and dropped from the program.

9.4.5 EUT Faces and Antenna Positions

Current EMI test methods for military equipment call for simultaneously scanning the frequency range to be measured while probing each face of the EUT with a small loop at approximately 5 cm from the surface. The intended purpose of this exercise is to localize the areas of maximum emission or susceptibility. The applicable test antenna is then located 1 m away from such crucial areas for performing the specified measurement for that face of the EUT.

The following is a brief discussion of ambiguities and problems associated with adherence to this procedure:

1. The concept of simultaneously or sequentially scanning frequency and positioning the probe is ambiguous, especially for narrowband emissions. An infinite number of observations taking an infinite amount of time would be required to ensure that no larger emission exists.
2. Presumably, at least four, and possibly six, faces would have to be scanned for the typical EUT. If the EUT consists of n modules, then 4n to 6n probings would be required. Such a procedure leads to conflicts with EUT layouts specified for multiple-module EUTs.
3. The concept is in conflict with automated measurement techniques, especially for multiple-module EUTs.

The following guidelines are suggested for the test plan, in lieu of the above.

9.4.5.1 Test Sample Faces

If the EUT has intentionally generated signals within it, such frequencies should have been identified in the test plan. All faces of the EUT should be probed at these frequencies to determine the face through which maximum radiation occurs. When the EUT does not include intentionally generated frequencies, the one-faced sampling procedure described below should be used. However, if during this procedure a previously unidentified signal is discovered as originating in the EUT, the procedure should then revert to finding the face of maximum radiation for that signal and using that face for testing.

One-Faced Sampling

If it is assumed that the EUT is housed in a metallic enclosure, and if economic considerations dictate that only a single face can be tested, that face should be the one with the most holes, slits and other apertures. With a multiple-module EUT, the selection for each module is made in accordance with the same criterion, and the respective preferred faces are aligned with the front of the test bench. If this multiple-module EUT is integrated into a single housing or cabinet, then either the front or back is chosen in accordance with the preceding rules. If one of the two main openings (usually the front) contains many more holes or slits, but the other (usually the back) contains greater cumulative length of interconnecting cables, there exists a potential conflict and sampling of both is suggested. If a single face must be chosen, the one with the greatest length of cabling should be selected, based on the propensity of cabling to act as radiating antennas, especially at HF and higher frequencies.

Multi-face Sampling

When the sampling of more than a single face is feasible, it is preferable to employ automation. Typically, the EUT and test stand are deployed as shown in Figs. 11.3 and 11.4 (Chapter 11). After completion of each sweep or scan, either the EUT faces or the test antennas are repositioned, and the measurements repeated until all faces are tested.

9.4.5.2 Antenna Considerations

When testing of the EUT must be done using both horizontal and vertical polarizations, it is sometimes possible to accomplish this in a single scan by using diagonal polarization. Since antenna sensitivity to both vertical and horizontal polarizations is thus reduced by 3 dB, this must be taken into account in the test plan and test report. Also, any signal found to be within 6 dB of the limit should then be tested to determine its amplitude using vertical and horizontal polarizations.

Similarly, it is sometimes most efficient to position the sensor onto its **ortho-axis**. This is the orientation from which it projects at an angle of 45° to each of the three orthogonal planes of the EUT, thus causing its response to a field polarized along any of the three axes to be down by 4.77 dB from maximum. The simplest procedure for attaining this position with a loop or a linear-element rod or dipole antenna is as follows:

1. Position the plane of the loop parallel to the nearest face of the EUT. Position the linear antenna horizontally and parallel to the nearest EUT face.
2. Rotate the loop 45° around its vertical axis. While keeping the linear antenna horizontal, rotate it 45° about a vertical axis.
3. Taking care not to disturb the orientation already established, rotate either antenna so that it makes an angle of 35° (actually, 35.3°) with the horizontal plane.

9.4.6 Susceptibility Scanning Speeds

As discussed briefly in Section 6.4.1, in the context of selecting scan speeds for automated susceptibility test systems, the response time of the EUT to potentially interfering energy must be considered in any sampling process.

Equations (9.7) and (9.8) repeat the relationships mentioned in Section 6.4.1:

$$SS_m \leqslant 1.73(f/Q)^2 \qquad (9.7)$$

$$\Delta f \leqslant f/1.65Q \qquad (9.8)$$

where,

f = frequency (usually subscripted, i.e., f_o)

Q = sharpness of resonance, f_o/B_3

SS_m = maximum analog scan speed

Δf = step size for digitally tuned (scanned) equipment

The generalized scan speed is designated as $SS_i = \Delta f/T$ if it does not by itself constitute the maximum scan speed. Equation (9.7) shows that the scan speed as limited by circuit or wiring resonance increases with frequency if Q remains constant. If this is not the only factor limiting the overall scan speed, it is combined with other factors by reciprocal addition as follows:

$$SS_m \leqslant 1/[(1/SS_1) + (1/SS_2) + ...] \tag{9.9}$$

9.4.6.1 Analog Scanning

The value of Eq. (9.7) varies with frequency; thus, its reciprocal must be integrated by frequency to determine the time to scan a given frequency range. The corresponding integral equation is:

$$T \geqslant 0.577 \, Q^2 \int_{f_L}^{f_H} df/f^2 \tag{9.10}$$

which, after integration, results in:

$$T \geqslant 0.577 \, Q^2(1/f_L - 1/f_H) \tag{9.11}$$

where,

T = time

Q = sharpness of resonance, f_o/B_3

f_L = lower frequency in the range

f_H = higher (upper) frequency in the range

Since the scan rate increases and the time needed to scan each increment of frequency decreases with increasing frequency, the practical electrical and mechanical agility of the test signal generator and amplifier becomes the limiting factor as frequency increases. For example, if a signal generator were capable of a maximum sweep rate of 100 kHz/s, this would imply a minimum scan time greater than 0.00001 s/Hz (>2.7 hr to scan from 14 kHz to 1.0 GHz). This is equal to the limitation defined by Eq. (9.11) at $f = 240\ Q$, so for $Q = 100$, $f = 24$ kHz; thus, above 24 kHz the scan speed should be constant at $SS_1 = 100$ kHz/s due to the limits of the test signal generator. These values, or course, would be different for other values of Q and other generators. In situations where the operator must tune the generator manually, the tuning process can be both tedious and a source of EUT response error because of incorrect scan speed.

The limiting value of scan speed may also result from the response time of the EUT. For an EUT with an indicator such as a panel meter, the scan speed limit given in Ref. 7 is:

$$SS_i \leqslant f/(\pi T_m Q) \qquad (9.12)$$

where,

$$T_m = \text{time constant of the meter}$$

This treats the EUT as if it were some sort of "receiver" with an audio or video channel driving a meter. In an EUT where the signal channel bandwidth, B_3, is less than the bandwidth of the wiring resonance, then B_3 is substituted for f/Q in Eq. (9.12). If the EUT is a digital device with a critical gate time or an electromechanical device with a certain **cycle time**, these respective times must be incorporated into the determination of overall scan speed. For such devices, the reciprocals of these cycle or gate times may be incorporated directly into the denominator of Eq. (9.9).

Equation (9.13) shows a combination of the limits from Eqs. (9.11) and (9.12) in terms of scan time, T_s, and Eq. (9.14) shows it in terms of scan speed. If the EUT has a fixed signal channel bandwidth, B_3, that is less than the bandwidth of the wiring resonance, then the second term of Eq. (9.13) becomes $[\pi T_m(f_H - f_L)/B_3]$ and $1/B_3$ is substituted for Q/f in the second term of Eq. (9.12).

$$T_s = 0.577 \ Q^2(1/f_L - 1/f_H) + 1.36 \ QT_m \ \log(f_H/f_L) \qquad (9.13)$$

$$+ \ T_g(f_H - f_L)$$

$$SS_m = 1/[0.577(Q/f)^2 + (\pi T_m Q/f) + T_g] \qquad (9.14)$$

where,

f_L and f_H = as previously defined

T_m = time constant of the EUT meter

T_g = minimum usable generator sweep time in s/Hz, the reciprocal of the maximum usable sweep rate $\Delta f/T_g$, in Hz/s

f = instantaneous measuring frequency

In most practical situations, the response time of the EUT will be the limiting factor in determining the scan speed, but in some cases the characteristics of both the test signal and its EUT response may be limiting factors. When the test signal is modulated, it must be scanned slowly enough to permit the completion of one cycle of modulation within the bandwidth of the EUT response. In this case, the scan speed is limited to:

$$SS_i \leqslant 0.39 \ B_3 \ f_{mod} \qquad (9.15)$$

where,

B_3 = 3 dB bandwidth of the EUT response, which may be a fixed RF, IF or video bandwidth, or the bandwidth, f/Q, of the resonance of a wire harness

f_{mod} = lowest modulation frequency of the test signal in the range being scanned

This equation or its results can also be added reciprocally in the previous overall scan speed equation, and its integral can be added to the previous scan time equation. Its integral becomes:

$$T = (6.0 \ Q/f_{mod}) \ \log(f_H/f_L) \qquad (9.16)$$

9.4.6.2 Stepwise Scanning

For step-scanned systems, which comprise most modern computer-automated test systems, the size of each step is $\leqslant f/1.65\,Q$, from Eq. (9.8). The number of steps in a given frequency range is found by integrating, as before, a frequency interval, df, multiplied by the reciprocal (time) of the step:

$$n = 1.65\,Q \int_{f_L}^{f_H} df/f \qquad (9.17)$$

$$= 3.8\,Q\,\log(f_H/f_L)$$

The test frequency must dwell on each step long enough for the EUT circuits to respond. The response of the wire-harness resonance is $0.35\,Q/f$. This is combined with the integrand of Eq. (9.17) before integration, giving, upon integration:

$$T = 0.577\,Q^2(1/f_L - 1/f_H) \qquad (9.18)$$

This is essentially identical to Eq. (9.11).

The step size was given as $f/1.65\,Q$, so to calculate the step, use:

$$f_2 = f_1(1 + 1/1.65\,Q) \qquad (9.19)$$

where,

$$f_2 - f_1 = \Delta f = \text{the step size}$$

The dwell time at each step is $T = 0.35\,Q/f_1$. At the completion of the test, the total scan time will be close to that given in Eq. (9.18), which was based on resonance Q effects.

Now allow sufficient time for EUT internal response. The total time at each step, T_s, is the dwell time discussed immediately above plus the EUT response time discussed earlier:

$$T_s = 0.35\,Q/f_1 + T_{rEUT} + T_{sys} \qquad (9.20)$$

where,

$$T_{sys} = T_{gs} + T_{cs}$$

$$T_{gs} = \text{test generator step time}$$

$$T_{cs} = \text{computer and interface delay}$$

The various values for T_{rEUT} are as calculated earlier for EUT video, meter, gate time, etc., and T_{sys} for test generator modulation, step time and settling time. The total step scanning time, T_{ss}, becomes:

$$T_{ss} = 0.577 \ Q^2(1/f_L - 1/f_H) + n(T_{rEUT} + T_{sys}) \qquad (9.21)$$

Table 9.1 gives some typical step-scanning times using the following parameters:

$$T_m = 0.2 \text{ s}$$

$$T_{gs} = 12 \text{ ms/step}$$

$$T_{mod} = 0 \text{ (unmodulated test generator)}$$

$$T_{cs} = 25 \ \mu s$$

These combined give a total step time $T_{rEUT} + T_{sys}$ of 0.64 s. From Eqs. (9.17) and (9.21):

$$T_{ss} = 0.58 \ Q^2(1/f_L - 1/f_H) + 2.4Q \ \log(f_H/f_L) \qquad (9.22)$$

Table 9.1—Required Scanning Times for Susceptibility Testing

Type of Susceptibility Test	Frequency Range	Scan Time in Minutes $T_{ss}/60$ for $Q = 100$
Conducted	30 Hz to 50 kHz	16
Conducted	50 kHz to 400 MHz	16
Radiated	30 Hz to 30 kHz	15
Radiated	14 kHz to 30 MHz	14
Radiated	14 kHz to 10 GHz	24

The value of 100 for Q is predicated on sharp resonances such as those involving parasitic responses of wiring. The time constant

T_m = 0.2 s is typical of panel meters used for status displays such as would be found in aircraft cockpits. Under these assumptions, the above analysis indicates that an exponential log-frequency spectrum scan for inducing susceptibility responses often should take one-half hour. A uniform frequency spectrum scan where step sizes are constant and satisfactory for the lowest frequency included in the scan often should take an hour or more.

It might be possible to reduce the scan time by moving the monitoring point ahead of the output display to a point in the circuitry having much shorter time constants. On the other hand, there are many situations in which T_{rEUT} is appreciably greater than 0.2 s. As an example, the EUT might have a 10 character per second (cps) printer as its output device, with a performance requirement of not more than one error per hundred characters. The resulting T_{rEUT} would be 100 characters divided by 10 cps = 10 s, which requires a scan time of five hours!

Other approaches can be taken to reduce the scan time. One would be to assume that most responses will have a Q factor of less than 100; although this would reduce the scan time proportionally, it would be at the cost of reduced certainty that all responses had been identified. For analog EUTs, the scan times can be reduced by using higher levels of driving power, provided that it is available and that it will not damage the EUT. An increase in level of x times permits a reduction in scanning time to 1/x of that required for the normal level of drive. Also, for some analog EUTs, a reduced indication of susceptibility may be used with a reduction of scanning time. Since the equations are based on responses within 1 dB of maximum, which is 2.3 time constants (T_{rEUT}), a still clearly apparent response of 1.0 time constant will reduce the scanning time by a factor of 2.3. When such a susceptible response is found, the test signal must then be tuned to it to find the full response and the threshold of susceptibility; however, this must be done regardless of the scanning technique used. This also risks missing susceptible responses, especially where the acceptable response indication is very low, e.g., at the level of EUT noise.

9.5 EMI Test Plans and Reports

The formulation of a test plan is a vital element of all EMI testing. Although military agencies and many other customers for equipment and systems mandate that a test plan be approved prior to commencement of testing, such a plan is always a catalyst to EMI testing efficiency and should be prepared even when no specific requirement exists.

9.5.1 EMI Test Plans

The outline and discussion of EMI test plans in this section are based largely on the outline and format required for testing products with military applications.[8] Although the orientation of Ref. 8 is directed toward military products, its basic content is pertinent for all products.

9.5.1.1 Introduction to the Plan

The introductory section of the plan should state the purpose of the plan and the relationship of the proposed EMI testing of the present equipment or subsystem to the applicable overall EMC plan for the system or environment in which it is intended to operate. Included in this first section should be a table of contents showing paragraph or page numbers, or both, for all tests to be performed. It should also identify the respective method of the controlling specification that is applicable to each. A description of the EUT should be included, with its operating frequency and line current.

9.5.1.2 Applicable Documents

All documents that are specifically applicable to the proposed tests should be listed, including those of the controlling government or military agency, company documents or standards which cover either EMI aspects or quality assurance programs, plus any other applicable industry or government standards.

9.5.1.3 Test Site

Pertinent information regarding the test site should include:

1. A description of the test facility, shielded enclosure or anechoic chamber showing features such as dimensions, power

availability, power source filtering, normalized site attenuation and shielding effectiveness of the test enclosure for magnetic, electric and plane-wave fields

2. A description of the ground plane, including its size and type, and methods used to ground or bond the EUT to simulate its actual installation

3. Measurements disclosing the ambient electromagnetic environment of the test facility, both radiated and conducted, with details on measures to be taken to solve problems created by any high-level ambient signals

9.5.1.4 Test Instrumentation

A section of the test plan should be devoted to a list and discussion, as appropriate, of all test instrumentation to be used. Among the parameters and descriptions included should be:

1. A listing of all equipment to be used, including basic descriptions, manufacturers and model numbers

2. Antenna factors and other conversion factors for all transducers to be employed, including the transfer impedance of current probes, the line impedance of LISNs and the insertion loss and impedance characteristics of 10 μF capacitors

3. The characteristics of any matching transformers or band-rejection filters used in the testing

4. The bandwidths of all EMI analyzers or other instrumentation used to receive or process EMI emissions

5. A description of the scanning speed capability and limitations of any automated EMI analysis instrumentation

6. A description of any monitoring equipment used

9.5.1.5 Setup of the EUT and Test Instrumentation

A diagram should be included showing the EUT, its interconnections and its connections and physical relationship to all other equipment included in the test procedures. Depictions should include the location of the EUT and feed-through capacitors or LISNs on the ground plane or other test surface, the dressing of leads, the placement of bonding straps, the deployment and connection of any real or simulated loads and the positioning of any other equipment involved in the test area or in any contiguous anteroom or staging area.

9.5.1.6 Operation of the EUT for Testing

A detailed description must be included covering the operation of the EUT during the EMI test procedures. Specific sets of data to be included are:

1. EUT modes of operation and operating frequency (where applicable) for each EMI test
2. A list of control settings on the EUT
3. A list of the settings on any test equipment employed, as well as a listing of the characteristics of any test signal used
4. A tabulation of the frequencies of operation of built-in EUT signal sources such as oscillators and clocks; also, their characterization as NB or BB at the EMI analyzer bandwidths to be used
5. A record of performance checks for the EUT sample being tested, showing its compliance to minimal operational requirements
6. Identification of those circuits, outputs, displays or other indicators to be monitored during susceptibility testing, as well as the criteria to be used to assess degradation of performance
7. A description of the specific malfunction or degradation of each performance criteria which will indicate susceptibility, such as change in output spectrum, change in (S + N)/N ratio, loss of synchronization and changes in output waveform

9.5.1.7 EMI Test Procedures

Test procedures to demonstrate compliance to the applicable EMI requirements should be described fully. As a minimum, the following information should be included:

1. A block diagram of the test setup used for each test method

2. The test instrumentation used in the performance of each test and the methods used for grounding, bonding or achieving its isolation
3. Detailed, step-by-step procedures for deployment and orientation of probes and antennas and for any probing of the EUT
4. Detailed tabulations or formats, with explanatory discussions as needed, of the frequency range of each test, the measurement frequencies selected, the detector functions utilized and the data to be recorded
5. For susceptibility testing, all pertinent characteristics of the test signal modulation, including its amplitude, type, degree and waveform

9.5.1.8 Data Formats

Outlines should be included for all data to be collected during the test, including:

1. Sample data sheets
2. Sample test log
3. Sample graphs

9.5.2 EMI Test Reports

The basic purpose of the EMI test report is to detail the results of the tests to determine compliance with applicable requirements regarding EMI emissions and susceptibility. As with the EMI test plan discussed in the preceding section, this outline and discussion is based largely on the outline and format prescribed for testing products with military applications.[8] However, its basic content is pertinent to EMI testing of all products.

9.5.2.1 Introductory Section

The introductory section of the report should state the purpose of the testing and its relationship to the EMC requirements for the system or environment in which the tested equipment is intended to operate. At this point in the report, an abstract of the results is appropriate and required by some sources of procurement. Included in this introductory section are administrative data such as the dates of the testing, by whom the tests were performed, the agency or customer for which the tests were performed, the number of the applicable contract or purchase order, certification of the test report by the appropriate executive, details on the source and disposition of the test specimen and a listing of any deviations or variances from applicable requirements which were granted prior to testing.

Also included in this first section should be a table of contents showing paragraph or page numbers, or both, for all tests performed and a listing of all documents applicable to the tests, including those of the controlling government or military agency, company standards or documents which cover either EMI aspects or quality assurance programs, plus any other industry or government standards.

9.5.2.2 Test Setup and Instrumentation

All of the following factual data regarding the test setups and instrumentation utilized should be included:

1. Nomenclature and serial numbers for all instrumentation actually used during the test procedures
2. Data for each item of test equipment, showing its most recent calibration, the calibration procedure used and its traceability to a national standard
3. Photographs or diagrams of the test setup and the EUT, with identification call-outs for all items shown. Accompanying information on test conditions should detail the location of the EUT and all other items in the setup, plus the methods used for their bonding or grounding. Details should also be given on all external loads and all cables, including their length, configuration and position relative to the ground plane.
4. Data for the pertinent characteristics of all transducers utilized in the testing, including transfer impedance of current probes, line impedance of LISNs, insertion loss and impedance of 10 μf capacitors and antenna factors for all antennas

5. All pertinent data on EUT operation, including the operating modes employed, all control settings, all monitoring points and all circuits and frequencies of operation for any intentionally generated RF signals

9.5.2.3 Test Results and Analysis

All results obtained during the testing must be presented in easily accessible formats showing comparisons to applicable specification limits. Although the data sheet format used for each test will depend on the data to be presented, the information shown in Fig. 9.10 should be shown for each emission test reading wherever it is applicable. Similarly, for susceptibility testing, data sheets should include the information shown in Fig. 9.11.[8]

When data is acquired using automated systems, the principal data presentation will likely be graphical; when this is the case, a few points of data can be taken from the graphical presentation and tabulated to demonstrate inclusion of all the pertinent factors shown in Figs. 9.10 and 9.11. When data is taken manually, graphical presentations should also be included to permit easy comparison to specified limits. Any presentations or calculations not appropriate to the main text of the report may be included as appendices.

Any special abstracts of results specifically required by the authority for which testing is performed should be highlighted in this section of the report. Some governing authorities require identification of the six highest emissions, while others request that all emissions within 10 dB or 20 dB of the specification limit be identified.

9.5.2.4 Conclusions and Recommendations

Each EMI test report should conclude with a set of conclusions and recommendations. Included should be clear statements of whether or not the EUT was found to comply with specified EMI limits. When the EUT fails to comply fully, the points of failure should be clearly stated, along with proposed remedies for correcting such failures.

Figure 9.10—Sample Data Sheet for Emission Testing

SUB-NOTE 3.2(1)	Sample Data Sheet—Emission Tests

Technician:

Equipment Nomenclature:

Test Method:

Measurement Point:

Frequency Range of Test:

Mode of Operation:

Test Equipment Used:

Date:

Serial:

Type of Measurement:
(Check as applicable)
Radiated: NB ☐ BB ☐
Conducted: NB ☐ BB ☐

Measurement Technique:
Calibrated Volt ☐
Slideback ☐
Substitution ☐
Automatic ☐

Test Frequency	Meter Indication	Attenuator Setting	Correction Factors A B C D	Corrected Reading	Limit	Remarks

A Current Probe   B Bandwidth   C Cable Losses   D Antenna Factor

9.56

Figure 9.11—Sample Data Sheet for Susceptibility Testing

SUB-NOTE 3.2(2)	Sample Data Sheet—Susceptibility Tests

Technician: **Date:**

Equipment Nomenclature: **Serial:**

Test Method: **Type of Measurement:**   (Check)

     Radiated: ☐

     Conducted: ☐

Measurement Point: **Mode of Operation:**

Frequency Range of Test:

Test Equipment Used: **Description of Test Signal:**

Test Frequency	Meets Limits Yes? No?	Susceptibility Threshold Level	Description of Degradation	Maximum Test Signal Applied if Not Susceptible	Remarks

9.6 Calibration and Its Documentation

Although it should be self-evident, it is important to emphasize that the accuracy of any EMI measurement is inherently limited by the accuracy of the instrumentation used to make it. The relationships among, and consequences of, measurement errors were discussed in Chapter 8. Although a program of periodic calibration for all EMI instrumentation will carry a significant cost, the consequences of performing EMI tests with uncalibrated instrumentation will certainly be more costly.

Specific programs for maintaining the calibration of test equipment in general are outlined in MIL-STD-45662. The basic principles for an effective calibration program are:

1. **Traceability to a national standard** must be ensured by maintaining at the local facility an adequate number of primary and secondary standards which can be submitted periodically for certification.
2. **A firm schedule for calibration** must be established and maintained. Adherence to this schedule must be diligent and fully supported by all levels of company management.
3. **The program must be complete.** All items involved in EMI testing must be included, despite any inherent difficulties in performing periodic calibrations on some of them (e.g., antennas).
4. **The program must be made as automatic as feasible.** In this regard, each item of equipment subject to calibration must carry its most recent calibration date as a prominent marking which is not vulnerable to smudging, erasure or forgery.

9.7 References

1. Bronaugh, E.L., "Overcoming High Ambient Noise in EMI Measurements on Open-Area Sites," 1985 Regional Conference and Exhibition on Electromagnetic Compatibility, Los Angeles, CA, January 1985.

2. IEC, CISPR Pub. 11-1975 (Amendment 1-1976 and Supplemented by Pub. 11A-1976), "Limits and Methods of Measurement of Radio Interference Characteristics of Industrial, Scientific, and Medical (ISM) Radio-Frequency Equipment (Excluding Surgical Diathermy Apparatus)" (Commission Electrotechnique Internationale: 1 Rue de Varembe, Geneve, Suisse).

3. Free, W.R., et al, "Electromagnetic Interference Measurements Methods—Shielded Enclosure," Final Report on Contract No. DA 28-043 AMC-02381 (E), EES, Georgia Institute of Technology, 1967.

4. Bronaugh, E.L., "Antennas for EMI Measurements," RF Design, Part 1: Vol. 9 No. 11, Part II: Vol. 9, No. 12, November-December 1986, pp. 45-49.

5. ANSI C63.7, "Guidelines for Construction of Open-Area Test Sites for Performing Radiated Emission Measurements," (New York: ANSI/IEEE).

6. ANSI C63.4-1981, "Radio-Noise Emissions from Low-Voltage Electrical and Electronic Equipment in the Range of 10 kHz to 1 GHz, ANSI Standard Methods of Measurement of" (New York: ANSI/IEEE).

7. Bronaugh, E.L., "Scan Speed Limits in Automated EMI Measurements", Proceedings of the Fifth Annual Conference on Electromagnetic Compatibility, Pub. No. 71 (York, England: IERE, University of York, 1986), pp. 293-299.

8. AFSC DH 1-4, Air Force Systems Command Design Handbook 1-4, Electromagnetic Compatibility, Sections 2A2, "Subsystem/Equipment EMI and Susceptibility Test Plan," and 2A3, "Subsystem/Equipment EMI and Susceptibility Test Reports."

Chapter 10

Test Procedures for Conducted EMI Emissions

The preceding nine chapters presented basic background information needed to understand and control the various forms of EMI testing. The remainder of the book covers the specific EMI test procedures for which the background material was provided.

Conducted EMI was defined in Chapter 1 as electromagnetic energy that is undesirably coupled out of an emitter or into a receptor via any of its connecting wires or cables. As stated in Chapter 2, the basic task of testing conducted EMI emissions is that of measuring accurately the EMI escaping from an emitter via any wires and cables connected to it and then comparing the results against allowable limits. Some EMI specifications call for measurement of the EMI current, using the current probes and other devices discussed in Section 4.1., while others specify their limits in terms of the EMI voltage, using the LISNs and voltage probes discussed in Section 4.2. In all of the specific test procedures described in Chapters 10 through 13, it is assumed that the reader will refer to related sections of Chapter 9 and follow these general setup and preparation guidelines. Also, use of the peak detector function of the EMI analyzer will be assumed for all military-oriented testing, and use of the quasipeak function will be assumed for CISPR-based testing.

10.1 Measuring Conducted EMI Current on AC and DC Power Leads

The purpose of measuring conducted EMI on power leads is to confirm that the EMI level is below a specified limit and thus not likely to produce a problem if those leads couple it into a potential victim. Ground or neutral lines are usually included in such measurements, but bonding straps are not. Figure 10.1 identifies, in a military context, the types of leads which require measurement of their conducted EMI.

10.1.1 Power Lead EMI Current, 30 Hz to 15 kHz

10.1.1.1 Test Preparation and Setup

Figures 10.2 and 10.3 illustrate typical setups used to measure 30 Hz to 15 kHz conducted EMI on ac and dc power leads. Figure 10.2 shows the actual physical layout given in MIL-STD-462 for a benchtop EUT, while Fig. 10.3 shows diagrammatically the preferred setup when an anteroom is available. As discussed in Section 9.2.2, many other variations in setup are possible, depending on factors such as the size of the EUT and the shielded enclosure. Also, as discussed in Section 4.1.1.2, the measurement task can be facilitated by the use of an inverse amplifier which complements the response characteristic of the current probe. Section 4.1.1 discusses various measures which can be taken to isolate EMI from the line source and prevent it from being measured along with the EMI from the EUT.

Substitution of 5 μH LISNs in place of, or in addition to, the 10 μF feed-through capacitors shown in Fig. 10.2 is preferred for some test requirements. The argument in favor of the LISNs is that they more adequately stabilize the line impedance and thus permit more uniform measurements using the same setup at different test locations with different line sources. For military testing, the LISN is to be a 5 μH type and must be in accordance with Fig. 7 of MIL-STD-462 Notice 3 (EL), dated 9 February 1971 (this is the same as Drawing no. ES-DL-198697). The signal output terminal of the LISN typically has been terminated in 50 Ω, thus making the power

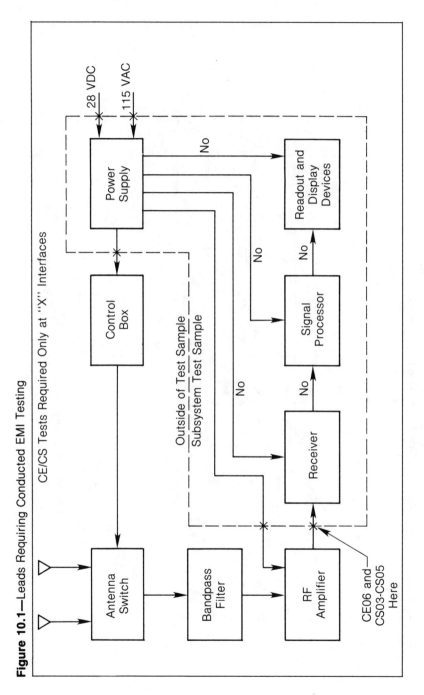

Figure 10.1—Leads Requiring Conducted EMI Testing

Figure 10.2—Setup for Conducted EMI Emission Testing of Power Leads

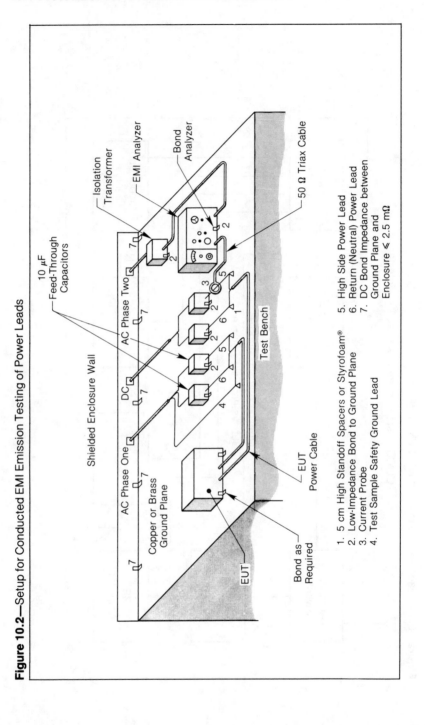

1. 5 cm High Standoff Spacers or Styrofoam®
2. Low-Impedance Bond to Ground Plane
3. Current Probe
4. Test Sample Safety Ground Lead
5. High Side Power Lead
6. Return (Neutral) Power Lead
7. DC Bond Impedance between Ground Plane and Enclosure ⩽ 2.5 mΩ

10.4

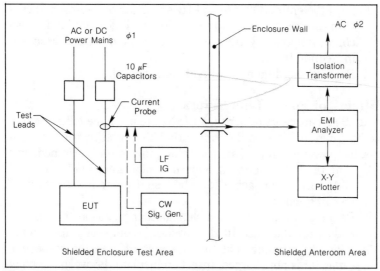

Figure 10.3—Conducted Emission Testing of Power Leads in Shielded Enclosure with Anteroom

mains impedance presented to the EUT also 50 Ω, over most of its useful range (see Figs. 4.14 and 4.15, Chapter 4). However, recent studies, as detailed in Ref. 1, have determined that a value of line impedance more often encountered in practice is 100 Ω, which makes a termination of this value more likely to simulate actual conditions. The length of the power lead between the EUT and the capacitor or LISN should be between 30 and 60 cm whenever possible.[1,2]

10.1.1.2 Validating the Setup

Ambient Suppression

The following procedure may be used to determine that ambient noise from the line source has been adequately suppressed by the 10 μF capacitors and any supplementary measures:

1. Substitute a dummy resistive load in lieu of the EUT, selecting its value to duplicate the current normally drawn by the EUT. Tungsten light bulbs and fixtures provide economical and readily available dummy loads.

2. Scan the entire 30 Hz to 15 kHz spectrum of interest and confirm that the ambient noise is adequately low, taking into account, if necessary, the noise correction techniques discussed in Section 9.1.1.
3. Remove the dummy load and reconnect the EUT.

Effects of Power Line Filters

If 10 μF capacitors rather than LISNs are used, the following procedure may be used to determine that the 10 μF capacitors, and not the power line filters, are controlling the power line impedance:

1. With the EUT energized, make one measurement of conducted EMI current on each lead to be tested at the lowest required test frequency.
2. Before performing the next step, disconnect all electrical power and assure that each 10 μF capacitor is completely discharged.
3. After determining that the power is off and the respective capacitor is not charged, insert an insulator between the body of the capacitor and the ground plane. Then restore the electrical power and remeasure each lead at the same frequency as used in step 1.
3. If the test setup is valid, the readings taken with the insulators in place should be at least 6 dB lower than those taken without the insulators.
4. If the readings with insulators remain the same, this indicates that the line filters are controlling the measurement and that valid results cannot be obtained. To correct the situation, an inductor must be installed between the line filter and the 10 μF capacitor. The impedance of the inductor should approximate that of the 10 μF capacitor at the lowest frequency of measurement.
5. Once the results are satisfactory, remove the insulators and proceed with the test.

10.1.1.3 Test Procedure

Because current probes usually have a lower impedance at lower frequencies, the use of an inverse amplifier is highly recommended, as discussed in Section 4.1.1.2. This device simplifies the measurement by complementarily amplifying the output of the current probe to produce a flat 1 Ω transfer impedance characteristic such that the input voltage to the EMI analyzer, in dBμV, is exactly equal to the current flowing in the test lead, in dBμA. The inverse amplifier is nearly indispensible for flattening the current probe response when simultaneous broadband measurement is required of the conducted EMI spectrum from 30 Hz up to 15 kHz. Although such simultaneous measurements of the entire audio range up to 15 kHz are no longer required for EMI testing for military applications, the ability of the inverse amplifier to integrate a pulse which is effectively differentiated by the current probe can be valuable in special situations.[3] The test procedure is as follows:

1. The first lead to be tested is selected and the current probe clamped into position, as shown in Fig. 10.2. Using the narrowest bandwidth available (5 to 10 Hz), the EMI analyzer is slowly and carefully tuned and the amplitude and frequency of any responses recorded from 30 Hz up to about 2 kHz. In the absence of discrete narrowband responses, the background noise is measured as required to produce a minimum of three readings per octave.

   Note that the use of bandwidth as narrow as 5 Hz requires that the EMI analyzer be tuned very slowly; using Eq. (6.1) from Chapter 6, $T > \Delta F/B_i^2$, for scan time. With responses down by 1.4 dB, the time required to tune a frequency segment 2 kHz wide using an impulse bandwidth of 5 Hz should be greater than $2{,}000/25 = 80$ s. If an X–Y plotter is used to record the responses, additional time must be allowed to overcome the inertia of the recording pen; for a typical plotter, a total scan time of about 200 s should be allowed for scanning with a 5 Hz bandwidth from 30 Hz to 2 kHz.[4]

2. The bandwidth closest to 100 Hz available on the EMI analyzer is then selected and the process continued up to 15 kHz or other highest frequency of interest.

3. The procedure is repeated for each power lead, including neutral. Any safety ground, or green wire, is exempt from the testing.

4. For presentation in the test report, the collected data is organized and plotted to show its relationship to the applicable test limits.

5. If emissions are found which exceed the specified limits, it may be advisable to effect the necessary suppression and retest while the test setup is still intact.

10.1.2 Audio Isolation Transformer Test for DC Power Leads, 30 Hz to 50 kHz

Available as an alternative to the current probe procedure discussed above, for dc power leads only, is the audio isolation transformer procedure detailed in Section 4.1.2. The purpose of this procedure, whereby a transformer is inserted in series with the dc power lead of the EUT, is to eliminate possible problems associated with current probe measurement sensitivity, change in transfer impedance or saturation of the inverse amplifier, as discussed in Section 4.1.1.

The isolation transformer is operated in reverse, with its secondary in series with the lead being tested and its primary driving the EMI analyzer. Once the calibration process is performed, as discussed in Section 4.1.2, the remainder of this procedure is the same as for the current probe, as discussed above.

10.1.3 Power Lead EMI Current, 15 kHz to 50 MHz

This test is essentially a continuation of the procedure given in Section 10.1.1, for 30 Hz to 15 kHz, but uses impulse bandwidths of at least 1 kHz to provide for the measurement of broadband as well as narrowband EMI. The basic setup and validation processes for each power lead are the same as given in Section 10.1.1.

10.1.3.1 Test Procedures

Testing for narrowband and broadband conducted emissions usually can be combined into a single frequency scan. For manual testing, this involves a quick-look assessment to identify each threatening emission as either narrowband or broadband, in accordance with the criteria of Table 2.1. For the X-Y-plotter level of automation, the operator follows the procedures for conducted measurements which are detailed in Section 6.2. When a computer automated system is used, as discussed in Section 6.3, the criteria of Table 2.1 are applied as part of the computer program which classifies all EMI signals as either narrowband or broadband and which then applies all correction factors to produce a final reading.

10.2 Measuring Conducted EMI Current on Control and Signal Leads

Unwanted electromagnetic energy on control or signal lines can create interference by being conducted directly into another piece of equipment or by radiating onto other lines and cables. The procedure covered in this section is intended to measure the extent to which such potentially interfering signals are present on a control or signal line; it is also applied to leads carrying secondary power, as derived from other equipments. Although any radiated emissions from the signals intentionally placed on the lines covered by this procedure must satisfy the appropriate radiated limits, such signals are usually exempt from conducted limits, based on requirements of the approved test plan.

Included in the exemption are the inherent components of intentional signals. For example, if a 5 V, 1 Mb clock signal having a 50 ns rise and fall time is required, the expected current for a 125 Ω impedance video line is:

$$I = V/R = 5 \text{ V}/125 \text{ } \Omega = 40 \text{ mA} = 92 \text{ dB}\mu\text{A}$$

However, the signal is broadband and has a 0.5 μs pulse width, τ. Thus, from Eq. (2.9) of Chapter 2:

$$I(f) = \frac{V(f)}{R} = \frac{2 \tau V}{R} \frac{\sin \pi \tau f}{\pi \tau f} \tag{10.1}$$

The envelope of this broadband emission in A/Hz is:

$$|I(f)| = \frac{2\tau V}{R} \qquad \text{for } f \leqslant \frac{1}{\pi \tau} \tag{10.2}$$

$$= \frac{2V}{\pi f R} \qquad \text{for } \frac{1}{\pi \tau} \geqslant f \geqslant \frac{1}{\pi \tau_r} \tag{10.3}$$

$$= \frac{2V}{\tau_r \pi^2 f^2 R} \qquad \text{for } f \geqslant \frac{1}{\pi \tau_r} \tag{10.4}$$

Figure 10.4 is a plot of Eqs. (10.1) through (10.4). The units of A/Hz have been changed to μA/MHz by multiplying by $10^6/10^{-6}$

= 10^{12} and expressing the result in dBμA/MHz. A comparison of this plotted level to typical broadband specification limits, also shown in Fig. 10.4, illustrates that the clock signal exemption would be necessary between 150 kHz and 21 MHz. However, since the EMI analyzer bandwidths used throughout this range will resolve these harmonics, this exemption will not apply to EMI signals falling at frequencies between them.

10.2.1 Test Apparatus and Setup

As with power leads, the use of a current probe is the most practical way of measuring interference on a signal or control lead without having to interrupt the lead and thus possibly alter significantly its impedance characteristics. The setup to be used is shown in Fig. 10.5. At the lower frequencies of measurement, the use of an inverse amplifier to flatten the response of the current probe and integrate pulse response can be worthwhile, as discussed in Section 10.1.1.3.

10.2.2 Test Procedures

The procedure steps 1 through 5 called for in Section 10.1.1.3

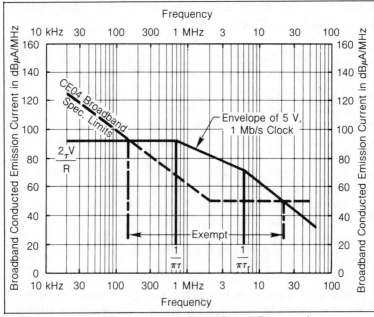

Figure 10.4—Example of Exempt Clock Signal Frequencies

Measuring Conducted EMI Current on Control and Signal Leads

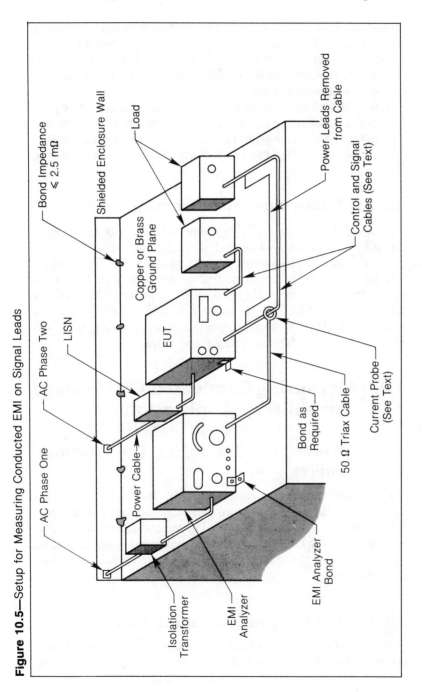

Figure 10.5—Setup for Measuring Conducted EMI on Signal Leads

should be followed, ignoring any comments which are unique to power leads. Also, the comments given for manual and automated testing of power leads in Section 10.1.3.1, relative to determining whether EMI signals are NB or BB, are equally applicable to testing of signal and control leads.

When the control or signal leads contain more than two wire pairs in a harness, following the sampling procedures outlined in Section 9.4.3.1, for wire lead sampling, and Section 9.4.3.2, for current probe positioning, can result in significant savings in testing time.

10.2.2.1 Baseband Measurement

Although broadband EMI limits generally are no longer imposed for military applications below 15 kHz, there are related applications, such as audio measurements with psophometric filters, which require simultaneous measurement of response over the entire range, typically from 16 Hz to 16 kHz.[4] A modern EMI analyzer for the audio and ELF ranges typically includes a wideband mode of operation in which the instrument functions as an amplified and metered bandpass filter covering these frequencies.

10.3 Measuring Conducted EMI Voltage for Military Applications

10.3.1 Power Lead Testing for Time-Domain Spikes

This section covers measurement of transients or spikes generated in the EUT which are conducted onto its power leads. No frequency scanning is involved. The method given is applicable for spikes or transients on all ungrounded power leads, including neutrals, having rise times $\leqslant 12$ μs and recurrence rates less than once per second.

10.3.1.1 Test Apparatus and Setup

As shown in Fig. 10.6, an LISN is inserted simultaneously in each power lead to be tested, including the neutral lead. For testing to U.S. military requirements, each LISN should be as described in Section 10.1.1.1.

Figure 10.6—Setup for Measuring Time-Domain Spikes on Power Leads

1. 5 cm Standoffs
2. Low-Impedance Bond to Ground Plane
3. Line Impedance Stabilization Networks
4. EUT Chassis Ground
5. High Side
6. Return (Neutral Line)
7. DC Bond Impedance between the Ground Plane and Enclosure Shall Not Exceed 2.5 mΩ
8. Line Impedance Stabilization Networks Shall Be Terminated in 50 Ω Resistive at Type N Connector

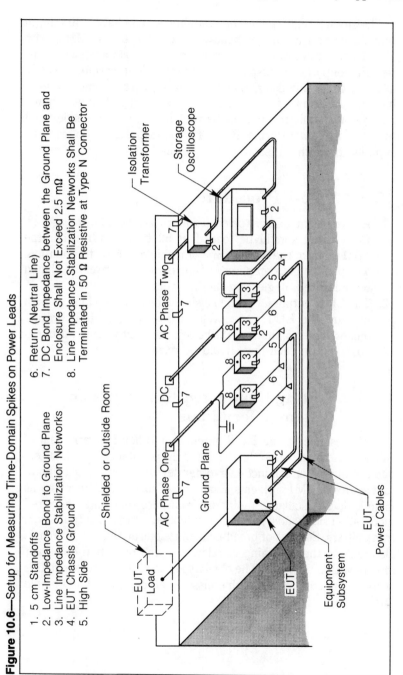

The storage-type oscilloscope required should have a 50 Ω input impedance and a storage bandwidth of at least 10 MHz, with 35 MHz being desirable. The writing rate of the storage mode must be sufficiently fast to display or store a transient waveform having a 35 ns rise time. It also should display or store a transient waveform having a rise time of 10 ns or less. These storage bandwidth and writing rate requirements must be available to measure single-event (nonrepetitive) waveforms. Power for the test oscilloscope is to be supplied through an isolation transformer.

10.3.1.2 Test Procedure

1. Any transient voltages on each power lead should be measured. Each LISN should be loaded at all times with either the 50 Ω input of the oscilloscope or a shielded 50 Ω termination. The peak-to-peak amplitude of each transient waveform should be measured, neglecting the line voltage.
2. The LISN output for each line should be observed long enough to allow the EUT to be cycled through all of its operating modes. The amplitude of the largest transient voltage waveform observed on each line should be recorded.

10.3.2 Testing Conducted Emissions on Antenna Terminals

The presence at the EUT antenna or other RF terminals of signals generated within the EUT, and the possibility of their subsequent radiation or conduction to other devices, represents a significant source of EMI problems. Examples of such potential emissions include local oscillator radiation from receivers and undesired modulation sidebands, harmonics and other spurious outputs from transmitters. Sources of broadband emissions at antenna terminals also include the switching of relays and the operation of blower motors within the EUT. The objective of the tests discussed in this section is to ensure that such emissions do not exceed acceptable levels.

10.3.2.1 Applicability

The testing discussed in this section covers measurement of both narrowband and broadband emissions from receivers under all their operation conditions and from transmitters both in their standby mode (key up) and, using different setups, in their transmitting mode (key down). The frequency ranges over which such EMI emissions are measured extend from 10 kHz to at least 26 GHz.

10.3.2.2 Test Preparation and Setup

Figures 10.7 through 10.10 illustrate typical setups for testing antenna-conducted emissions from receivers and transmitters under various sets of conditions. Figure 10.7 typically is used for receivers, RF amplifiers and transmitters in the key-up position. The purpose of the buffer pad in Fig. 10.7 is to establish a low VSWR for more accurate measurements; its typical value is 10 dB, but it can be smaller if necessary to maintain measurement sensitivity.

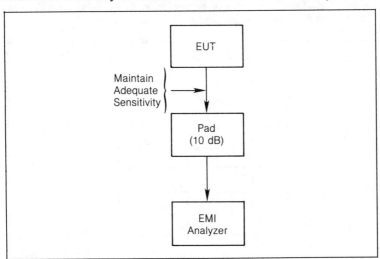

Figure 10.7—Setup for Receivers, RF Amplifiers and Key-Down Transmitters

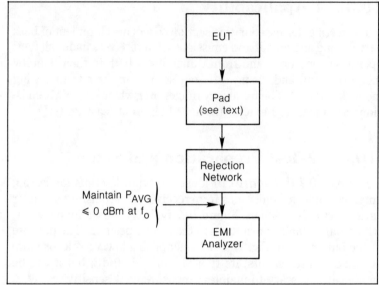

Figure 10.8—Setup for Transmitter Key-Down; Average Power ⩽43 dBm and Highest Frequency ⩽ 26 GHz

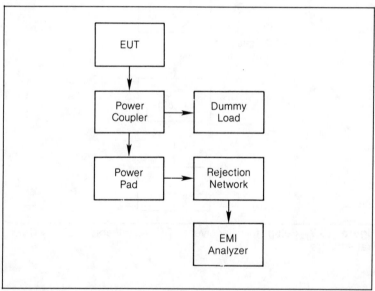

Figure 10.9—Transmitter Key-Down; 43 dBm < Average Power < 67 dBm; 10 kHz ⩽ f_o ⩽ 300 MHz; No Antenna

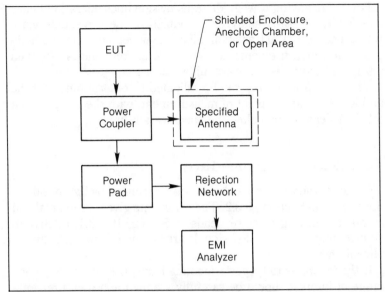

Figure 10.10—Transmitter Key-Down; 43 dBm < Average Power < 67 dBm; 10 kHz ⩽ f_o ⩽ 1,240 MHz; Specified Antenna

The setup in Fig. 10.8 is used for transmitter key-down measurements in which the average power output does not exceed 43 dBm (20 W) and the highest intentionally generated frequency does not exceed 26 GHz. The RF pad should be approximately 20 dB, or large enough to reduce the 20 W output level of the transmitter down to a level which will not damage the EMI analyzer input. The rejection network shown in the figure is tuned to the fundamental frequency of the EUT and is intended to reduce the post-pad transmitter power to a level that will not desensitize or induce spurious responses in the EMI analyzer. For typical instruments, the total power reaching the receiver input should not exceed about 0 dBm.

Either the setup shown in Fig. 10.9 or that in Fig. 10.10 is used for transmitter key-down measurements in which the average power output exceeds 43 dBm but is less than 67 dBm (5 kW). The choice between the two is determined by the operating range of the EUT and whether it must be operated with a specified antenna. When output power exceeds 5 kW, radiated measurements are usually made in the far field of the transmitting antenna. Specific measurement proposals are always subject to approval of the respective test plan.

For EUTs having waveguide transmission lines operating below 1.24 GHz, the EMI analyzer is coupled to the waveguide via a waveguide-to-coaxial transition. Since the waveguide acts as a high-pass filter, measurements are not made at frequencies less than $0.9\ f_{co}$, where f_{co} is the waveguide cutoff frequency.

The appropriate setup can be validated by determining that the ambient level at the point of measurement, with the EUT turned off, is at least 6 dB below the specification limit.

10.3.2.3 Test Procedure

Choice of the test setup to be used is determined by the considerations given in Section 10.3.2. The comments given for manual and automated testing of power leads in Section 10.1.3.1, relative to determining whether EMI signals are NB or BB, are equally applicable here.

If the testing is to be performed manually, the entire frequency range of interest should be carefully scanned and measurements made to determine whether each response is NB or BB, in accordance with the criteria of Table 2.1 (Chapter 2). The respective NB or BB amplitude and center frequency of each significant response should be recorded; at least three readings should be made within each octave of coverage, including readings of the respective noise levels as required. Resulting data are plotted or otherwise processed for easy comparison to applicable specification limits and for integration into the test report. The process is repeated for each antenna or RF terminal to be tested. Automated test systems should be operated to obtain the same information, as a minimum, with the specific process dependent on the system being used.

10.4 Measuring Conducted EMI Voltage on Power Lines

10.4.1 Measurements Using LISNs

In contrast to military-oriented testing for EMI conducted on power lines, which specifies the measurement of EMI **current** using a current probe, testing in accordance with CISPR-based standards of the FCC, ANSI, VDE and other regulators is based on the measurement of EMI **voltage** using a LISN (also called an "artificial mains network"). Figure 10.11 shows a schematic for the LISN used for such testing from 10 to 150 kHz (or up to 30 MHz in some cases), while Fig. 10.12 shows the comparable LISN used from 0.15 to 30 MHz. The appropriate LISN network is inserted in series with each current-carrying conductor in the EUT power cord. The basic design and functions of the LISN are discussed in Section 4.2.1.[5-7]

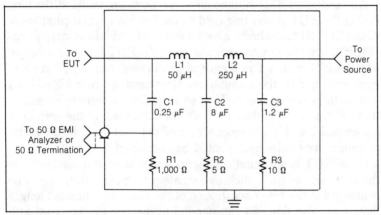

Figure 10.11—LISN for Testing from 10 to 150 kHz (or 30 MHz)

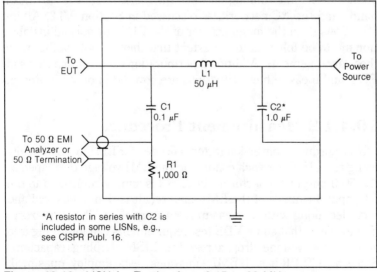

Figure 10.12—LISN for Testing from 0.15 to 30 MHz

10.19

10.4.1.1 Test Preparation and Setup

The shielded enclosure test setup to be used for measurement of conducted EMI voltage on power lines is described in Section 9.3.2 and diagrammed in Fig. 9.8 (Chapter 9). Included are details on such subjects as spacing of the EUT from grounded surfaces, arrangement of power cords, simulation of hand effects and bonding of the LISN to ground.

All conducted EMI voltage measurements are made at the plug end of the EUT power line cord when this is a normal component of the EUT. If furnished without a line cord and no distinctive type of cord is specified by the manufacturer, the EUT is to be connected to the LISN with a 1 m length of unshielded line. Any length of cord furnished by the manufacturer in excess of 1 m is folded back and forth in serpentine fashion so as to form a bundle no longer than 40 cm. This is placed so that the total span of the cord does not exceed 1 m. If resonances are found to result from the cord after bundling, its total length should be shortened to 1 m.

If the EUT has ground connections that are not integrated into the main power cord, such as for safety purposes, they are to be connected to the reference ground of the LISN by a line not longer than 1 m. The line will run parallel to the main power cord at a distance not greater than 10 cm from it. This same arrangement applies to the line running between the metal foil of the "artificial hand" and the RC network, as discussed in Section 9.3.2. All instructions from the manufacturer of the EUT for normal installation are to be followed to the extent that they do not conflict with these arrangements. Additional permutations and combinations of EUT and measurement situations are covered in detail in Ref. 5.

10.4.1.2 Measurement Procedure

No transducer conversion factor is needed for EMI measurements using the LISN; for each conductor, the EMI voltage developed at the 50 Ω output connector of the LISN is simply connected to the RF input terminals of the EMI analyzer. It is then measured and recorded along with its measurement frequency. The only exception to this is that some VDE test requirements call for taking into account the voltage drop across the LISN coupling capacitor.[8] Since all CISPR-based EMI emissions tests employ quasipeak detection and a single specified IF measurement bandwidth, no classification of signals as NB or BB is necessary. Whether measured manually or through use of an automated system, each reading is compared to the respective specification limit and plotted versus frequency for presentation in the test report.

10.4.2 In Situ Testing and Other Voltage Probe Applications

FCC and other CISPR-based procedures for testing conducted EMI at the user's equipment installation provide for use of the high-impedance (1.5 kΩ) voltage probe shown schematically in Fig. 4.14 (Chapter 4). The specified probe impedance of 1.5 kΩ is the minimum allowed; for some installations and power mains impedances, values as high as 100 kΩ might be required to avoid excessive loading of the lines being tested.

For this type of unique measurement, special attention must be accorded to the selection of a suitable reference ground and to other considerations pertinent to obtaining an accurate assessment of the conducted EMI effects of the installation on its electromagnetic environment.[5]

10.4.2.1 Selection of a Reference Ground

If possible, the existing earth ground at the place of installation should be used as the reference ground by means of a short, low-RF-impedance connection to grounded items such as water pipes or lightning protection systems. In general, the safety and neutral conductors of the power line installation are not suitable for this use because of their unknown EMI content and their undefined impedance with respect to the earth ground.

10.4.3.2 Length of Ground Connection

To avoid measurement anomalies from standing waves, the length of the ground connection should not exceed λ/10 at the maximum frequency of measurement, which is 1 m at 30 MHz. Although much greater lengths can be used at lower frequencies, they should not exceed 10 m. This restriction avoids coupling loops and thus minimizes magnetic coupling of EMI from the power mains.

10.5 References

1. SAE ARP 1972 (January 1986), "Recommended Measurement Practices and Procedures for EMC Testing" (Warrendale, PA: Society of Automotive Engineers), prepared by SAE AE4 Committee on Electromagnetic Compatibility.
2. MIL-STD-462, "Electromagnetic Interference Characteristics, Measurement of," 31 July 1967.
3. MIL-STD-461C, "Electromagnetic Emission and Susceptibility Requirements for the Control of Electromagnetic Interference," 4 August 1986.
4. Bronaugh, E.L., "Scan Speed Limits in Automated EMI Measurements," *Proceedings of the Fifth International Conference on EMC,* Publication no. 71 (London: IERE, 1986), University of York, York, England, 1-3 October 1986, pp. 293-299.
5. CISPR 16, "Specification for Radio Frequency Measuring Apparatus and Measurement Methods."
6. ANSI C63.4-1981, "Radio-Noise Emissions from Low-Voltage, Electrical and Electronic Equipment in the Range of 10 kHz to 1 GHz, American National Standard Methods of Measurement of" (New York: IEEE/ANSI).
7. FCC MP-4, "FCC Methods of Measurement of Radio Noise Emissions from Computing Devices" (Washington, DC: Federal Communications Commission, August 1983).
8. VDE 0876, "Radio Interference Measuring Apparatus."

Chapter 11

Test Procedures for
Radiated EMI Emissions

This chapter describes specific procedures for testing radiated
EMI emissions and is the second of four chapters covering specific
procedures for EMI testing (10 through 14). All procedures in these
are based on the background information presented in Chapters
1 through 9.

Radiated EMI was defined in Chapter 1 as electromagnetic
energy that is undesirably coupled out of an emitter or into a receptor by means other than conduction. As stated in Chapter 2, the
basic task of testing radiated EMI emissions is that of measuring
accurately, and then comparing to appropriate limits, any undesired
electromagnetic fields emanating from the EUT. Some EMI
specifications, particularly those of the U.S. military, call for such
measurements to be made in shielded enclosures. Others, which
typically are based on CISPR recommendations, specify that
measurements be performed in open-area test sites or their
equivalents.

In all of the specific test procedures described in this chapter,
it is assumed that the reader will refer to and follow relevant sections of Chapter 9 in regard to the general setup and preparations
for such testing. Also, unless specifically stated otherwise, use of
the peak detector function of the EMI analyzer will be assumed
for all military-oriented testing, and use of CISPR quasipeak detector function will be assumed for all civilian-oriented testing.

11.1 Testing Magnetic Fields in Shielded Enclosures

The purpose of testing the levels of magnetic fields radiated from EUTs and their associated cables and interconnecting wiring is to assure that such fields are sufficiently low to avoid interference to nearby equipment and subsystem receptors. The wiring which should be checked includes that used for control and power as well as transmission lines that carry RF, digital data, video and audio information.

11.1.1 Testing EMI Magnetic Emissions Close to EUT (7 cm)

Measurement of the magnetic field at a distance of only 7 cm from the EUT originally was intended to apply only to equipment intended for installation in very tight quarters, such as submarines. It is now the accepted practice for most testing for military applications. The frequency range over which such testing is normally prescribed is 30 Hz to 50 kHz.[1-3]

11.1.1.1 Loop Antenna and Setup

The loop antenna and test setup to be used for magnetic-field measurement is shown in Fig. 11.1. Commercially available versions of this loop are built so that the plane of the loop is spaced 7 cm from the face of the EUT when a built-in spacing rod is butted against that EUT face.

11.1.1.2 Specification and Loop Conversion Factors

Typical specification limits for this type of testing are in terms of decibels relative to one picotesla (dBpT). Since the EMI analyzer with which the loop is used measures in terms of decibels relative to one microvolt (dBμV), it is necessary to apply a conversion fac-

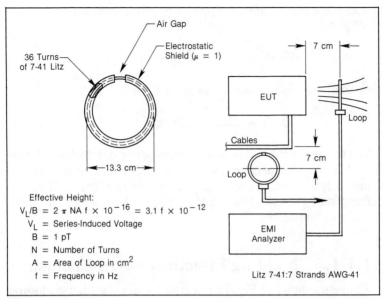

Figure 11.1—Loop Antenna and Test Setup for Magnetic Emission, Testing at 7 cm

tor. The ratio of voltage available from the loop to magnetic flux density in V/pT is:

$$V_L/B = 2\pi NAf \times 10^{-16} \qquad (11.1)$$

$$= 3.1f \times 10^{-12} \qquad (11.2)$$

where,

V_L = series-induced voltage, in volts, produced into an EMI analyzer with minimum input impedance of 10 kΩ

B = magnetic flux density in picotesla (pT)

N = number of loop turns in loop antenna = 36

A = area of loop in cm² = 139

f = frequency in Hz

Converting the units of Eq. (11.2) to μV/pT yields:

$$V_L/B = 3.1f \times 10^{-6}$$

Expressing this ratio of microvolts to picotesla in terms of dBμV/pT:

$$V_L/B = -110.2 + 20 \log f$$

Changing sign to reverse the ratio, to dBpT/μV:

$$B/V_L = 110.1 - 20 \log f \qquad (11.3)$$

Thus, to convert the EMI analyzer reading in dBμV to dBpT, simply add the number of dB shown in Eq. (11.3) to the measurement. Conversely, to convert a specification limit in terms of dBpT to the corresponding level in dBμV produced by the loop, simply subtract that same number of dB.

11.1.1.3 Shielding Effectiveness of Enclosure

The setup shown in Fig. 11.1 is installed in a shielded enclosure with the monitoring and auxiliary equipment located outside of the testing area, such as in an anteroom. Since many shielded enclosures do not exhibit any significant magnetic shielding effectiveness at the low frequencies involved in these tests, the ambient magnetic field should be measured to confirm that it is lower than the specification limit; if not, one of the techniques given in Section 9.1.1 for measuring emissions in the presence of high ambient levels must be applied. If ambients are a problem, different locations within the shielded enclosure should be investigated to find the lowest ambient levels.

11.1.1.4 Bandwidth Selection

Note that the use of relatively narrow bandwidths at these lower frequencies requires that the EMI analyzer be tuned very slowly, in accordance with Eq. (6.1): $T > \Delta F/B_i^2$. If a 10 Hz bandwidth were used to scan a segment 50 kHz wide, the time required should be greater than $50 \times 10^3/10^2 = 500$ s (8.3 min). This points out the necessity of switching the EMI analyzer to a wider bandwidth as the scan reaches higher frequencies: the bandwidth should be switched to 100 Hz at 500 Hz and to 1 kHz at 10 kHz. If an X-Y plotter is used to record the responses, additional time must be allowed to overcome the inertia of the recording pen.

11.1.1.5 Test Procedures

1. To select the face of the EUT most likely to provide the maximum field for measurement, first tune the EMI analyzer to any intentionally generated frequencies in the EUT that lie in the measurement range. At each such frequency, physically scan the loop over all faces of the EUT and select the face that produces the highest emission level. In the absence of any intentional signals, select the face of the EUT which is likely to provide the greatest magnetic field leakage or radiation because of factors such as its proximity to a strong magnetic source within the EUT.

2. With the loop positioned at an angle of 45° relative to all three axes of the EUT (see Section 9.4.5.2), scan the entire frequency range of interest and record the frequencies of the two per octave (below 200 Hz) or three per octave (above 200 Hz) largest responses.

3. Tune the EMI analyzer to each of the responses noted and, with the plane of the loop as in step 2, move the loop over the face of the EUT and record the location of maximum indication.

4. Orient the loop for maximum indication at the location in step 3. Record the loop orientation and the EMI analyzer reading.

5. Repeat steps 3 and 4 for each frequency recorded in step 2.

6. Repeat steps 1 through 5 for each side of each module of the EUT unless it can be shown clearly that the level of emissions is lower than for the first face selected.

7. Locate the loop so that its plane includes that of one cable of the EUT at a distance of 7 cm from the center of the loop, as shown in Fig. 11.1.

8. Scan the frequency range and measure and record the frequency and amplitude of the largest responses, two per octave below 200 Hz and three per octave above 200 Hz.

9. Repeat steps 7 and 8 for each cable of the EUT.

Automated test systems should be operated to obtain the same data as results from the manual procedure, as a minimum, with the specific process dependent on the system being used. However, because of the degree of operator involvement implied by the foregoing procedure, automation will produce limited savings in test time in comparison to manual testing.

11.1.2 Testing Radiated Magnetic EMI Emissions at 1 m Spacing

This section covers shielded-enclosure testing of EMI magnetic field radiation performed over the frequency range from 20 Hz to 50 kHz with the pickup loop positioned 1 m from the EUT, as compared to the 7 cm spacing of the preceding section.

11.1.2.1 Test Antenna and Setup

As shown in the typical test setup illustrated in Fig. 11.2, the magnetic loop sensor is to be located 1 m from the most central face of the equipment being tested. Unlike the military requirement for 7 cm spacing discussed in the preceding section, the antenna design is not precisely prescribed. The types of magnetic-field sensors suitable for this task are discussed in Section 4.3.2.

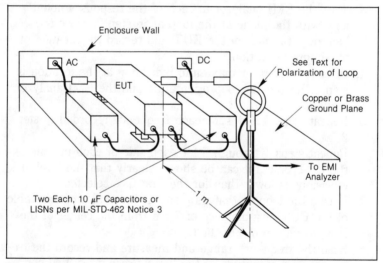

Figure 11.2—Setup for Testing Magnetic EMI Emissions at 1 m

11.1.2.2 Test Procedures

A typical test procedure calls for the magnetic field sensor to be placed in three positions, each with its center spaced 1 m from the EUT (a) with its plane parallel to the face of the EUT, (b) with its plane vertical and perpendicular to the EUT face and (c) with its plane horizontal. The corresponding positions for a ferrite sensor with respect to the EUT face are with the axis of the ferrite rod (a) perpendicular to it, (b) horizontal and parallel to it and (c) vertical and parallel to it.

The following test procedure is generic in nature and aimed at finding and quantifying all magnetic-field EUT emissions of potential concern. Before proceeding further, review Section 11.1.1 to highlight various pertinent considerations.

1. Select the initial EMI analyzer bandwidth while taking into account the selectivity required and the limitations on scan rate implied [see Eq. (6.1) in Chapter 6]. Position the center of the loop or other magnetic sensor 1 m from the center of the EUT as shown in Fig. 11.2. Then orient the plane of the loop 45° to all three orthogonal axes of the EUT (see Section 9.4.5.2).
2. Scan the entire frequency segment of interest to locate the frequency of maximum flux-density indication.
3. At this frequency, move the sensor horizontally and vertically, parallel to the EUT, while monitoring for maximum indication. Maintain the 45° orientation of the sensor relative to the three axes of the EUT. When a peak is noted, secure the loop in this position.
4. Scan the EMI analyzer over the entire frequency range of interest and record the levels of at least three emissions of maximum flux-density emission per octave, including those at critical frequencies of the EUT, as applicable. Apply the appropriate conversion factors for comparison to specification limits and, if pertinent, determine if each emission is NB or BB. In the data analysis consider that, because of the 45° orientation of the field sensor, 6 dB must be added to each measurement to account for possible polarization loss. That is, the actual radiation may be orthogonal or parallel to the EUT axes.

5. Measure accurately the maximum value of each emission that is determined by the analysis of step 4 to be within ± 6 dB of the limit.
6. Process the data and, on semilogarithmic graph paper, plot the flux-density units of each emission versus frequency, showing the respective specification limit for comparison.

Illustrative Example 11.1

The test configuration of Fig. 11.2 is used with the loop shown in Fig. 11.1. In performing step 4, above, an EMI analyzer reading of 25 dBμV was produced by an emission at 5 kHz. Is the emission within the specification limits of 71 dBpT?

From Eq. (11.3), the conversion factor from μV to pT in dBpT/μV is:

$$
\begin{aligned}
B/V_L &= 110.1 - 20 \log f \\
&= 110.1 - 20 \log (5 \times 10^3) \\
&= 110.1 - 74.0 \\
&= 36.1 \text{ dBpT}/\mu V
\end{aligned}
$$

Adding this to 25 dBμV yields 61.1 dBpT. Adding 6 dB to account for the diagonal polarization used, the resulting level becomes 67.1 dBpT, which is 3.9 dB below the specified limit. Because of its proximity to the limit, orient the loop so as to measure the maximum signal level.

11.2 Testing Electric Fields in Shielded Enclosures

The purpose of testing the levels of electric fields (E-fields) radiated from EUTs and their associated cables and interconnecting wiring is to assure that they are sufficiently low to avoid interference to nearby equipment and subsystems. Wiring that should be checked includes that used for control and power as well as transmission lines carrying RF, digital data, video and audio information. Such testing excludes deliberate emanations from antennas and stresses possible leakage from any electrical, electronic or electromechanical sources within the EUT housing or from its cables.

11.8

11.2.1 Test Preparation and Setup

Typical setups for electric-field measurements in shielded enclosures are shown in Figs. 11.3 and 11.4. Although both figures show the EMI analyzer located in the shielded enclosure, it is preferable to locate it in an adjacent anteroom to reduce the potential for influence on measurements from radiation of its local oscillator.

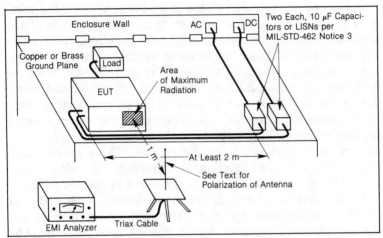

Figure 11.3—Test Setup for Electric-Field Testing of Benchtop Equipment

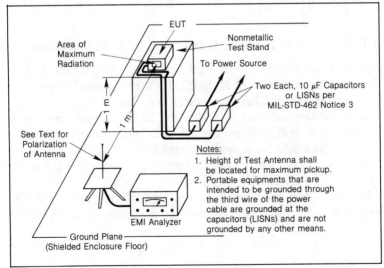

Figure 11.4—Test Setup for Electric-Field Testing of Portable Equipment

11.9

11.2.1.1 Error-Reducing Measures

As detailed in Chapter 8, radiated EMI measurements in shielded enclosures probably are subject to sources of larger error than any other type of EMI testing. It is useful at this point to refer to the sections of Chapter 8 which deal with the errors particularly associated with radiated EMI measurements in shielded enclosures and the measures which can be taken to ameliorate them.

Of particular significance are the errors that result from the proximity of the EUT and test antenna to the metallic walls of the enclosure. Discussed in Section 8.2.2.1 are the effects from reflections off these walls and the degree to which they can be reduced with absorbing material. Other solutions to reflection problems discussed in Section 9.2.1.3 are hooded and optically isolated antennas. Section 8.2.2.2 covers the subject of the antenna being detuned by its proximity to the walls and ceilings and recommends keeping the antenna as far as possible from the walls and using an active antenna with very small elements. The effects of enclosure resonances and the concomitant advantage of using larger enclosures to reduce their effects is covered in Section 8.2.2.3.

Another type of error in shielded-room testing of radiated EMI results from the physical proximity (typically 1 m) of the EUT and the test antenna. As discussed in Section 8.4, precautions must be taken to reduce gradient errors associated with the beamwidth patterns and physical dimensions of the EUT.

11.2.1.2 EUT Deployment Considerations

A basic difference between Figs. 11.3 and 11.4 is that the former simulates the deployment of the EUT above a ground plane. The arrangement in Fig. 11.3 is intended to simulate the common situation in military settings in which the EUTs are mounted on a metallic deck, bulkhead, rack or cabinet. The arrangement in Fig. 11.4, on the other hand, uses a nonmetallic test stand and is intended to simulate the situation for portable, hand-held EUTs such as electric power tools.

In both figures, however, the respective deployments of the EUT, its power cable and its interconnecting leads are specified rather meticulously as discussed in Section 9.2.2. Reviewing briefly the rationale for this deployment:

1. It permits recognition of the existence of any represen- tative ground current loop area by controlling the height of the cable leads above a ground plane to 5 cm and by requiring a specific lead length. The size of the loop is significant because any magnetic or electric-field emis- sions (or its corresponding susceptibility) are proportional to its area.
2. It permits the exposure of a nominal length of cable. The apparent rationale for the 2 m length typically specified for military testing is that this minimum length is suffi- cient to establish its radiative or susceptive characteristics. Disregarding contributions by ground loop currents, any common-mode emission (or susceptibility) of cables is primarily by electric-field media. For a constant-level signal applied to the cable, coupling increases with fre- quency and begins to be significant at length, $L = \lambda/8$.

The lengths of cable shown in Figs. 11.3 and 11.4 are approx- imately 2 m and 1 m, which is $\lambda/8$ at 18 MHz and 36 MHz, respec- tively. Thus, if an EUT is either an emitter of, or susceptible to, electric fields, it may be expected to display this primarily through its power and interconnecting cables at frequencies of 30 MHz and higher. This propensity is consistent with the growing use of the absorbing clamp as a substitute for radiated measurements of EUT emissions at these frequencies (see Section 11.8).

It should be noted that any specification of cable length in Figs. 11.3 and 11.4 is superseded by use of the cable actually furnished as a normal part of, or accessory to, the EUT. If EMI test results are desired on the EUT without any contribution to results from its cable, the cable can be shielded by aluminum foil or by running it in a sheet metal trough, with any shield grounded along its en- tire length.

A cable much longer than 1 m which is furnished as part of the EUT and intended for testing with it should be deployed as discussed in Section 9.2.2.2. In brief, a coiled cable can produce the worst case of emissions and susceptibility (highest radiation and maximum coupling), a serpentine configuration presents the best case, and a straight run represents an intermediate situation. Consequently, either the straight run should be chosen or the cable should be arranged as it would be in its actual installation. In any case, the deployment should be detailed in the test plan.

11.2.2 Testing Large EUTs

This section examines the procedures to be followed for testing radiated EMI from EUTs which are larger than the approximately 0.1 m size implied by Figs. 11.3 and 11.4 or which consist of multiple modules. In some cases, these modules are interconnected by cables as long as 10 to 30 m.

11.2.2.1 Test Setups

Figure 11.5 shows a plan view of one such multiple-module system which illustrates the problem presented. The various modules of the EUT are aligned in a single row, with the interconnecting cables exposed in front of the modules. Depending on the number and size of the modules, this type of system can extend for a length of 2 to 6 m. Thus, as suggested by Fig. 11.5, there will exist a significant field gradient between the closest approach of

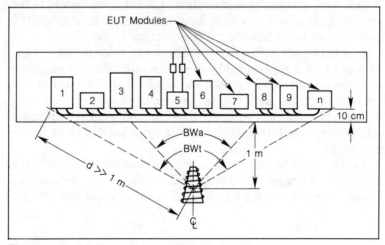

Figure 11.5—Multiple-Module EUT Setup Illustrating Gradient and Beamwidth Errors

the pickup antenna (at 1 m) and the farthest distance (at the edge of the EUT lineup). Further, at frequencies above 30 MHz, when an antenna with a more sharply directional pattern is used, the angle subtended by the ends of the EUT may exceed the antenna beamwidth.

One solution for reducing the magnitude of the resulting error is shown in Fig. 11.6. By using a corner of the shielded enclosure and deploying the test benches appropriately, the gradient resulting from changing antenna distance is reduced significantly. Because of the narrower beamwidths of the antennas used above 30 MHz, two runs may be required, with the antenna facing each of the two test benches. However, as suggested by the rays from the antenna in Fig. 11.5, more than two are needed for a linear array of the EUT.

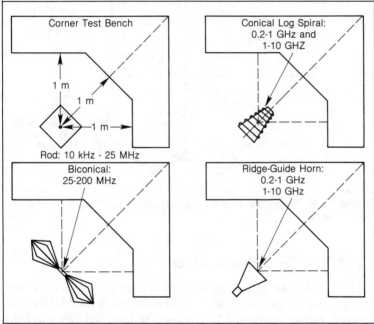

Figure 11.6—Gradient Effect Reduction by Testing in Corner of Shielded Enclosure

A third solution which is most appropriate for automated testing is to use the type of test stand shown in Fig. 9.6 and arrange the EUT modules as shown in Fig. 11.7. The antennas are repositioned by 90° after each test scan.

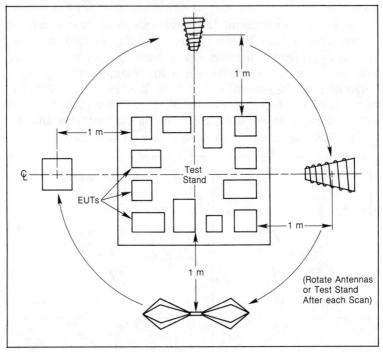

Figure 11.7—Setup for Automated Radiated EMI Testing of Multiple-Module EUT

11.2.2.2 Test Procedures

The appropriate test setup is selected from among those shown in Figs. 11.3 through 11.7 and the antenna(s) to be used for the first frequency scan positioned 1 m or another specified distance from the EUT. Operating the EMI analyzer or automated EMI system in accordance with the manufacturer's directions, select the peak detector function and the widest bandwidth position that will provide an adequate margin of sensitivity for both NB and BB measurements. Be sure to observe scanning speed limitations as a function of the selected bandwidth and frequency range to be scanned, as given by Eq. (6.1) in Chapter 6:

$$T > \Delta F/B_i^2$$

If the testing is to be performed manually, the entire frequency range of interest should be carefully scanned and measurements made to determine whether each response noted is NB or BB, in accordance with the criteria of Table 2.1 (Chapter 2). The respective NB or BB amplitude and center frequency of each significant response should be recorded; at least three readings should be made within each octave of coverage, including readings of the respective noise levels as required. Resulting data are plotted or otherwise processed for easy assessment versus applicable specification limits and for integration into the test report. Automated test systems should be operated to obtain the same information, as a minimum, with the specific process dependent on the system being used.

1. With the EUT deactivated, obtain a plot of the ambient noise to determine that it is suitably low, as discussed in Section 9.1.
2. Scan and record or plot the amplitudes of radiated emissions versus frequency, comparing them to the specified limits. If the setup in Fig. 11.7 is used, proceed to step 5.
3. If the corner setup of Fig. 11.6 is used and the angle subtended by the EUT exceeds the antenna beamwidth, rotate the antenna 45° clockwise and repeat step 2. If the linear setup in Fig. 11.5 is used, reposition the antenna horizontally to the right by a distance calculated in accordance with the considerations given in Section 8.4.1, then repeat step 2. Plot or record the data, superimposing it on the data acquired in step 2.
4. Repeat step 3, either by rotating the antenna 45° counterclockwise from its original position (Fig. 11.6) or by moving it to the left by the same distance from its original position (Fig. 11.5) as calculated for step 3, as applicable. Proceed to step 7.

5. For the test setup shown in Fig. 11.7, rotate either the antennas or the test stand by 90° and repeat step 2, superimposing the plotted data over the previous data. The antennas usually are rotated because the test stand is bonded to the floor of the enclosure.
6. Repeat step 5 for the other two 90° antenna positions.
7. As applicable, rearrange the EUT to expose additional faces to the antenna. Repeat steps 2 through 4 or 5 and 6, as applicable.
8. Process the data for incorporation into the test report, identifying out-of-specification NB and/or BB responses, as applicable.

11.2.3 Specialized Testing of EMI Emissions from Signal Cables

Reference 2 describes a method using a special fixture to position a signal-carrying cable bundle under test to measure the extent to which it radiates emissions into an adjacent bundle of conductors. A 1 m length of copper tubing positioned a fixed distance from the cable under test was used to intercept emissions and thus to serve as surrogate for a receptor cable.

Results obtained by this method with the pickup conductor both open-circuited and shorted were compared to measurements made with a current probe. Since fixed differences between measurements made with the probe and fixture were obtained for both conditions, with varying loads installed on the cable under test, it was concluded that the standard conducted EMI test method using the current probe, as discussed in Section 10.2, is a simple and valid method for determining the propensity of cables to radiate EMI.

11.3 Open-Field Testing of Transmitter Spurious and Harmonic Emissions

As discussed in Section 10.3.1 in the context of conducted testing, signals generated within the EUT may be present at the EUT antenna or other RF terminals. These signals may be radiated or conducted to other devices, and this constitutes a significant source of EMI problems. Examples of such potential emissions include local oscillator radiation from receivers and undesired modulation sidebands, harmonics and other spurious outputs from transmitters. Sources of broadband emissions at antenna terminals also include the switching of relays and the operation of blower motors within the EUT. The objective of the tests discussed in this section is to ensure that radiated levels of such emissions do not exceed acceptable levels.

Whenever the governing document allows a choice of conducted or radiated testing of these types of emissions, because of the relative complications of open-field testing, the conducted method should always be chosen. The choice is not available for military testing, and the radiated methods must be used when any of the following conditions apply:

1. The average transmitted power exceeds 5 kW (+67 dBm)
2. The fundamental transmitted frequency is higher than 1.24 GHz
3. The EUT antenna is an integral part of the transmitter and cannot reasonably be replaced by a suitable dummy load

Note that the frequency restriction of condition 2 does not apply to nonmilitary testing; low- to medium-power transmitters which do not have an integral antenna may be tested for antenna terminal **conducted** emissions, regardless of their operating frequency. Availability of directional couplers functioning to 40 GHz and notch filters tuning up to 12 GHz make conducted measurements quite feasible.

The limits for these types of emissions are usually specified relative to the peak transmitted power. The frequency ranges over which testing is performed typically are determined by the particular transmitted frequency and range from 10 kHz to at least 40 GHz.

11.3.1 Preparation for Testing

One of the fundamental parameters to be considered prior to testing is the distance from the transmitting antenna required to place the measuring antenna in the far field. As covered in Section 2.5.2, for an error in antenna gain of 0.3 dB:

$$R = D^2/\lambda \qquad \text{for } D > \lambda/2 \qquad (11.4a)$$

$$R = \lambda/2\pi \qquad \text{for } D < \lambda/2 \qquad (11.4b)$$

where,

D = largest dimension of transmitter antenna

λ = wavelength of fundamental transmission

It should be noted that conditions imposed by some military procedures are much more restrictive. For example, above 1.24 GHz, for a height above ground of D^2/d:

$$R = 2D^2/\lambda \qquad \text{for } d < 0.4D \qquad (11.5a)$$

$$R = (D + d)^2/\lambda \qquad \text{for } d > 0.4D \qquad (11.5b)$$

where,

d = largest dimension of the smaller antenna

For measurements on EUTs operating below 1.24 GHz, when the conducted procedure cannot be used and radiated testing is necessary, the separation between the transmitting and test antennas should be D^2/λ or 3λ, whichever is larger.

The next step involves determining the required sensitivity for the antenna(s), the EMI or spectrum analyzer and, if necessary, the low-noise preamplifier with protective filter that constitutes the receiving system. The far-field power density, P_D, for free-space conditions in watts per meter square (W/m^2), is:

$$P_D = E^2/Z = P_t G_t/4\pi R^2 \qquad (11.6)$$

Electric field strength, E, at that measuring site in volts per meter (V/m) is:

$$E = \sqrt{\frac{P_t G_t Z}{4\pi R^2}} = \sqrt{\frac{30 P_t G_t}{R^2}} \qquad (11.7)$$

where,

P_t = peak transmitted power in watts at f_o

G_t = gain of transmitter antenna at f_o

Z = wave impedance in far field = 120π = 377 Ω

R = distance from EUT to measurement site in meters

Since the antenna factor, AF, in dB(1/m) is by definition (see Section 2.5.5) AF = E − V, where V is the two-terminal voltage delivered into a 50 Ω load:

$$V = 10 \log \left(\frac{30 P_t G_t}{R^2} \right) - AF \qquad (11.8)$$

Since the typical purpose of this development is to determine the sensitivity needed to measure harmonics as much as 100 dB below the level of the fundamental transmission, 100 dB is subtracted from the expression in Eq. (11.8). Finally, 10 dB is subtracted to allow a 10 dB signal-to-noise margin, and 120 dB is added to convert from dBV to dBμV, producing a required sensitivity, in dBμV of:

$$V = 10 \log \left(\frac{P_t G_t}{R^2} \right) - AF + 25 \text{ dB} \qquad (11.9)$$

Using Eq. (2.31) of Chapter 2 to express this as power in a 50 Ω system (in dBm):

$$P_s = V_s - 107 \qquad (11.10)$$

where,

P_s = system power in dBm

V_s = system voltage in dBμV

Equations (11.9) and (11.10) are plotted in Fig. 11.8 for the system sensitivity versus transmitter effective radiated power, ERP (i.e., P_tG_t), and distance, R, with the antenna factor as a measurement parameter. Note that this sensitivity is defined as that into a 50 Ω load at the receiving antenna and that any loss in the transmission line connecting the antenna to the receiver must still be taken into account. Also note that Fig. 11.8 is based on harmonic levels of –100 dBc (100 dB down from fundamental carrier). For other harmonic levels γdBc, add $100 - |\gamma|$ to resulting receiver sensitivity.

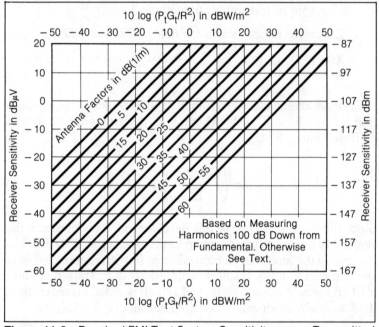

Figure 11.8—Required EMI Test System Sensitivity versus Transmitted Power

Illustrative Example 11.2

Determine the required minimum distance and measurement system sensitivity to perform harmonic measurements on a Loran C transmitter. Here, P_t = 10 kW, G_t = 2(3 dB), and f = 100 kHz (λ = 3 km). Since D ≈ λ/4, D < λ/2 and Eq. (11.4b) applies to make

$R = \lambda/2\pi = 3,000/2\pi = 477$ m. Also, according to Eq. (11.9), the required measurement system sensitivity in dBμV is:

$$V_s = 10 \log (2P/R^2) + 25 - AF$$

$$= 10 \log (2 \times 10^4/477^2) + 25 - AF$$

$$= 14.4 - AF$$

Because of the relatively high antenna factors of passive rod antennas, an active rod antenna should be used; however, to minimize intermodulation in its active circuits, it should incorporate a high-pass filter capable of suitably rejecting the 100 kHz fundamental.

When additional sensitivity is required in the measurement system, the solution is to use either a receiving antenna with a lower antenna factor (higher gain), a more sensitive EMI analyzer or both. The sensitivity of an available EMI analyzer or spectrum analyzer can be improved by preceding it with a low-noise, wideband amplifier, suitably protected by a band-pass filter. As discussed in Section 3.4.2, the resultant noise factor, $\underline{F}$, of three networks in series is:

$$\underline{F} = \underline{F}_1 + \frac{\underline{F}_2 - 1}{G_1} + \frac{\underline{F}_3 - 1}{G_1 G_2}$$

Applying this to the measurement system being discussed, where the resulting overall noise figure, in dB, is F_T:

$$F_T = 10 \log [1 + (\underline{F}_2 - 1)/G_1 + (\underline{F}_3 - 1)/G_1 G_2]$$

where,

$\underline{F}_1$ = noise factor of passive band-pass filter = 1

$\underline{F}_2$ = noise factor of low-noise amplifier

$\underline{F}_3$ = noise factor of EMI analyzer

G_1 = insertion gain of band-pass filter (fractional for lossy elements such as this (see Section 3.4.2)

G_2 = gain of low-noise amplifier

Note that G2 should be large enough to make $G_1 G_2 > (\underline{F}_3 - 1)$ to make the third term within the parentheses negligible. When this is the case:

$$F_T \approx 10 \log [1 + (\underline{F}_2 - 1)/G_1]$$

Thus, the improvement in system sensitivity, ΔS in dB, is the original noise figure, $F_3 = 10 \log \underline{F}_3$, minus the new noise figure, F_T, or:

$$\Delta S \approx \underline{F}_3 - 10 \log [1 + (\underline{F}_2 - 1)/G_1] \qquad (11.11)$$

Illustrative Example 11.3

Calculate the improvement in system sensitivity and the required traveling wave tube (TWT) amplifier gain when its noise figure, $\underline{F}_2 = 6$ dB, $\underline{F}_3 = 30$ dB and the insertion loss of the protective band-pass filter is 3 dB.

$$\Delta S = 30 \text{ dB} - 10 \log [1 + 2(4 - 1)] \approx 21 \text{ dB}$$

In addition:

$$G_1 G_2 > (1{,}000 - 1), \text{ or } G_2 > 2 \times 999$$

This is slightly less than 33 dB. Thus a gain of 33 dB or greater would be adequate. See Section 3.4.2 and its accompanying reference for a discussion of the impact of preamplifier addition on overall dynamic range.

11.3.2 Test Setup

Illustrated in Figs. 11.9 and 11.10 are test setups for the open-field measurement of spurious and harmonic emissions. Some existing military standards specify the use of spectrum analyzers as the measuring instrument. At the time these standards were written, uncalibrated microwave spectrum analyzers were much more commonly available in military and industrial communications laboratories than were microwave EMI analyzers. As discussed in Section 3.7, the advantages provided by the spectrum analyzers'

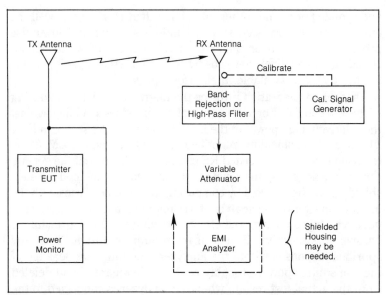

Figure 11.9—Typical Setup for Testing Radiated Spurious and Harmonics, 10 kHz to 1 GHz

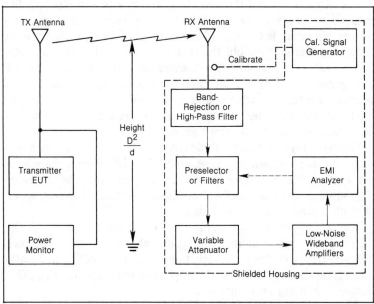

Figure 11.10—Typical Setup for Testing Radiated Spurious and Harmonics, 1 to 18 GHz

wide dispersion and other attractive features might well be outweighed by the need to use band-pass filters and low-noise preamplifiers to compensate for their vulnerability to overload, poor shielding and relatively low sensitivity. Since EMI analyzers suitable for the task are available, their use is preferred.

Another consideration involves the degree to which the housing of the EMI analyzer or spectrum analyzer provides shielding against the relatively high power of the EUT transmitter. As shown in Figs. 11.9 and 11.10, shielding might be necessary around the EMI/spectrum analyzer and associated RF components to prevent the generation of spurious responses within the analyzer. The need for such shielding can be checked by comparing measurement runs with the input connector of the analyzer terminated in its characteristic impedance and comparing the effect of having the EUT transmitter passive versus active. In lieu of or in addition to shielding, any spurious responses within the analyzer resulting from leakage of the transmitter power probably could be disregarded and deleted from the actual test results when the analyzer is connected to the receiving antenna. Additional suppression measures could be required to provide a measurement margin, such as 10 dB.

The RF cable from the receiving antenna to the input of the measurement equipment should always be kept as short as possible, to minimize both signal loss and signal pickup. One way of achieving this is to mount the receiver front end at the antenna. Direct cable pickup of the transmitter fundamental can be minimized by use of triaxial cable or by slipping a 0.3 m piece of suppressant tubing over the end of the cable nearest the input to the band-rejection filter. The outer shield of the triaxial cable should be grounded only at the analyzer end.

The band-rejection filters shown in Figs. 11.9 and 11.10 are needed to block the transmitter fundamental and thus reduce any propensity of the EMI/spectrum analyzer to generate spurious responses or exhibit suppression effects because of the presence of such a strong out-of-band signal.

The calibration signal generators shown in the setups are for the purpose of substitution calibration ahead of the unknown characteristics of the band-rejection filter. However, it is usually more convenient to calibrate the measurement system at this point before beginning an actual run.

Where the azimuth and elevation of the transmitter antenna can be varied, this should be done to produce a maximum signal at the test antenna. After the maximum signal is found, record the azimuth and elevation angles of the effective boresight condition.

The receiving antenna should be raised or lowered to obtain a maximum reading on the EMI or spectrum analyzer at each frequency of measurement. Theoretically (based on geometric optics), for flat terrain having no obstacles, the receiving antenna height, h_a, corresponding to the **first** maximum in the resultant of the direct and ground-reflected waves is, in meters:

$$h_a = R\lambda/4h_t = 75R/h_t f$$

$$\lambda \ll R \text{ and } h_t < R$$

where,

R = distance between EUT antenna and receiving antenna, meters

λ = wavelength at test frequency

h_t = height of EUT antenna above ground

f = test frequency in MHz

11.3.3 Test Procedures

As already mentioned, each test procedure, including the following one, assumes that the reader has read and heeded the related sections of Chapter 9.

1. Set the transmitter frequency at the mid value of any tuning range and adjust all controls for typical performance. Measure the transmitter power output using a suitable power monitor.
2. Select a bandwidth for the EMI/spectrum analyzer that encompasses at least 90 percent of the signal spectrum intentionally radiated by the transmitter antenna. This should be at least as wide as the 10 dB transmitter bandwidth. For a pulsed signal, it should be at least $2/\tau$, where τ is the pulse width.
3. Key the transmitter. Tune the EMI/spectrum analyzer for maximum output indication at the transmitted frequency.

If either or both of the antennas have directivity, align them to obtain maximum indication. This might involve adjusting the elevation or azimuth angle of the antennas for maximum indication. Verbal communication between the sites via radiotelephone will facilitate this process.

4. As appropriate, disconnect the receiving antenna and connect a substitution calibration generator to the input of the EMI/spectrum analyzer. (Note that the use of a substitution generator is no longer necessary when using a modern calibrated EMI analyzer.) Tune the signal generator to the receiver frequency and modulate its output to simulate the EUT transmission. Set the generator output to give the same EMI/spectrum analyzer reading as that previously obtained from the EUT transmission. Record the signal generator frequency, with the accuracy of the frequency counter and the signal generator output level in dBm or $dB\mu V$ into 50 Ω.

5. Using Eq. (11.8), calculate the transmitter ERP (i.e., P_tG_t) and compare it to the product of the antenna gain times the power monitor readings from step 1. From Eq. (11.8), the voltage, V, in dBV, produced at the EMI/spectrum analyzer by the transmitter fundamental is:

$$V = 10 \log(30\ P_tG_t/R^2) - AF$$

or,

$$V = 10 \log 30 + 10 \log(P_tG_t) - 20 \log R - AF$$

Therefore, the effective transmitter power, ERP = $10 \log (P_tG_t)$, in dBW is:

$$ERP = 10 \log (P_tG_t) = V - 15 + 20 \log R + AF$$

Or, subtracting 120 dB to change dBV to $dB\mu V$:

$$ERP = V + 20 \log R + AF - 135 \qquad (11.12)$$

Or, using Eq. (2-31) to convert V in $dB\mu V$ to power, P, in dBm:

$$ERP = P + 20 \log R + AF - 28 \qquad (11.13)$$

The results should agree within ± 5 dB. If the difference exceeds this amount, check the test setup for errors such as in measuring distance, amplitude calibration or substitution, power monitoring of the transmitter, frequency tuning or drift, antenna factors and antenna boresight alignment. It should be noted that some military requirements specify agreement of the two measurements to within ± 2 dB; however, this is not believed to be realistic because an error analysis conducted in accordance with the principles of Chapter 8 will show that perhaps only 10 percent of the measurements will agree to within ± 2 dB.

Assuming that the results are within limits, the relative ERP value becomes a zero reference from which amplitudes at spurious and harmonic frequencies will be referenced to determine compliance to specification limits.

6. With the band-reject filter connected, tune the analyzer to f_0 and scan below and above f_0 to locate spurious and harmonic transmitted products, concentrating on harmonic radiations from the second to the tenth harmonics. Verify that apparent harmonic transmissions truly are originating at the transmitter and not from other radiators in the environment by keying the transmitter on and off. This process can be facilitated by watching the modulation on a CRT video or spectrum display. The apparent spurious signal could be an intermodulation product or harmonic developed at points of complete or partial discontinuity such as rusty bolts or corroded connections in local structures. See Section 11.5 for methods of localizing such a product. If found to be bona fide transmissions, measure their respective amplitudes by repeating step 4.

11.4 Radiated Emissions from Vehicles and Engine-Driven Equipment

This section discusses the testing of radiated EMI from a wide variety of tactical and special-purpose vehicles and engine-driven equipment, including their normally installed electrical and electronic equipment. The purpose of such testing is to reduce the probability that radiated emissions will be coupled to nearby vehicles and systems, thus disrupting their normal operation. The categories of vehicles to which this type of testing is applied by the military include both tactical and special-purpose and range from armored personnel carriers to bulldozers to sedans and staff cars. For civilian-type vehicles, the military specifications reference and adapt procedures developed by the Society of Automotive Engineers (SAE), including J551 and J1816.

11.4.1 Test Preparation and Setup

Figures 11.11 and 11.12 illustrate typical setups used in radiated EMI testing of military vehicles. The measuring antennas are deployed around the vehicle as shown in Fig. 11.11. The number of test positions is usually not specified, but is to be sufficient to obtain an accurate measurement of the maximum radiation from the vehicle. This requires the use of sampling techniques such as those discussed in Chapter 9.

Typically, the horizontal location of antennas, as shown in Fig. 11.11, is at a distance from the EUT, $X_m = 2$ m. The distance between sampling stations, Y_m, should be the lesser of X_m, or X_m times the beamwidth in radians of the measuring antenna. That is:

$$Y_m = X_m \tag{11.14}$$

or,

$$Y_m = X_m(\Theta_H/57.3) \tag{11.15}$$

where,

Θ_H = antenna horizontal beamwidth in degrees

Equation (11.15) results in a distance $Y_m < X_m$ when $\Theta_H < 57.3°$ (one radian). Thus, $Y_m = X_m$ for a rod antenna ($\Theta_H = 360°$), the biconical antenna ($\Theta_H \approx 120°$) and the conical log spiral ($\Theta_H \approx 70°$). However, if the antenna used is a double-ridged-guide type ($\Theta_H \approx 37°$), the result is $Y_m \approx 1.3$ m, which is the measuring distance to be used.

The vertical location of the measurement antenna corresponds to a station sampling distance, Z_m, starting at 1 m above ground

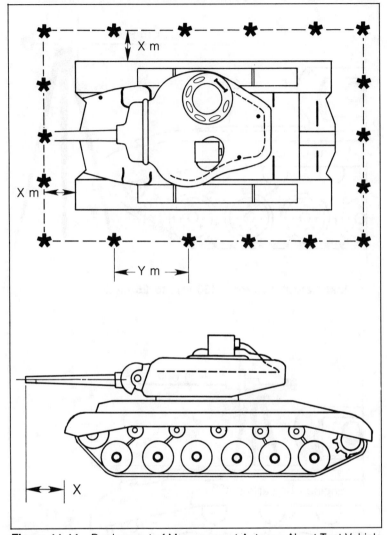

Figure 11.11—Deployment of Measurement Antenna About Test Vehicle

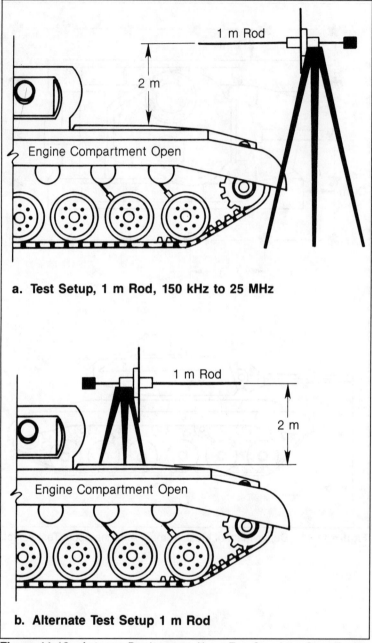

a. Test Setup, 1 m Rod, 150 kHz to 25 MHz

b. Alternate Test Setup 1 m Rod

Figure 11.12—Antenna Deployment About Top Openings Over Engine Compartments

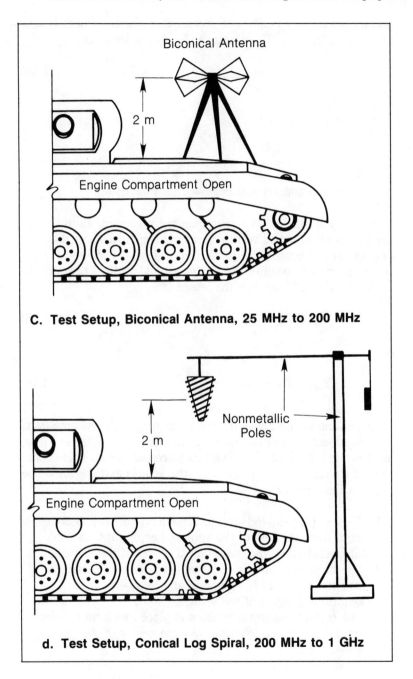

C. Test Setup, Biconical Antenna, 25 MHz to 200 MHz

d. Test Setup, Conical Log Spiral, 200 MHz to 1 GHz

and extending to a height not greater than the maximum height of the vehicle, h_{max}. The distance, Z_m, is the lesser of:

$$Z_m = X_m \tag{11.16}$$

or,

$$Z_m = X_m(\Theta_V/57.3) \tag{11.17}$$

where,

Θ_V = antenna vertical beamwidth in degrees

Diagonal polarization measurements are preferred, so to reduce separate horizontal and vertical measurements to a single diagonal one, the actual beamwidth to be used in Eqs. (11.15) and (11.17) is the geometric mean of the horizontal and vertical beamwidth, $\Theta = \sqrt{\Theta_H \Theta_V}$. Thus, use the lesser of:

$$Y_m = Z_m = X_m \tag{11.18}$$

or,

$$Y_m = Z_m = X_m \frac{\sqrt{\Theta_H \Theta_H}}{57.3} \tag{11.19}$$

Exceptions to the above involve measuring radiated emissions from top openings over the engine compartments of vehicles. Here, as shown in Fig. 11.12, the antenna is placed as follows, while maintaining a clearance of 2 m between the vehicle and the reference point of the antenna:

1. The 1 m (41-inch) rod antenna is tilted over the engine compartment from the end of the vehicle, keeping the antenna horizontal along the longitudinal center of the vehicle.
2. The biconical antenna is placed with its axis horizontal over the center of the opening and in a vertical longitudinal plane of the vehicle.
3. The conical log spiral antenna is placed with nose pointing down, its axis vertical, over the center of the opening.

11.4.2 Test Procedure

The EUT vehicle is operated or exercised in a manner which causes maximum radiated emissions within normal operating procedures; thus, the test is to be performed with all electrical equipment in operation. Load conditions should be adjusted so that the electrical charging system is operational throughout the test; voltage regulators, hydraulic power packs and pneumatic pumps are all to be exercised.

Unless otherwise specified, starting motors and switches associated with starting the vehicle, short-duration starting aids and engine-protective warning devices usually do not require tests. However, low-air warning devices for air-brake vehicles usually are required to meet the emission limits while warning of low air pressure.

The measurements proceed as follows:

1. Place the antennas as shown in Fig. 11.11 or 11.12, as applicable. Select the maximum available receiver bandwidth(s) or those specified in the test plan for the respective portions of the frequency spectrum to be scanned. Shut down the EUT and measure the ambient level to determine that it is suitably low (see Section 9.1.1). Reactivate the EUT and allow it to warm up, as appropriate.
2. Scan and plot or record the amplitude versus frequency of the radiated emissions.
3. Shift the antennas clockwise by a distance Y_m from the original deployment and repeat step 2, superimposing new data over the old as appropriate.
4. Repeat step 3 as many times as necessary to encircle the vehicle.
5. Elevate the antenna by a distance Z_m above the 1 m height of the first series of measurements. Repeat steps 2 through 4.
6. Repeat step 5, if applicable [see the text associated with Eqs. (11.16) and (11.17)].
7. Where top openings exist over engine compartments, repeat step 2 in accordance with Fig. 11.12.
8. For any signal within 6 dB of the limit, adjust the polarization of the test antenna for maximum pickup.

11.5 Testing Emissions from Overhead Power Lines

This section covers the measurement of EMI radiated from overhead power lines. For military testing, even when such measurements are not required for compliance to current versions of MIL-STD-461 and -462, they still apply for determining compliance to earlier versions mandated by continuing contracts. In the civilian sector of testing, they will always be essential for evaluating the electromagnetic environmental impact of new overhead power line installations.

The following is a brief survey of the various sources of EMI emissions from overhead power lines:

Narrowband Reradiations

Overhead power lines can act as extended antenna systems which can intercept and then conductively transmit for many miles various communication-electronic and other narrowband radiated transmissions. Such signals can be inductively coupled to nearby receptors. Also, discontinuities in RF impedance on the lines, caused by such factors as cracked or broken insulators, can result in the reradiation of RF signals. In severe situations, such transmissions could include intermodulation products developed at the points of discontinuity or partial discontinuity such as rusty bolts or corroded connections.

Broadband Reradiations

External broadband transmission sources external to the lines can be picked up, modified and reradiated by the same mechanisms as discussed above for narrowband sources.

Line-Originated Broadband Radiations

This class of EMI includes line-originated broadband emissions from the following sources:

1. Load changes: The switching on and off by large users or substations of inductive or high-current loads develops transients on the overhead lines having pulse durations and rise times on the order of 10 ns.

2. Gap-Type Discharges: This phenomenon is an arcing over, or sparking, which occurs at twice the line frequency (120 Hz in the U.S.A.). It typically is oscillatory in nature and exists at dirty or defective insulators, tie wires or other hardware. It tends to be the predominant EMI source for lines carrying less than 70 kV and is most significant in the VHF and lower UHF ranges.

3. Corona Discharge: This is a partial electrical discharge due to ionization of the air at or near the surface of the conductor. As compared to dry and ideal conditions, it is enhanced up to 20 dB by factors such as rain, snow, frost, fog, high relative humidity, conductor contamination and surface burrs. This type of noise tends to predominate for overhead lines carrying voltages greater than 110 kV and has an RF spectrum which falls off rapidly above about 15 MHz.

Because of their diverse origins and manifestations, emissions from overhead lines may be predominantly either coherent or non-coherent and may fall off with distance, d, from the apparent source at rates ranging from $1/d$ to $1/d^3$. Observation of the difference in EMI analyzer readings as its bandwidth is switched will be necessary to determine whether the noise is predominantly coherent ($\Delta V = 20 \log \Delta B_i$) or noncoherent ($\Delta V = 10 \log \Delta B_i$). Use the criteria of Table 2.1 to determine whether the noise is NB or BB for compliance with military specifications.

11.5.1 Military Testing

11.5.1.1 Test Preparation and Setup

Figure 11.13 illustrates a typical deployment of electric-field antennas for testing of radiated EMI emissions. The antennas typically are deployed for measurements on only one side of the tower if the line rating is 70 kV or less, but on both sides for lines carrying voltages higher than 70 kV.

To eliminate the possibility of inadvertently measuring signals not originating on the line, as discussed above, a second measurement should be made on any suspected signal at a <u>distance from the line</u> roughly twice that of the first, or at $d = 2\sqrt{15^2 + h^2}$. At frequencies for which $d < \lambda/2\pi$, the level should decrease by 12 to 18 dB and at frequencies for which $d \geqslant \lambda/2\pi$, the level should decrease by about 6 dB if the source is the overhead line or its hardware. (If an ambient source were within 300 m or so of the measured line, changes in level exceeding 6 dB could be observed when changing the measurement distance.) However, if the change in level is significantly less than 6 dB, the source is probably not the overhead line or its hardware. A possible exception to this rule arises when the power line is acting as a large-area radiator; in this event, for $d < \lambda/2\pi$, the rate of decrease in level becomes unpredictable and can be much less than 6 dB. A shielded loop antenna or probe can prove very useful in finding the sources of suspected ambient signals. Much useful information on the nature of the EMI and probable sources can be derived by monitoring its demodulated audio or video using headphones or video/spectrum displays.

Measurements should always be made in a clear area, free of any nearby objects, including personnel. This eliminates proximity effects on the measurement antennas. A separate monitoring receiver should be tuned to a frequency at which it is clearly responding

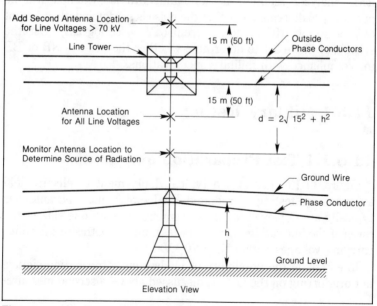

Figure 11.13—Deployment for Military Testing of Radiated EMI from Overhead Lines

only to noise from the line, and it should be left at that frequency during any test run. If its indication changes by more than 6 dB during the run, this can be taken as an indication that conditions affecting the line under test have changed and that the run is not valid.

Before beginning any test, it should be verified that the operating conditions for the line under test are typical and not subject to some anomaly such as brownout. Measurements should be made during daylight hours in fair weather to minimize condensation conditions on the line. Avoid other unusual conditions under which measurements would be abnormally high, including the presence of electrical storms sufficiently close to affect readings and prolonged periods of dry weather when insects, dust or other contaminants may temporarily accumulate on the line and its tower hardware.

11.5.1.2 Test Procedures

1. Select the maximum available bandwidth(s), or bandwidths as specified in the test plan, B_m, in the EMI analyzer or measurement system for the frequency segments to be scanned. Deploy the measurement and monitoring antennas as shown in Fig. 11.13, orienting each for maximum reading from the line under test.
2. Scan and record the levels of radiated emissions across the frequency spectrum of interest. Repeat the scan and superimpose the new data on top of the original data to confirm repeatability.
3. If the emissions have not been automatically identified as NB or BB by the measurement system, select the next narrower bandwidth, B, without disturbing the system in any other way and repeat the scan, juxtaposing the data on that obtained in step 2. Then determine whether data showing a lower reading for the narrower bandwidth is coherent or noncoherent by noting the difference, Δ, in dB, between the two readings and then applying the following formula:

$$\Delta = N \log (B_m/B) \qquad (11.20)$$

where,

$N = 20$ for coherent emissions

$N = 10$ for noncoherent emissions

$10 < N < 20$ for composite emissions

See Table 2.1 (Chapter 2) for other methods of NB/BB determination.

4. Calculate the broadband field strength, E_B, for each EMI response of interest by first applying the appropriate antenna factor to determine its apparent narrowband level, E, in dBμV/m. Then, apply the following formula to convert E, in dBμV/m, to E_B in dBμV/m/MHz:

$$E_B = E + N \log (1 \text{ MHz}/B_m)$$

Be sure to indicate for all data in the test report the calculations used to determine both N and the BB levels.

5. Should any doubt exist as to whether emissions originated from the power line, repeat steps 1 and 2 at a second distance from the line as discussed in Section 11.5.1. Repeat further steps only as necessary.

6. For overhead power lines with voltages in excess of 70 kV, repeat steps 1 through 5 with antennas on the other side of the tower as shown in Fig. 11.13. Choose the higher of the levels measured on opposite sides as the measured level of radiated emissions.

11.5.2 Power Distribution Industry Testing

As exemplified by procedures detailed in ANSI/IEEE Std 430[4], the principal orientation of nonmilitary EMI testing of overhead lines is toward measurement of noise from corona discharges. Although they are also applicable to other continuous or repetitive noise sources such as gap discharges and harmonics, the Std 430 procedures are not appropriate for transient sources such as switching or breaker operations.

Measurements to determine the environmental impact of a new overhead line installation are often made in sets of three. As the first step, the ambient EMI is measured in the right-of-way prior to power line installation. Then, it is measured again after installation is physically complete, but before power is applied. Finally, the measurements are repeated with the line fully operational.

Power authorities also measure radiated EMI from overhead lines in conjunction with investigating and mitigating complaints of EMI to television or radio signals at locations near the overhead lines. Measurements near the line of magnetic fields at the power frequency and its harmonics as they relate to possible biological effects are beyond the scope of this volume.

Except for the specific procedures of Section 11.5.1.2, all of the foregoing information in Section 11.5 is equally pertinent to non-military testing. Therefore, the following discussion emphasizes only those aspects which are unique to civilian-oriented testing. Reference 4 should be read and understood in its entirety before actual test performance.

11.5.2.1 Techniques Used to Characterize EMI from Overhead Lines

The power distribution industry uses both a **short-term survey** and a **long-term survey** to characterize the EMI performance of overhead lines. A short-term survey requires both a **lateral profile** and a **frequency spectrum** while a long-term survey consists of a statistical sampling presented in an amplitude-probability distribution (APD) format.

The **lateral profile** is a plot of the ground-level EMI field strength at a frequency of 0.5, 73.5 or 150 MHz as a function of horizontal distance from, and at a right angle to, the power line conductors. The test site for such a profile is prescribed either as midspan, opposite a self-supporting tower or both. The measurements for a lateral profile are usually taken out to 80 m from the outer phase conductor(s), (for ac lines) or from the positive pole (for dc lines). The lateral profile is always to be accompanied by a sketch of the line configuration, as shown in Ref. 4.

The **frequency spectrum** is a plot of the ground-level EMI field strength versus frequency measured at a midspan test site at a lateral distance of 15 m from the outer phase conductor(s) (for ac lines) or the positive pole (for dc lines). For two bipolar dc lines in close proximity that have the positive poles as the inner conductors, the measurements should be made at 15 m from the outer, or negative, conductor. If an X-Y plotter or other scanning technique is not used, measurements are required at a minimum of the 10 highest-level responses per decade. Measurements are made on only one side of the line unless the EMI radiation is likely to be assymmetrical.

The purpose of the **long-term survey** is to obtain statistical data on the ground-level EMI field strength from the line at a frequency of 0.5, 73.5 or 150 MHz over an extended period of time. The measurement location is a midspan test site at a lateral distance of 15 m, as projected along the ground, from the outer phase conductor(s) (for ac lines) or the positive pole (for dc lines). When two positive poles are the inner conductors of two bipolar lines in close proximity, the measurement is dimensioned from the outer, or negative, conductor. The sampling rate must be sufficiently high and the total period of the data collection must be sufficiently long to reflect the normal distribution of weather conditions at the site. The resulting data is then presented in a graphical format showing on its Y-axis the percentage of time that each amplitude on the X-axis is exceeded. See Ref. 4.

11.5.2.2 Other Aspects of Power Industry EMI Testing

Although obviously constrained by the required location with respect to the line being measured, the test site to the extent feasible should be free of buildings, trees, fences and other overhead lines. Background noise at each frequency of measurement should be at least 6 dB below the EMI level from the line under test. As detailed in Ref. 4, a number of pertinent environmental parameters should be recorded to accompany all measurements, including the elevation above sea level and all aspects of the weather conditions.

Whenever possible, the test site selection should be at least 10 km from obvious discontinuities such as those created by terminations, abrupt transitions and traps. The extent to which the site selected is vulnerable to standing waves from such discontinuities can be determined by taking a **longitudinal profile:** this is a plot of the ground-level EMI field strength at a single frequency at a constant distance from the power line as a function of distance along the line. The typical distance from the line is 15 to 30 m, and the EMI level is measured at a minimum of 10 equal consecutive increments along the line for a distance centered at midspan of 150 m or one-half wavelength at the test frequency, whichever is longer. Standing waves are considered to exist if a plot of the resulting field strengths versus distance approximates that of a sine wave with its negative half inverted.

The EMI analyzer and antennas used for testing overhead lines should conform to requirements of ANSI C63.2[5] and CISPR Publication 16.[6] Although quasi-peak detection is preferred for measurements concerned with protection of radio and television broadcasting, use of other detector processes is allowed for EMC evaluation of overhead lines relative to their influences on other communication services. In many cases, power industry investigators make both a broadband measurement using quasipeak detection and a narrowband measurement using average detection. Reference 4 includes a number of precautions for measurement antennas unique to their use near overhead power lines, including techniques for avoiding corona at the tips of their elements and possible erratic behavior resulting from the discharge onto them of ions or charged aerosols.

11.6 Radiated EMI Emission Testing on Open-Area Test Sites

This section discusses the procedures used for EMI testing of radiated emissions from products with nonmilitary applications which typically are tested on open-area test sites. Sections 9.3.1 through 9.3.1.5 cover various details of the test installation and should be referred to as background for the procedures discussed.

11.6.1 Test Preparation and Setup

All test instrumentation should be in conformance with the recommendations and specifications of ANSI C63.2, CISPR 16 or other appropriate documents. Radiated emissions to be measured include those from the EUT and all of its signal and power cabling. The EUT should be set up and operated in a manner representative of its actual intended use.[6-8]

Since each predominant emission typically is to be measured at the azimuth at which it produces maximum field strength, it is necessary to rotate the EUT with respect to the receiving antenna. The preferred method of accomplishing this rotation is use of a properly designed and installed turntable as discussed in Section 9.3.1.1. For heavy, large or stationary EUTs for which an adequate turntable is not available, it is necessary to move the test antenna and much of its associated measurement equipment around the EUT to determine the radial of maximum emission. When such rotation of antenna positions around the EUT is necessary, it should be noted that dimensional criteria applicable to turntable operation do not apply; instead, the minimum clearance distance is a circular area centered on the EUT and having a diameter three times the maximum distance between the measuring antenna and the closest point of the EUT.[8]

Tests of radiated emissions are normally performed at standardized distances of 3, 10 or 30 m from the EUT. Provided that equivalency can be shown, tests specified for 10 or 30 m frequently are permitted at shorter distances, but usually not less than 3 m. When tests are made at the shorter distances of 3 or 10 m, at frequencies between 30 MHz and 1,000 MHz, they are extrapolated to distances of 10 m or 30 m using a 20 dB/decade relationship unless a different relationship can be validated. Extrapolations from greater to lesser distances are not recommended.

At frequencies above 30 MHz, the measuring antenna should be scanned in height from 1 to 4 m above the ground plane for measurement distances of 10 m or less. For a measurement distance of 30 m, the range of antenna height should be from 2 m to 6 m above the ground plane. At frequencies above 300 MHz, it may be necessary to reduce the antenna height to avoid null effects in determining the maximum radiation levels. If the EUT comprises extended radiating elements such as receivers or transmitters with integral antennas, it will be necessary to search in height for the maximum radiation.

A typical test configuration for testing in open-area and alternate sites is shown in Fig. 11.14. The LISN, which is used for conducted power line EMI testing, may be left in place to provide a consistent ac source impedance.

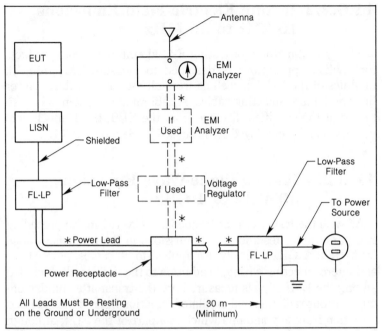

Figure 11.14—Suggested Layout for Open-Area Testing

11.6.2 Test Procedures

11.6.2.1 Testing Magnetic-Field Emissions, 10 kHz to 30 MHz

The typical procedure for testing magnetic emissions from products with nonmilitary applications is used to measure EMI from all modules of the EUT as well as all cables, power lines and interconnecting wiring. A calibrated loop antenna, such as discussed in Section 4.3.2, is positioned vertically at the specified distance from the EUT and is oriented for maximum response.

It should be noted that it is common for regulatory agencies to specify measurements of magnetic fields using a shielded loop antenna but to require that the measured H-fields be expressed in terms of their equivalent E-fields by multiplying them by 377 (adding 51.5 dB). Many loop antenna manufacturers accommodate this convention by furnishing calibration data in E-field terms.

11.6.2.2 Testing Electric-Field Emissions, 10 kHz to 30 MHz

The typical method for testing E-field emissions from products for civilian applications is designed to measure EMI from all modules of the EUT as well as from all associated cables, power lines and interconnecting cables. A calibrated rod antenna is positioned at the specified distance from the EUT; the 1 m (41-inch) version usually employed is discussed in Section 4.3.3.1.

11.6.2.3 Testing Plane-Wave Emissions, 30 MHz to 1 GHz

As with the tests at lower frequencies covered in the preceding two paragraphs, tests for EMI emissions in the frequency range 30 MHz to 1 GHz typically are applied to all cables, power lines and interconnecting wiring, in addition to the EUT itself. Included among the EMI signals measured are the transmitter fundamental, spurious radiation and oscillator radiation but not the intended radiation from any antenna which is a part of the EUT; although both broadband and narrowband signals are measured, typically, a quasipeak detection process is used. This produces a reasonably meaningful reading regardless of the bandwidth characteristics of the noise.

Frequency scans to characterize the EMI profile of the EUT typically are made at a minimum of four azimuth angles spaced by 90°. Additional azimuths are examined if directional radiation patterns are suspected. Measurements are always made at the azimuth which produces maximum readings of the radiated levels. Linearly polarized antennas are positioned at specified distances from the EUT and measurements made in both horizontal and vertical polarizations. Portable uncalibrated probe-type antennas such as discussed in Section 4.3.1 and 4.3.4 are useful in establishing the azimuth of maximum radiation.

11.7 In Situ Testing of Radiated EMI

When the EUT is tested as installed at the end user's location, the results are regarded as unique to both the EUT and the environment of its installation. However, after testing has been performed showing compliance at three or more such sites, the cumulative results can be considered representative for all sites. Unless detailed instructions for testing appear in the instructions for the individual equipment, measurements should be made to locate the radial of maximum radiated emission at a distance of 30 m from the EUT. If measurements at 30 m are impractical, measurements can be made at lesser distances and extrapolated to 30 m on the basis of 20 dB/decade or on the basis of the relationship determined by taking measurements at a minimum of two different distances. Insertion of a LISN into the setup is frequently not practical and, to make the results truly representative of the particular site, a LISN should not be used.

11.8 Use of the Absorbing Clamp for Testing Radiated EMI Power

This method is a substitute for the actual measurement of radiated EMI emissions, as discussed above, but with the advantage of being unaffected by either the reflection problems of shielded enclosures or the high ambient levels of open-area testing. It is the standard method recommended by the CISPR for testing radiated EMI from small appliances at frequencies from 30 MHz to 1 GHz.

Rationale for use of the absorbing clamp, which is described in detail in Section 4.4.1, is based on the fact that EMI from small EUTs such as household appliances is radiated primarily from the first meter or two of their power cords and not from the EUTs themselves. As detailed in Section 4.4.1, the absorbing clamp transforms the EMI current flowing in the power cord into a proportional voltage which is fed to the EMI analyzer; since the current flow in the cord is proportional to the EMI power, the EMI analyzer thus indicates the level of EMI power available to be radiated.

Figure 9.9 shows the setup for using the absorbing clamp to measure EMI power. The EUT is placed in an insulating support at least 40 cm from any other metallic object, with its power cord positioned horizontally at the same height and connected to the power source. If the EUT is a floor-standing unit, it is placed on the floor and its power cord oriented at an angle of 45° until it reaches a height of 40 cm above the floor.

The absorbing clamp is closed around the cord and located so that it can be shifted along the power cord on its rollers. At each frequency of measurement, as the clamp is shifted along the cord away from the EUT, the current transformer portion of the device couples to the EMI analyzer standing wave maxima which result from the power line acting as a resonant antenna. The first maximum nearest the EUT is taken as representing the EMI potential. If this point is not accessible, the measurement is taken at the second maximum. After application of any correction factor furnished by the probe manufacturer, the EMI voltage in dBμV is directly translatable into EMI power in specified units of dBpW.[6, 7]

11.9 References

1. MIL-STD-462, "Electromagnetic Interference Characteristics, Measurement of," 31 July 1967.
2. SAE ARP 1972 (January 1986), "Recommended Measurement Practices and Procedures for EMC Testing," (Warrendale, PA: Society of Automotive Engineers), prepared by SAE AE4 Committee on Electromagnetic Compatibility.
3. MIL-STD-461C "Electromagnetic Emission and Susceptibility Requirements for the Control of Electromagnetic Interference," 4 August 1986.
4. ANSI/IEEE Std 430-1986, "IEEE Standard Procedures for the Measurement of Radio Noise from Overhead Power Lines and Substations" (New York: IEEE).
5. ANSI 63.2, "American National Standard Specification for Electromagnetic Noise and Field-Strength Instrumentation, 10 kHz to 1 GHz" (New York: IEEE).
6. CISPR 16, "Specification for Radio Frequency Measuring Apparatus and Measurement Methods."
7. ANSI C63.4-1981, "Radio-Noise Emissions from Low-Voltage, Electrical and Electronic Equipment in the Range of 10 kHz to 1 GHz, American National Standard Methods of Measurement of" (New York: IEEE/ANSI).
8. FCC/OST MP-4, "FCC Methods of Measurement of Radio Noise Emissions from Computing Devices," August 1983.

Chapter 12

Test Procedures for
Conducted EMI Susceptibility

This chapter covers procedures for testing conducted EMI susceptibility and is the third of four chapters on specific procedures for
EMI testing. The background for understanding and controlling
such testing was presented in Chapters 1 through 9.

Conducted EMI was defined in Chapter 1 as electromagnetic
energy which is undesirably coupled out of an emitter or into a
receptor via any of its connecting wires or cables. As stated in
Chapter 2, the basic task of testing susceptibility to conducted EMI
is that of injecting specified levels of EMI onto the wires or cables
connected to a receptor EUT and of then noting any deterioration
in performance of the EUT in response to this conducted EMI.

In all of the specific test procedures described in this Chapter,
it is assumed that the reader will refer to and follow related sections of Chapter 9 which cover the general setup and preparations
for such testing. Also, although manual test procedures are outlined,
it is assumed that the procedures will be automated wherever practical, consistent with the caveats and discussions of Section 6.4
(Chapter 6).

The setups used for testing EUT susceptibility to EMI signals
are nearly identical to those used for testing EMI emissions from
the EUT. However, one important point of difference is that the
EUT performance degradation or malfunction which indicates that
the threshold of susceptibility has been attained is not usually so

clear cut as the simple reading of an EMI level. Since the same degradation can be caused by other phenomena not directly related to the level of EMI energy conducted into or radiated at the EUT, the test plan should state clearly the measures, such as redundancy, which will be used to establish the causal relationship.

Caution: Many of the tests for conducted susceptibility involve potentially hazardous levels of voltage and current. Every feasible effort should be made to protect personnel from contact.

12.1 Conducted Susceptibility Testing of Power and Control Leads

12.1.1 Power Lead Conducted Susceptibility, Testing, 30 Hz to 50 kHz

The purpose of power lead conducted susceptibility tests is to confirm that injection of CW signals of specified levels and modulation onto EUT power leads will not cause degradation of performance or malfunction. The levels injected are intended to simulate power line EMI in a typical system environment. For military applications, this test requirement is usually applied to all ac and dc power leads, including those grounds and neutrals which are not grounded internally within the equipment or subsystem. It is usually not applicable within ±5 percent of the power frequencies being carried on the respective line.

12.1.1.1 Test Preparation and Setup

Shown in Fig. 12.1 is a typical setup for testing power lead susceptibility at frequencies between 30 Hz and 50 kHz. The isolation transformer (see Section 5.2.1.1) permits series injection of the susceptibility signal onto the power leads; however, for heavy current loads into the EUT, it may be necessary to compensate for the drop in supply voltage that occurs across its output winding. The injection transformer should be located as closely as possible to the EUT.

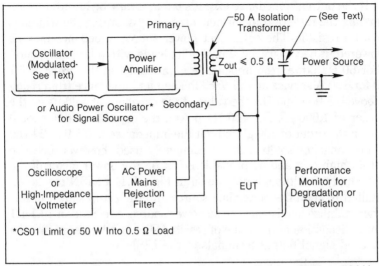

Figure 12.1—Setup for Power Lead Susceptibility Testing, 30 Hz to 50 kHz

To calculate the output impedance, Z_0, of the isolation transformer when it is terminated by the signal source in its primary, use the following equation:

$$Z_0 = R_L (V_{oc} - V_{cc})/V_{cc} \qquad (12.1)$$

where,

V_{oc} = open-circuit secondary voltage measurement corresponding to an applied signal to the transformer primary

V_{cc} = closed-circuit secondary voltage measurement across a known load, R_L, corresponding to the same applied signal for V_{oc}

The measurements and calculations typically are performed at one frequency per decade from 30 Hz to 50 kHz, including the end frequencies (i.e., 30 Hz, 300 Hz, 3 kHz, 30 kHz and 50 kHz). The measured impedance should be less than 0.5 Ω to assure that the correct signal source input voltage is presented to the EUT and does not appear across the transformer (or the power source impedance).

If the output impedance exceeds 0.5 Ω, it may be lowered by adjusting the ratio of transformer turns or by shunting the windings with a resistor. The equivalent power source impedance may be lowered, if necessary, by shunting its leads with a large capacitor. For 60 Hz power, the impedance is probably on the order of 0.1 Ω for 100 A service at 115 Vac. To keep its impedance from rising above 0.5 Ω at 300 Hz, the value of the capacitor should be on the order of 1,000 μF. For 400 Hz power, the capacitor value should be on the order of 200 μF to limit the impedance to 0.5 Ω at 2 kHz. This capacitor solution is not commonly used, however, because of its high cost and its probable effect on the power factor of the ac supply.   Although not shown in Fig. 12.1, a LISN can be installed beween the power line source and the setup shown to further stabilize and isolate the ac power source. See Section 10.1.1.1 for a discussion of the value of resistor to be used to terminate the unused signal output terminals of the LISN.

12.1.1.2 Test Procedures

The following procedure is recommended when testing power lead conducted susceptibility. It is based on the test setup of Fig. 12.1.

1. Set the signal source to provide the greatest value, V_o, called for at the lower frequency end of the applicable test limits (typically 30 Hz). Tune the oscillator slowly through the range of frequencies for which that maximum value remains applicable while taking care to observe the limitations on scanning rate discussed in Section 9.4.6. Observe the EUT for any malfunction, performance degradation or deviation beyond allowable tolerance, as previously detailed in the test plan, that would indicate that the susceptibility threshold has been exceeded (see Section 9.1.6).

2. Typical limits call for a decreasing test level starting at 1.5 kHz and continuing to the upper limit of the test, which is typically 50 kHz. A **stair-step** approach to the resulting curve is recommended: the previous level is maintained with increasing frequency until it exceeds the specified limit level by about 2 dB; the level is then reduced to that of the limit and the process repeated until the upper frequency end of the test range is reached.

3. Return to each frequency corresponding to a malfunction, degradation or deviation. Adjust the output of the signal source for a threshold condition of susceptibility. Approach the threshold condition from test signal levels which are both higher and lower than the threshold and record the smallest level at which the threshold is exceeded. Also record all data pertinent to the adverse behavior induced in the EUT.

4. After confirming that an applicable limit has not been met, it may be advantageous to implement corrective measures and retest while the setup is still intact.

12.1.2 Power and Control Lead Conducted Susceptibility Tests, 50 kHz to 400 MHz

This section covers the injection of EMI signals into signal, control and power leads, over the frequency range from 50 kHz to 400 MHz, to determine the levels which cause the EUT to malfunction or exhibit degradation in performance.

12.1.2.1 Test Preparation and Setup

Three setups will be discussed in this section. Those in Figs. 12.2 and 12.3 are intended primarily for testing power leads, while that in Fig. 12.4 is applicable both to power leads and cable bundles of leads carrying control and other signals.[1-3] Many governing documents do not explicitly specify test signal modulation. However, in accordance with Section 9.1.7, the signal should always be modulated in the manner to which the EUT is most susceptible.

The series coupling capacitor in Fig. 12.2 is used to block the power line frequency so that the signal generator, EMI analyzer or other monitoring receiver will not burn out from excessive exposure to 115 Vac or other power source. The value of the capacitor is selected to make its impedance 5 Ω or less at the lowest frequency of measurement (e.g., 1 μF for 50 kHz) and may have to be changed to avoid self-resonant effects at higher frequencies. A series inductor about 25 μH in value, installed in the mains, may help to reduce loading of the injected signal.

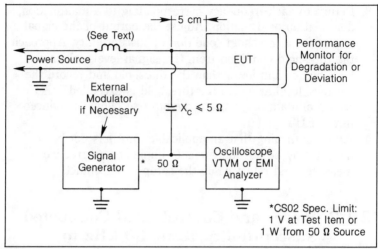

Figure 12.2—Setup for Conducted Susceptibility Testing, 50 kHz to 400 MHz

As shown in Fig. 12.3, some military testing specifies the use of a LISN to provide both the coupling capacitor and the series inductor. The signal source is normally connected to the type-N connector of the LISN, which usually is used for testing conducted emissions. Both current and voltage are monitored on the power leads between the LISN and the EUT. The applicable limit for this type of setup is specified in terms of apparent power and is calculated as the product of the voltage and current levels monitored on the power leads. It is expressed in terms of dBm.

The setup in Fig. 12.4 can be used to test either power leads or bundles of cables carrying various control and signal leads. This setup uses a current probe to inject the test signal and is intended to overcome various difficulties encountered with other methods of injection. Limits for testing using this setup are expressed in terms of the injected current. Reference 2 specifies a calibration procedure for the current probe which is to be used in lieu of similar data supplied by its manufacturer. Over the frequency range of intended measurements, the forward power into the current probe to produce specified levels of current in the conductor is determined. In the actual tests, the corresponding power flow into the probe is determined by using a directional coupler with its low-power output connected to an EMI analyzer or receiver, as shown in Fig. 12.4. Reference 3 covers common-mode injection of test signals for testing susceptibility in the context of automotive use.

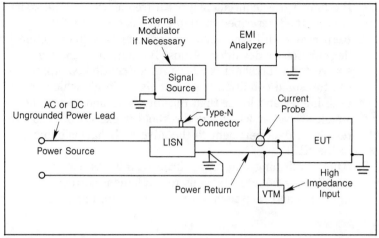

Figure 12.3—Alternate Setup for Conducted Susceptibility Testing Using LISNs

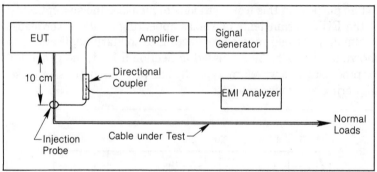

Figure 12.4—Setup for Conducted Susceptibility Testing of Cable Bundles

12.1.2.2 Test Procedures

The following procedure is intended to be generally applicable to any of the three test setups for power and control lead conducted susceptibility.

1. Set the signal source to the level corresponding to the highest level of test signal to be applied. Tune the signal source slowly, taking into account the considerations presented in Section 9.4.6, checking frequently to confirm that the signal level is that desired and observing the EUT for any malfunction or performance deterioration. If

the limit varies continuously with frequency, use the stair-step method described in step 2 of Section 12.1.1.2.

2. Return to each frequency corresponding to a malfunction, degradation or deviation. Adjust the output of the signal source for a threshold condition of susceptibility. Approach the threshold condition from test signal levels which are both higher and lower than the threshold and record the smallest level at which the threshold is exceeded. Also record all data pertinent to the adverse behavior induced in the EUT.

3. After confirming that an applicable limit has not been met, it may be advantageous to implement corrective measures and retest while the setup is still intact.

12.1.3 Testing Susceptibility to Spikes Conducted on Power Leads

The purpose of this test method is to measure the susceptibility of the EUT to transients or spikes appearing on its power leads. A standard waveform used for testing to military applications is shown in Fig. 12.5. As discussed in Section 5.1.2.1, the generator for producing this waveform typically has variable controls for pulse triggering and pulse rate.

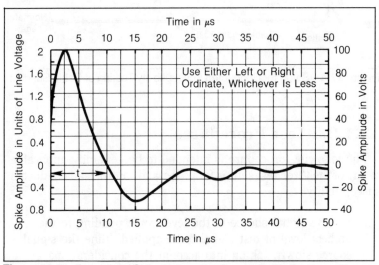

Figure 12.5—Example of Spike Voltage for Susceptibility Testing of Power Leads

A typical specification limit is based on developing at the power input of the EUT a spike of 200 V peak amplitude. For purposes of confirming the spike rise time, duration and approximate amplitude, the spike generator is terminated in a 5 Ω noninductive resistor. Its test amplitude is then set and measured in the actual test setup as shown in Figs. 12.6 or 12.7. Depending on the application of the EUT, the width of the test spike typically ranges from 0.15 to 10 μs as shown in Fig. 12.5.

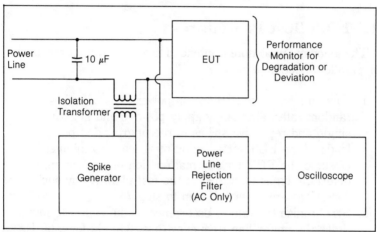

Figure 12.6—Series Injection of Spike for Susceptibility Testing

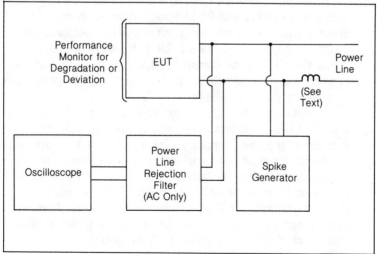

Figure 12.7—Parallel Injection of Spike for Susceptibility Testing

12.1.3.1 Test Preparation and Setup

The choice of series or parallel injection is based on several considerations, including the RF impedances of both the power lines and the EUT. The purposes of the 10 μF capacitor and the 25 μH inductor were discussed in Section 12.1.2.1. Basically, both are intended to reduce the extent to which injection of the spike is influenced by the impedance of the power mains.

12.1.3.2 Test Procedures

The following procedure is intended to apply to either the series- or parallel-injection setups.

1. To simulate the occurrence on power lines of spikes at random rates, alternately apply positive and negative, single and repetitive spikes to the ungrounded power leads of the EUT for a period of at least 10 minutes. Observe the EUT for any malfunction or performance deterioration as identified in the test plan. If any such conditions are observed, skip to step 7.
2. Synchronize the rate of occurrence of the spikes to four times the power line frequency (e.g., 240 Hz for a 60 Hz line) and trigger the spikes so that they occur at X-axis crossings and maximum positive and negative line voltages. Run this test for at least five minutes and observe the test sample for malfunctions or performance degradations. The rationale behind this technique is to check the EUT to determine if anything about its logic or performance is especially sensitive to either zero crossings or peak supply line voltages.
3. As an option to step 1, remove the synchronization in step 2 so that the pulse repetition rate is slightly different from four times the line frequency. The result should appear on the oscilloscope as pulses which slowly advance or retard with respect to the line voltage waveform. Run this test for about 10 minutes and observe the EUT for malfunctions or performance degradations. The rationale here is to seek out any pulse phasing or amplitude pedestal situation to which the EUT might be susceptible.

4. For EUTs containing digital circuitry, the spikes are synchronized and triggered to occur within the strobe gates of
clocks. When the clock rate is 50 kb/s or faster, the spike
pulse must be narrower than 10 μs so that it will not occupy both a 0 and 1.
5. If susceptibility is observed, reduce the amplitude of the
spikes to a threshold condition to determine and record
the repetition rate, phase position on the ac waveform and
time of occurrence with respect to circuit gates.
6. Repeat steps 1 through 5, as applicable, for other
ungrounded power leads of the EUT.
7. If a susceptible condition appears, it may be advantageous
to take the necessary corrective measures and retest while
the setup is still intact.

12.2 Susceptibility Tests on Receiver Performance

This section covers receiver testing for susceptibility to various
signals imposed on their input terminals. The collective frequency
range of testing is very broad, extending from 30 Hz to above 20
GHz. The purpose of these conducted susceptibility tests is to confirm that intermodulation products, cross-modulation products and
rejection of the receivers to out-of-band emissions all are within acceptable limits.

The following are working definitions of the phenomena to be
tested:

Intermodulation

Intermodulation occurs when two or more emissions, located outside of the receiver bandwidth but not sufficiently rejected by the
front end, mix by nonlinear action in the RF or mixer stages. They
produce sum and difference frequencies, one of which lies in the
receiver passband. This new signal is then processed as if it were
an intentional signal.

Cross Modulation

Cross modulation occurs when an adjacent-channel emission sufficiently penetrates the receiver front end to cause any stage of the

RF amplifier section to perform nonlinearly. When the intentional signal is processed through this stage, it becomes cross modulated with the modulation of the undesired signal.

Rejection to Out-of-Band Emissions

An undesired signal penetrates the receiver front end and mixes with the local oscillator to produce sum and difference frequencies, one of which lies at the receiver IF to be processed like an intentional signal. Examples of such spurious responses are image response, harmonics of the local oscillator plus and minus the IF, and the same frequencies divided by harmonics of the interfering signal.

These phenomena are illustrated in Fig. 12.8 which shows an idealized receiver block diagram and basic superheterodyne frequencies across the top of the figure. Below this, the three phenomena are illustrated in terms of the spectrum responses which would occur at various points in the receiver. Note that only the simplest circumstances of occurrence are illustrated. Also, the receiver configuration shown is relatively simple, with only a single IF. The presence in the receiver of additional IFs can reduce the number of susceptible responses or, if not carefully chosen, can cause additional susceptible responses of one or more of the three types.

12.2.1 Intermodulation, 30 Hz to 10 GHz

This section covers testing the susceptibility of a receiver or tuned amplifier to intermodulation products generated in response to two out-of-band signals appearing at its input terminal, such as would occur with two neighboring transmitters.

12.2.1.1 Background Information on Intermodulation

Although any amplifier exhibits some degree of nonlinearity, it becomes progressively worse as the signal level approaches saturation. Because the typical RF receiver is designed to be very sensitive, it is also more vulnerable to nonlinear effects than most amplifiers.

Figure 12.8—Illustration of Receiver Susceptibility Products

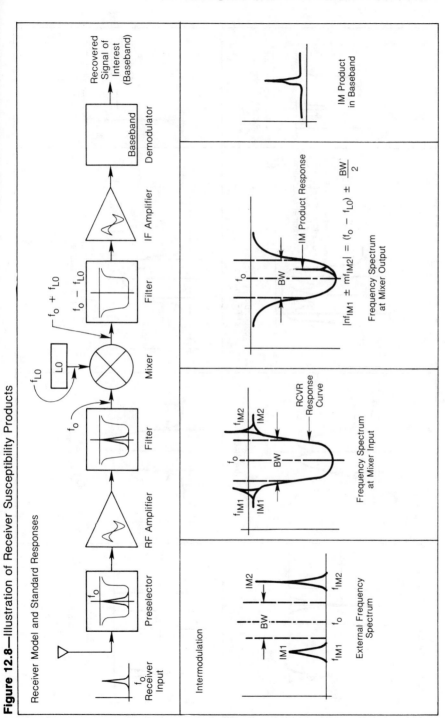

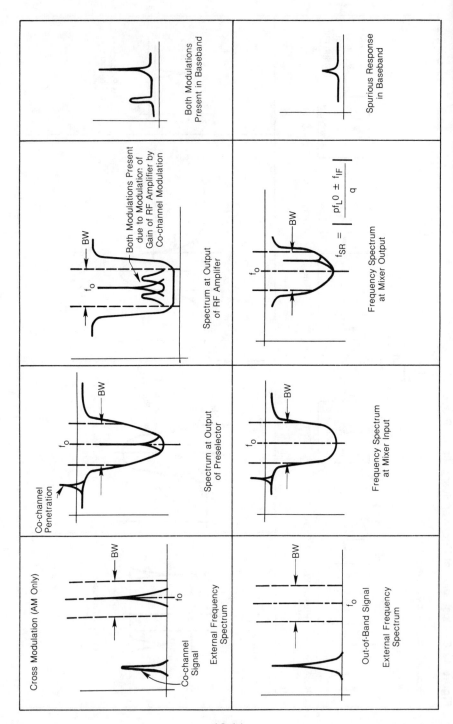

12.14

To produce intermodulation products, two or more out-of-band signals must be sufficiently strong to penetrate the receiver front end (e.g., any preselector) and mix in a nonlinear stage. The mixing action then produces additional signals at the sum and difference frequencies of the culprit signals and their harmonics. Any of the resulting products which lie within the passband of the receiver will be processed along with the signals of interest, as expressed by:

$$|mf_1 \pm nf_2| = f_o \qquad (12.2)$$

or,

$$|mf_1/f_o \pm nf_2/f_o| = 1 \qquad (12.3)$$

where,

f_1 and f_2 = frequencies of the two interfering emissions

m and n = integers (1, 2, 3, etc.)

f_o = tuned frequency of the receiver

It should be noted that this formulation is only an approximation of the actual situation to the extent that it neglects any modulation on the signals and the degree to which the spectrum of the intermodulation products is passed by the receiver bandwidth. More accurately, "1" in Eq. (12.2) should be replaced by $1 \pm \Delta N$, where ΔN is one-half the normalized sums of these bandwidths.

The order of an intermodulation product mix is determined by adding the integers m and n. Other than the second order (m = n = 1), the even-order products result in insignificant levels of EMI. The second and third order products, which are usually the most significant, are shown in Fig. 12.9 in a form normalized with respect to the receiver tuned frequency as presented in Eq. (12.3). Examples

12.15

of the second, third, and fifth order intermodulations are shown in the following table.

Order of Intermodulation	Intermodulation Product
Second $(m + n = 2)$	$f_1/f_o + f_2/f_o = 1$ $\|f_1/f_o - f_2/f_o\| = 1$
Third $(m + n = 3)$	$f_1/f_o + 2f_2/f = 1$ $\|f_1/f_o - 2f_2/f_o\| = 1$ $2f_1/f_o + f_2/f_o = 1$ $\|2f_1/f_o - f_2/f_o\| = 1$
Fifth $(m + n = 5)$	$f_1/f_o + 4f_2/f_o = 1$ $\|f_1/f_o - 4f_2/f_o\| = 1$ $2f_1/f_o + 3f_2/f_o = 1$ $\|2f_1/f_o - 3f_2/f_o\| = 1$ $3f_1/f_o + 2f_2/f_o = 1$ $\|3f_1/f_o - 2f_2/f_o\| = 1$ $4f_1/f_o + f_2/f_o = 1$ $\|4f_1/f_o - f_2/f_o\| = 1$

Curve A in Fig. 12.10 shows the response of a superheterodyne receiver without preselection. Note the dual selectivity curves at $f_{LO} \pm f_{IF}$. The RF selectivity is that of the IF amplifier as translated to RF by mixing with the LO.

Curve B shows the response of the preselector alone. Although its response is broad in comparison to that of the IF, it is still able to provide significant rejection of the image frequency ($f_{LO} + f_{IF}$). Curve C shows the combined effects of Curves A and B for low-level signals; since high-level signals will produce any intermodulation products at or before the mixer, it is curve B that will control their potential effect, not curves A or C. Thus, it is Curve B that is denoted in Fig. 12.9 as a region of major and secondary significance.

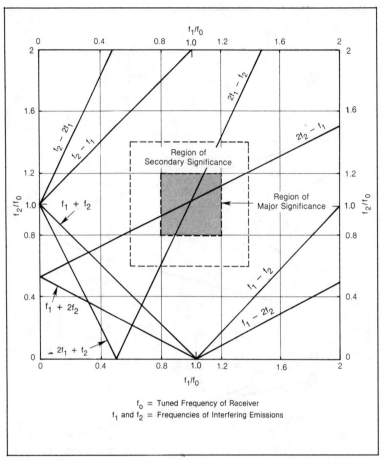

Figure 12.9—Chart of Second and Third Order Intermodulation Products

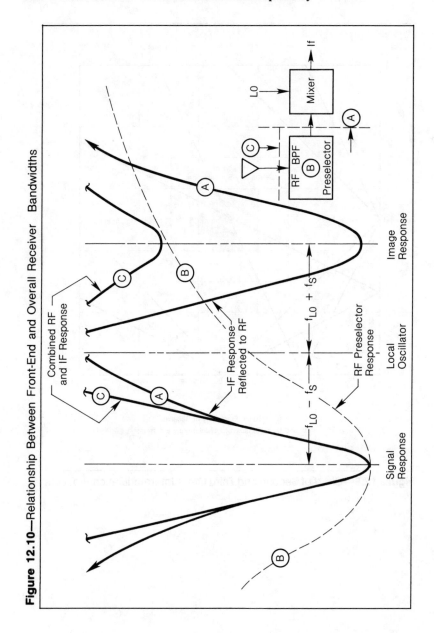

Figure 12.10—Relationship Between Front-End and Overall Receiver Bandwidths

Illustrative Example 12.1

Assume that an air traffic control communication transmitter is tuned to 360 MHz. Determine other transmitter emission frequencies that may combine with the 360 MHz emission to produce second and third order intermodulation frequencies in a receiver used by the air traffic controllers to receive transmissions from pilots. The receiver is tuned to 300 MHz and co-located with the transmitter. For this situation, the transmitter frequency is 1.2 times the receiver frequency (i.e., $f_1/f_o = 1.2$).

Referring to Fig. 12.9, potential second and third order intermodulation frequencies within the region $0 \leqslant f_2/f_o \leqslant 2$ are:

$$0.1, \text{ third order, } = (f_1 - 2f_2)$$

$$0.2, \text{ second order, } = (f_1 - f_2)$$

$$1.1, \text{ third order, } = (2f_2 - f_1)$$

$$1.4, \text{ third order, } = (2f_1 - f_2)$$

The most significant frequencies from the standpoint of potential intermodulation interference for the specified situation are $f_2/f_o = 1.1$ and 1.4. Thus, $f_2 = 330$ MHz and 420 MHz emission sources could be potentially hazardous to the air-to-ground receiver tuned to 300 MHz; this is especially true of 330 MHz. The frequencies corresponding to $f_2/f_o = 0.1$ and 0.2 would be 30 MHz and 60 MHz, respectively, and these frequencies should be sufficiently rejected by the front-end selectivity.

12.2.1.2 Test Preparation and Setup

Typical requirements for the rejection of intermodulation products cover receivers and tuned amplifiers operating over the frequency range from 30 Hz to 10 GHz and specify that these products from two signals not be detectable when the two signals are 66 dB above a standard response level (see Section 9.1.6.2).

Figure 12.11 illustrates a typical setup for measuring conducted susceptibility to intermodulation from 30 Hz to 10 GHz. The two signal generators are usually models from the same manufacturer and typically provide a calibrated output from −120 dBm to ≈

0 dBm. Performance of the required tests usually requires that they cover about two decades in frequency, centered around the tuned frequency of the receiver EUT. The purpose of the low-pass filters is to remove from the generators harmonics that otherwise might confuse the test results. However, it is common to omit these filters because of the need to retune or switch them so often with changes in test frequencies and to restore them to the setup in the event of an out-of-specification condition.

The outputs from the two signal generators are combined in a three-port network, which is typically a 6 dB power divider (see Section 5.2.1.2) with two 10 dB pads, one located at each arm of the divider. This provides at least 20 dB of isolation between the two signal generators to prevent interactions such as frequency pulling or intermodulation. The output arm of the 6 dB power divider thus carries both test signals. The use of hybrid junctions for combining the signals is recommended because it eliminates the 10 dB pads while still providing the required isolation between the signal generators.

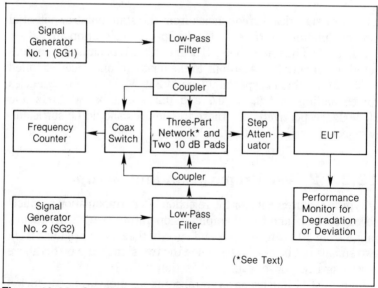

Figure 12.11—Setup for Testing Conducted Susceptibility of Receivers

12.2.1.3 Test Procedures

Although the following sequence of procedures is believed to be the most generally efficient, certain steps can be interpósed to accommodate special situations.

1. To test for intermodulation products in the test instrumentation, substitute an EMI analyzer for the EUT. Set the signal generator outputs to a level 66 dB above the planned receiver standard response level (see below) with one generator tuned to the planned EUT frequency, f_0, and the other to 1.3 f_0. Any intermodulation products which exist will be at $0.3f_0$ and $2.3f_0$ (second order) and $0.7f_0$, $1.6f_0$, $3.3f_0$ and $3.6f_0$ (third order). Harmonics from the signal generators should not be a problem at these frequencies. Any apparent intermodulation products should be checked by the method outlined in Section 9.1.8 to confirm that they are not being generated in the EMI analyzer. If it is determined that intermodulation is resulting from interaction of the generators, it may be reduced by a different isolation network or more padding in the network arms. Once the setup is declared valid, restore the connections to those shown in Fig. 12.11.

2. Tune the receiver to perform each of the following steps at each frequency, f_0, defined in the test plan; otherwise, perform at three frequencies per receiver band or octave (see Section 2.2.4 for frequency selection). Set the receiver EUT controls to the same positions as specified in the detailed equipment specification for the sensitivity measurement.

3. Turn off signal generator no. 2 (SG2) by increasing the output attenuator to a maximum and tune signal generator no. 1 (SG1) to f_0 (see Fig. 12.12). SG1 is modulated as required by the detailed equipment specifications to produce a standard output. If not specified, use the values presented in Section 9.1.6.2. Adjust the SG1 output level to produce a standard reference output. If this level is not specified in the detailed specification on sensitivity measurements of the EUT, use the values specified in Section 9.1.6.2. Record the frequency and level of SG1.

12.21

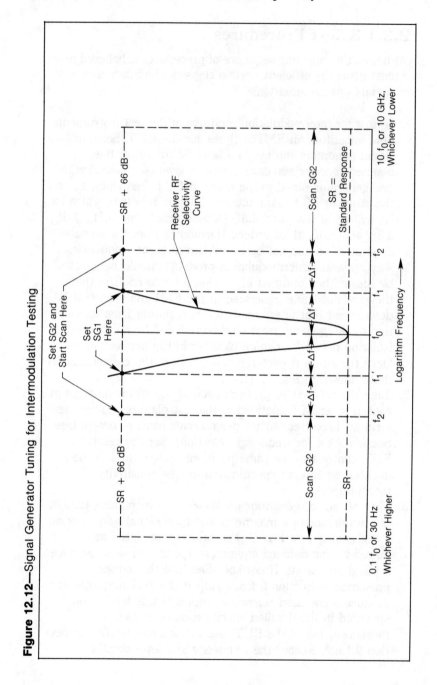

Figure 12.12—Signal Generator Tuning for Intermodulation Testing

4. Repeat step 3 with SG1 turned off and SG2 tuned to f_o with the required modulation to give a standard response. Record the output level and frequency of SG2 with a frequency counter.

5. For the remainder of the test, turn both signal generators on with SG1 modulated as above but SG2 unmodulated. Turn down the level of SG2. Some generators may drift in frequency. Therefore, during the remainder of the test steps, it may be necessary to retune each generator to be sure that the maximum response is being measured.

6. Increase the level of SG1 by 66 dB above that recorded in step 3. Slowly tune SG1 above f_o until there is no longer a response. In Fig. 12.12, this corresponds to sliding down the EUT receiver selectivity curve until frequency f_1 is reached. Measure f_1 with a frequency counter. Note that $f_1 - f_o = \Delta f$. Leave SG1 at f_1.

7. Set SG2, unmodulated, to Δf above f_1. This is $2\Delta f$ above f_o and corresponds to the closest-in third order intermodulation products:

$$[2f_1 - f_2 = 2(f_o + \Delta f) - (f_o + 2\Delta f) = f_o]$$

Adjust SG2 level to 66 dB above that recorded in step 3. Note whether there is a response. If not, slowly increase the frequency of SG2, maintaining a constant output level, until a frequency of 10 f_o or 10 GHz, whichever is less, is attained. Note any and all EUT receiver responses.

8. Test each response observed in step 7 by reducing SG1 output to a level well below that in step 6. If the response is still present, it is not an intermodulation product and can be neglected for purposes of the test.

9. When an intermodulation response is confirmed, reduce the levels of both signal generators equally until the standard response is attained. The amount of equal reduction in dB is the number of dB by which the EUT exceeds the limits. Record the levels and frequencies of each intermodulation response. The difference between the new signal generator levels and the standard reference level in step 6 is the intermodulation rejection.

10. Repeat steps 6 through 9 with SG1 now set at $f_1 = f_o - \Delta f$ and scanning SG2 from $f_o - \Delta f$ to $0.1f_o$ or 30 Hz or another minimum frequency, whichever is the higher, as shown in Fig. 12.12.

11. Repeat steps 1 through 10 with SG1 = f_1 set to generate frequencies in the 200 to 400 MHz frequency range. Select f_1 so that it is not tuned to a spurious response. Temporarily reduce the output level of SG2 below that recorded in step 4. The test is performed with SG1 set at 80 dB above the reference level. The purpose of this test is to simulate a nearby high-level transmitter in the UHF communications and P-band radar bands. This step does not apply to receivers designed to operate between 200 and 400 MHz.

12. Repeat steps 1 through 10 with SG1 = f_1 now set for frequencies in the 2 to 25 MHz range at an output level of 80 dB above that in step 3. Select f_1 so that no spurious response occurs with the output level of SG2 temporarily set below that recorded in step 4. The purpose of this test is to simulate a nearby high-level HF transmitter. This step does not apply to receivers designed to operate in the 2 to 25 MHz frequency range.

12.2.2 Cross Modulation, 30 Hz to 20 GHz

This section covers testing of conducted susceptibility to cross modulation of its intended signals by strong adjacent-channel signals which penetrate its front-end preselection.

12.2.2.1 Background Information

Cross modulation differs from intermodulation and spurious responses in that it does not involve a carrier transposition process involving front-end mixing. Instead, the offending signal typically cross modulates by imposing nonlinear operation onto the final RF stage preceding the mixer. Any baseband information modulated on the culprit signal is thus modulated onto the intended signal. Under certain circumstances, offending signals can simultaneously cause both cross modulation and spurious responses; however, by definition there is no cross modulation unless a desired signal is being received.

12.2.2.2 Test Preparation and Setup

This test can be performed using the same setup configuration used for testing intermodulation and cross modulation, as shown in Fig. 12.11. However, whereas SG2 must be tunable over the total range implied by Fig. 12.13, SG1 need only furnish f_0 modulated to produce the standard output specified for the EUT. Otherwise, the comments of Section 12.2.1.2 apply as pertinent to the following test procedure.

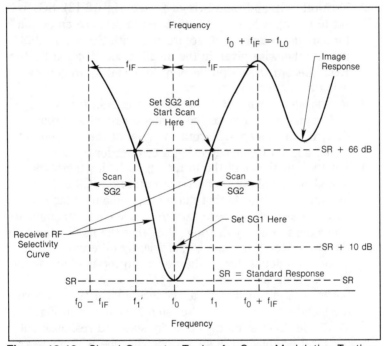

Figure 12.13—Signal Generator Tuning for Cross Modulation Testing

12.25

12.2.2.3 Test Procedure

1. Tune the receiver to perform each of the following steps at each frequency f_o defined in the test plan; otherwise, perform at three frequencies per receiver band or octave (see Section 2.2.4 for frequency selection). Set the receiver EUT controls to the same positions as specified in the detailed equipment specification for sensitivity measurement.

2. Turn off SG2 and tune SG1 to f_o (see Fig. 12.13). SG1 is set to a proper level and modulated to produce an output for standard response in accordance with Section 9.1.6.2 unless otherwise given in the detailed specification for the EUT. Record the output level of SG1 and its frequency using a counter for accuracy.

3. Repeat step 2 with SG1 turned off and SG2 tuned to f_o and adjusted to produce the standard response output determined in step 2. Record the level of the SG2 output signal and its frequency using a counter for accuracy.

4. For the remainder of the test, turn on both generators modulated as above. Reduce the output of SG2 to its minimum level. Note that during the remaining steps it may occasionally be necessary to retune each generator to overcome frequency drifting. Note that the modulations on the two generators must be sufficiently different so that there is no doubt during the test when the modulation on SG2 is being observed.

5. Set SG1, still tuned to f_o, to produce a level 10 dB above the standard response level of step 2 as shown in Fig. 12.13. Set SG2 at 66 dB above its standard response output level established in step 3. Slowly tune SG2 above f_o until the original standard response condition with SG1 exists alone as in step 2. In Fig. 12.13, this corresponds to moving away from f_o until f_1 is reached.

6. Slowly increase the frequency of SG2 from f_1 to $f_o + f_{IF}$ while maintaining a constant output level. When responses are noted, remove the modulation from SG2 only; if the response disappears, it is due entirely to cross modulation.

7. When a cross modulation response is confirmed, reduce the level of SG2 until the standard response condition established in step 2 is restored. The amount in dB by

which SG2 was reduced below conditions shown in Fig. 12.13 is the extent to which the EUT exceeds specified limits. The difference between this value and the standard reference output is the degree of rejection to cross modulation.

8. Repeat steps 5 through 7 with SG2 now tuned down to f_1'. Then slowly scan SG2 from f_1' to $f_o - f_{IF}$ as shown in Fig. 12.13.

12.2.3 Rejection of Undesired Signals, 30 Hz to 20 GHz

This section covers testing of susceptibility to conducted out-of-band signals appearing at the input terminals of receivers or tuned amplifiers.

12.2.3.1 Background Information

The susceptibility test covered in this section results in spurious responses other than intermodulation (see Section 12.2.1) or cross modulation (see Section 12.2.2). For receivers with AGC, the response may be more subtle, taking the form of lowered sensitivity to desired signals as a result of AGC activation by the interfering signal.

While any type of receiver can display spurious responses because of inadequate front-end selectivity, the superheterodyne receiver is particularly vulnerable because of its heterodyne process. Any high-level signal which reaches the mixer generates signals at frequencies which are the sum and difference of the culprit signal, the LO and its harmonics. Any signal thus generated which falls in the IF bandpass of the EUT receiver will be processed along with the signals of interest. Neglecting the effects of any modulation present on the interfering signal, as discussed in conjunction with intermodulation in Section 12.2.1.1, signals capable of producing spurious responses in superheterodyne receivers satisfy the following relationship:

$$|pf_{LO} \pm qf_{SR}| = f_{IF} \qquad (12.4)$$

or,

$$f_{SR} = |pf_{LO} + f_{IF}|/q \qquad (12.5)$$

where,

f_{LO} = local oscillator frequency of superheterodyne

f_{SR} = spurious-response frequency

f_{IF} = intermediate frequency of superheterodyne

p = integer or harmonic number of local oscillator

q = integer or harmonic number of interfering signal

The smaller the integer p and q in Eqs. (12.4) or (12.5), the more potentially damaging the spurious response. This is illustrated conceptually in Fig. 12.14. For the first three integers of p and q, the results are tabulated below:

Computation of 2nd, 3rd, and 4th Order Spurious Responses

p	q	f_{SR} Spurious Response	Approximate f_{SR} for $f_{LO} \gg f_{IF}$
1	1	$f_{LO} + f_{IF}$ $f_{LO} - f_{IF}$	Intentional (or image) Response* Image (or intentional) Response*
1	2	$0.5(f_{LO} + f_{IF})$ $0.5(f_{LO} - f_{IF})$	$0.5\,f_{LO}$ $0.5 f_{LO}$
2	1	$2f_{LO} + f_{IF}$ $2f_{LO} - f_{IF}$	$2f_{LO}$ $2f_{LO}$
2	2	$f_{LO} + 0.5f_{IF}$ $f_{LO} - 0.5f_{IF}$	f_{LO} f_{LO} Near region of intentional (or image) response
1	3	$0.33\,(f_{LO} + f_{IF})$ $0.33\,(f_{LO} - f_{IF})$	$0.33\,f_{LO}$ $0.33\,f_{LO}$
3	1	$3f_{LO} + f_{IF}$ $3\,f_{LO} - f_{IF}$	$3f_{LO}$ $3\,f_{LO}$

*Descriptions are for intentional high-side or (low-side) mixing.

Computation of 2nd, 3rd and 4th Order Spurious Responses

Most spurious response situations for superheterodyne receivers result at the fundamental of $f_{SR}(q = 1)$. Thus, the victim receiver is more sensitive in the region of $f_{SR} \approx p f_{LO}$.

Illustrative Example 12.3

A VHF receiver, tuned to 130 MHz in the aeronautical band, evidences interference from a nearby L-band radar transmitting at 1,250 MHz. The pulse repetition frequency (PRF) of the radar is heard in the audio of the receiver as the radar antenna scans through its direction. Since the receiver has a 30 MHz IF (f_{IF}) and the LO (f_{LO}) is situated above the frequency to which it is tuned, is this an example of heterodyne spurious response (out-of-band susceptibility) in the receiver?

From the above, the receiver LO frequency is $f_{LO} = f_o + f_{IF} = 130 + 30 = 160$ MHz. Applying Eq. (12.5) for the eighth harmonic (i.e., p = 8) of the LO and for q = 1:

$$f_{SR} = (8 \times 160 \text{ MHz} \pm 30 \text{ MHz})/1$$

$$= 1,250 \text{ and } 1,310 \text{ MHz}$$

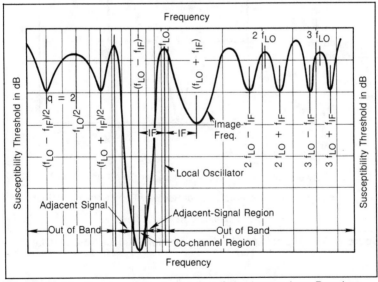

Figure 12.14—Spurious Responses in a Superheterodyne Receiver

12.29

Thus, it is confirmed that this is a valid example of a heterodyning, spurious-response action. In this instance, the EMI effect probably can be eliminated by inserting a low-pass filter with a cutoff frequency between 200 and 500 MHz ahead of the antenna terminals of the receiver.

Typical limits for this type of testing specify that there shall be no undesired responses as the test signal is scanned at the frequencies and levels shown in Fig. 12.15. The maximum rate of scanning should be determined by Eq. (6.1) of Chapter 6, using the bandwidth of the EUT receiver.[4] The start frequency for the test scan should be $0.2f_{IF}$ or $0.05f_o$, whichever is lower. The stop frequency should be $5f_{LO} + f_{IF}$ or $20f_o$, whichever is higher. The 80 dB bandwidth of the receiver selectivity curve is exempt from testing.

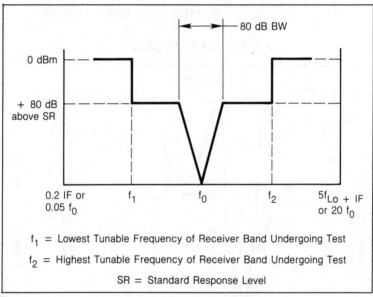

Figure 12.15—Typical Specification Limits for Spurious Response Levels

12.2.3.2 Test Preparation and Setup

The test for conducted susceptibility to out-of-band signals can be performed using the same setup configuration used for testing intermodulation and cross modulation as shown in Fig. 12.11. However, whereas SG2 must be tunable over the total range specified in the preceding paragraph, SG1 need only furnish f_o modulated to produce the standard output specified for the EUT. Otherwise, the comments of Section 12.2.1.2 apply to the following test procedure.

12.2.3.3 Test Procedures

1. Tune the receiver to perform each of the following steps at each frequency, f_o, defined in the test plan; otherwise, perform the test at three frequencies per receiver band or octave (see Section 2.2.4 for frequency selection). Set the receiver EUT controls to the same positions as specified in the detailed equipment specification for sensitivity measurement.

2. Turn off SG2 and tune SG1 to f_o (see Fig. 12.16). SG1 should be set to a proper level and modulated to produce an output for standard response, in accordance with Section 9.1.6.2, unless otherwise specified in the detailed specification for the EUT. Record the level and counter-accurate frequency of the resulting SG1 output signal.

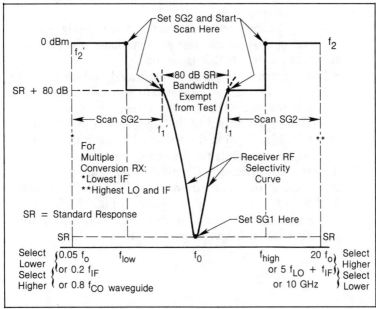

Figure 12.16—Signal Generator Tuning for Testing Spurious Responses

3. Repeat step 2 with SG1 turned off and SG2 tuned to f_o and adjusted to produce the standard response output determined in step 2. Record the characteristics of the output signal as in step 2.

4. For the remainder of the test, turn on both generators, with SG1 modulated as above but SG2 unmodulated. Reduce the output of SG2 to its minimum level. Note that during the remaining steps it may occasionally be necessary to retune each generator to compensate for frequency drift.

5. Set SG1 to the level and modulation obtained in step 2 and set SG2, unmodulated, to produce a level 80 dB above that of step 3. Slowly tune SG2 above f_o until the EUT reading of step 2 is duplicated. Referring to Fig. 12.16, this corresponds to moving away from maximum response of the selectivity curve until frequency f_1 is reached.

6. Slowly increase the frequency of SG2 from f_1 to f_{HI} (the upper tuning extreme of the EUT receiver) while maintaining a constant output level. At f_{HI}, increase the level of SG2 to 0 dBm and scan to f_2 (see Fig. 12.16) while maintaining a constant level. Note and record any and all receiver responses.

7. Although an intermodulation product is unlikely with the level of SG1 so low, test each response observed in step 6 to confirm that it is not one.

8. When a spurious response is confirmed, reduce the output level of SG2 until the standard response condition of step 2 is restored. The amount in decibels by which the reduction in the output of SG2 exceeds the conditions shown in Fig. 12.16 is the amount by which the respective response exceeds the specified limit.

9. Repeat steps 5 through 8 with SG2 now tuned downward in frequency from f_o to f_1'. Then slowly scan SG2 from f_1' to f_{low} to f_2' as shown in Fig. 12.16.

10. As required by the test plan, repeat the above steps for any other tuned frequencies of the EUT.

12.3 Testing Conducted Susceptibility of Squelch Circuits

The purpose of the test covered by this section is to determine whether receiver squelch circuits are susceptible to inadvertent operation in the presence of impulsive EMI at the receiver input terminals. Two tests typically are required to establish whether the squelch circuit of the EUT receiver is satisfactory:

Test 1

Squelch circuits shall not open when the EUT is subjected to the 90 dBμV/MHz output of a 50 Ω impedance impulse generator matched to its input.

Test 2

Squelch circuits shall not open when the EUT is subjected to two signals applied to its input. One signal is an unmodulated RF signal at the tuned frequency, f_o, at a voltage level two-thirds of that used to adjust the squelch threshold. The other is the output from an impulse generator set to a level of 50 dBμV/MHz.

12.3.1 Test Preparation and Setup

As diagrammed in Fig. 12.17a, the first test determines squelch circuit performance in the presence of impulsive EMI alone to simulate squelch activation by such impulsive EMI before the arrival of an intended signal. As diagrammed in Fig. 12.17b, the second test evaluates its performance in the presence of both CW and impulsive EMI. A discussion of the isolation network used to decouple the signal generators is contained in Section 12.2.1.2.

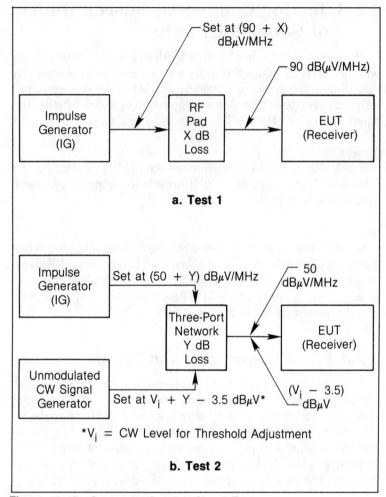

Figure 12.17—Setups for Squelch Circuit Tests

12.3.2 Test Procedures

12.3.2.1 Test 1, Impulsive EMI Input

1. Adjust the squelch circuit for a threshold opening at the level of injected voltage, V_i, as stated in the EUT specification, at its antenna input terminals.

2. Taking into account the insertion loss in any matching pad, adjust the impulse generator for a level at the antenna input terminals of 90 dBμV/MHz.
3. If the squelch circuit opens, reduce the IG level until it closes. The amount of reduction below 90 dBμV/MHz is the amount in dB by which the EUT fails to satisfy the specified limits.

12.3.2.2 Test 2, CW and Impulsive Inputs

1. Adjust the squelch circuit for a threshold opening at the level of injected voltage, V_i, as stated in the EUT specification, at its antenna input terminals.
2. Tune the frequency of the unmodulated CW signal generator in Fig. 12.17b for maximum response on the EUT receiver and set its output to a level two-thirds of (3.5 db less than) that in step 1. Set the IG to produce a level of 50 dBμV/MHz at the EUT input terminals. Any loss in the coupling network must be taken into account for both inputs.
3. If the squelch circuit opens, reduce the IG level until it closes. The amount of reduction necessary is the amount in dB by which the EUT fails to satisfy the specified limits.

12.4 Testing Susceptibility to Common-Mode Current on the EUT Structure

The purpose of the test covered in this section is to measure the susceptibility of an EUT to common-mode currents flowing on its surface. This test is usually restricted to equipment with an operating frequency of 100 kHz or less and with a sensitivity of 1 μV or better.

12.4.1 Test Preparation and Setup

Shown in Fig. 12.18 is the basic method of testing susceptibility to currents flowing on the surface of an EUT. Typically, a current ranging from 1 A at 60 Hz to 1 mA at 100 kHz is made to flow between two diagonal extremes on one or more surfaces of the EUT chassis or cabinet. Resistor R is inserted in the lead to provide a suitable load (typically 50 Ω) for the signal source, with the test current being measured by a suitable low-frequency current probe closed around the return lead to the output terminal of the signal source.

The signal source must be capable of supplying at least 6 dB more current than required for the test limit; thus, for a current limit of 1 A at 60 Hz, the source should have a 2 A capability. Both the current probe and the EMI analyzer or selective RF voltmeter must be capable of operation over a frequency range from 60 Hz to 100 kHz.

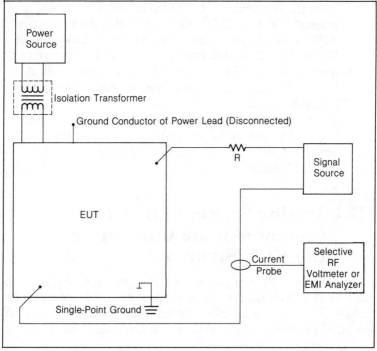

Figure 12.18—Setup for Measuring Susceptibility to Structure Currents

If the EUT is not battery operated, its ac power source must be connected through a suitable isolation transformer. This isolation from any ground connection is equally applicable to all items of test equipment including the signal source, the EMI analyzer and any equipment used to monitor EUT performance. Contrary to most military tests, the EUT itself must be mounted on a nonconductive surface, such as a wooden bench, to permit establishment of a single-point ground. **Great care must be taken to ensure safety since the "safety ground" is removed throughout this test.**

The current connection points on the EUT depend on the manner in which it is installed for actual operation. They are as follows:

Installation or Mounting	Current Connection at Diagonal Extremes
Not rack-mounted	Across bottom surface only
Rack-mounted	Across all surfaces
Assembly (deck-resting)	Across all surfaces
Bulkhead-mounted	Across rear surfaces only

The intent is to minimize any damage to the EUT; any screw heads or protuberances near the diagonal corners should be used whenever possible. If none are available, a sharply pointed test probe should be used to contact the metallic chassis.

12.4.2 Test Procedures

The following procedure can be used to test EUT susceptibility to structure currents:

1. Adjust the signal source so that 1 A of 60 Hz current is flowing through R, as measured using the current probe.
2. Slowly (see Section 9.4.6) tune the signal source and the monitoring selective volt meter or EMI analyzer from 60 Hz to 100 kHz, maintaining a level that produces a current greater than that specified in the applicable limit but not exceeding 2 A.

3. While tuning is in process, determine whether the performance of the EUT is being degraded beyond the tolerances indicated in the EUT equipment specification and the test plan.
4. At each frequency of susceptibility, or at a minimum of three such frequencies per octave (see Section 2.2.4), adjust the current level to the threshold of susceptibility and record that level of current and all associated pertinent data.

12.5 Testing Susceptibility to Damped Sinusoidal Transients (EMP)

The purpose of the test discussed in this section is to determine the conducted susceptibility of the EUT to a damped sinusoidal electromagnetic pulse (EMP) of relatively large magnitude. This type of transient typically would be induced on the various leads and cables by a nuclear detonation in the atmosphere. These conducted tests are usually applied to items which will be installed in a relatively shielded area; EUTs for installation in more exposed locations should be subjected to the radiated emission test of Section 13.4.

CAUTION: All of the tests simulating response to both conducted and radiated EMP involve potentially hazardous voltage and current levels. Every effort should be made to protect personnel from exposure.

Conducted testing for this type of susceptibility typically is divided into two categories: common-mode testing of cables and individual testing of pins and terminals. Both tests use the same sinusoidal waveform shown in Fig. 12.19; peak amplitudes of current applied are a function of frequency, as shown in Fig. 12.20. The sinusoidal waveform is defined by:

$$I(t) = 1.05\ I_{max}\ e^{-\pi ft/Q}\ \sin(2\pi ft) \qquad (12.6)$$

12.38

where,

$I(t)$ = common-mode current in amperes

I_{max} = peak common-mode current in amperes

f = frequency in hertz

t = time in seconds

Q = decay factor

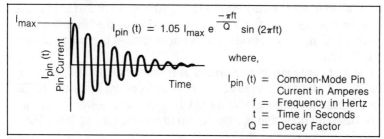

Figure 12.19—Waveform for EMP Conducted Susceptibility Testing

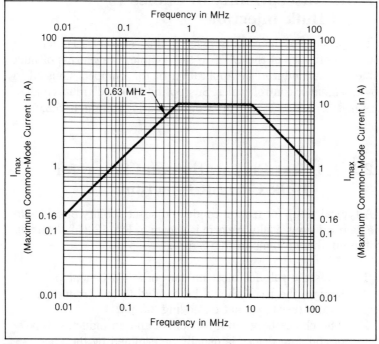

Figure 12.20—Typical Test Limit for EMP Conducted Susceptibility Testing

The **decay factor** (or **damping factor**) usually will be specified as between 10 and 20; for Q = 10, the eighth cycle will have about 10 percent of the amplitude of the first cycle, while for Q = 20, the waveform will not diminish to that value until the fifteenth cycle.[5]

The specified sinusoidal current is not necessarily applied to the EUT cables, pins, or terminals; it is first injected into a noninductive calibration resistor. Once the output level of the signal generator is established for the current in Fig. 12.20 (see 5.1.2.2), the current actually injected into the EUT is a function of the impedance at the point of injection. However, it is not to exceed the values shown in Fig. 12.20.

The tests are usually performed at frequencies of 0.01, 0.1, 1.0, 10, 30 and 100 MHz, plus at any critical frequencies of the EUT. These include frequencies of its LO, IF, clock and power switching, both fundamentals and harmonics up to a maximum of 100 MHz.

12.5.1 Susceptibility of Cables to Bulk Injection

The purpose of the test discussed in this section is to determine the susceptibility of the EUT to the complex waveforms of bulk cable current induced by application of the damped sinusoid to power, signal or control cables. Susceptibility of individual conductors is determined by the tests described in Section 12.5.2.

12.5.1.1 Test Preparation and Setup for Bulk Current Injection

A typical setup for testing conducted susceptibility of cables to the damped sinusoidal waveform is shown in Fig. 12.21.[6] Referring to the numbered items in this figure:

1. As is the rule for most military-oriented benchtop testing, the EUT should be bonded to the ground plane with a resistance not exceeding 2.5 mΩ.
2. The choice between a capacitive and an inductive type of coupling device is usually determined by the applicable specifications and is governed by factors discussed in Section 5.2.1.3.

3. A filter or isolator may be used to prevent possible damage to test loads or instruments that are not subject to the test.

4. The current probe is to be located within 15 cm of the EUT cable connector. Its transfer impedance should be at least 0.5 Ω over a frequency range of 10 kHz to 100 MHz, and not more than 3 dB down at the extremes. It should function into an input impedance of 50 Ω and be capable of measuring at least 10 A of current. Two current probes may be used to cover the entire range, one operating from 10 kHz to 1 MHz and the other operating from 100 kHz to 100 MHz.

5. As in most military-oriented benchtop testing, the cable under test is to be positioned 5 cm above the ground plane.

6. An isolation transformer is used to protect the oscilloscope from any portion of the test waveform that might otherwise be coupled in through its ac power supply.

7. Each wire of the EUT power mains should be connected through a LISN with a 50 Ω termination at the coaxial port.

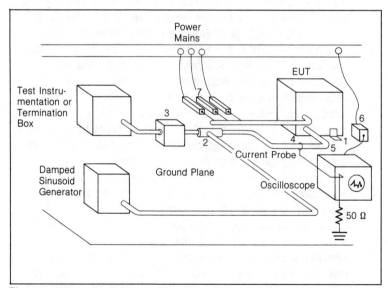

Figure 12.21—Setup for Indirect Bulk Current Injection of Sinusoid

Shielded cables are handled in accordance with the applicable specification. In some instances the shield is removed; in others, the shield is bonded to the entry and exit of a test box and the un-shielded cable tested within the box.

12.5.1.2 Test Procedures

The following procedure is recommended for testing susceptibility to bulk current injection:

1. Calibrate and set the output of the test signal generator at each test frequency, in accordance with the procedure in the applicable specification, to produce the desired level of current into a 100 Ω noninductive load. At each test frequency, record the generator output level setting that produces the test limit level. Reduce the generator output to its minimum setting and disconnect the calibration setup.

2. At each test frequency, apply the output of the generator to the current injector and monitor on the oscilloscope the level and wave shape of the resulting test signal current as fed from the output of the current probe. Slowly increase the level of the generator until the EUT exhibits performance degradation or until the test limit level is attained, as indicated by the calibrated oscilloscope display, whichever comes first. Do not exceed the calibration output setting of the generator established in step 1, even if the oscilloscope current reading falls short of the limit level. In this event, try to maximize the value of the observed current by varying the position of the coupling device along the cable under test, taking care not to exceed the calibration level.

3. Apply a minimum of 10 positive first-half-cycle waveforms, followed by at least 10 negative first-half-cycle waveforms at each test frequency and for each EUT operating mode specified in the test plan. Include a sequence with the EUT power off. Also, vary the repetition rate of the waveform from one per minute to one per second, as allowed by the generator capability. Record the maximum current level attained or the level of susceptibility as appropriate. For each susceptible

condition, determine and record the cable under test, the test frequency, threshold level and timing (for logic circuitry).

4. Repeat steps 2 and 3 for each cable in sequence.

12.5.2 Susceptibility of Individual Leads (Pins and Terminals)

The purpose of the test discussed in this section is to determine the susceptibility of the EUT to application of the damped sinusoid of Fig. 12.19 to individual cable leads. The test current waveform may be coupled to the individual lead via the capacitive or inductive injection devices used in the preceding section for bulk cables. Alternatively, it may be directly connected to a pin or terminal which is connected to the respective lead. The rationale of this testing is that the distribution among the individual leads of the bulk current injected in the test procedure of the preceding section cannot be predicted, especially at higher frequencies.

12.5.2.1 Test Preparation and Setup for Indirect Coupling

A typical setup for testing conducted susceptibility of individual leads to the damped sinusoidal waveform by the indirect method, as shown by Fig. 12.22, is essentially identical to that shown in Fig. 12.21 for bulk current injection. The single important difference is that a "breakout box," such as shown in Fig. 9.3 (Chapter 9), is used to segregate each lead, one at a time, and make it available for injection of the test current. Items 1 through 7 of Section 12.5.1.1 should be implemented with the following alterations (numbers in parentheses refer to numbered items in Fig. 12.22):

1. As an alternative to the filter or isolator (3A), a common-mode filter (3) may be inserted in series with the lead under test, between the breakout box and the injection device.

2. The lead under test takes the place of the cable under test (5) in Fig. 12.21. The surrogate lead from the breakout box should be AWG-10 or larger and as short

as possible. The length of this lead which is not surrounded by the coupling device shall not exceed 25 cm.

3. The current probe is positioned around the bulk cable
between the EUT and the breakout box. The length of
this cable is to be 1.0 m, ±0.1 m.

12.5.2.2 Test Preparation and Setup for Direct Coupling

Figure 12.22 shows a typical setup for testing susceptibility by
direct coupling of the test waveform to an individual terminal. Multiple wire combinations such as balanced leads, twisted pairs, shielded twisted pairs or triaxial cable shall be treated as a single wire
and tested accordingly.

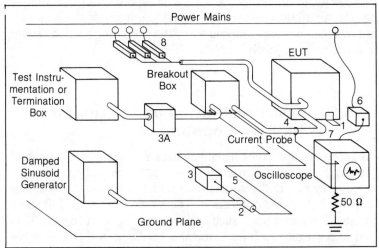

Figure 12.22—Basic Setup for Injecting Sinusoid at Individual Terminals

12.5.2.3 Test Procedure

Except as noted in the following statements, the procedure for
testing individual leads, pins and terminals is the same as given
in Section 12.5.1.2 for testing entire cables. Considerations unique
to these tests are:

1. The test signal is to be applied sequentially to each interface pin or terminal of the EUT. The current flow in
the test lead, or to the test terminal, should exhibit the

specified wave shape as viewed and measured on the oscilloscope. The peak current is to be adjusted to meet the specified level but is not to exceed the precalibrated current level (which could occur for individual lead/terminal impedances of less than 100 Ω). Thus, the peak voltage injected at a terminal is not to exceed the calibrated current level in amperes times 100 Ω.

2. For each susceptible condition noted, determine and record the lead or terminal under test, the test frequency, threshold level, operational mode of the EUT and timing (for logic circuits) at which the condition occurs.

12.6 References

1. MIL-STD-462, "Electromagnetic Interference Characteristics, Measurement of," 31 July 1967.
2. SAE ARP 1972 (January 1986), "Recommended Measurement Practices and Procedures for EMC Testing," (Warrendale, PA: Society of Automotive Engineers), prepared by SAE AE4 Committee on Electromagnetic Compatibility.
3. SAE J1547, "Electromagnetic Susceptibility Procedure for Common Mode Injection (1-400 MHz), Module Testing" (Warrendale, PA: Society of Automotive Engineers).
4. MIL-STD-461C, "Electromagnetic Emission and Susceptibility Requirements for the Control of Electromagnetic Interference,"[4] August 1986.
5. Press, J., and Komp, M., "EMP Test Methods and Equipment," *Test and Measurement World*, June 1987.
6. MIL-STD-462, "Electromagnetic Interference Characteristics, Measurement of, Interim Notice 5 (NAVY)," 1 April 1986.

Chapter 13

Test Procedures for Radiated EMI Susceptibility

This chapter covers testing for susceptibility to radiated EMI. It is the last of four chapters on specific EMI test procedures. All procedures are based on the background material presented in Chapters 1 through 9. Throughout each of these last four chapters, it is assumed that the reader has referred to and followed relevant sections of Chapter 9 which cover the general setup and preparations for such testing.

Radiated EMI was defined in Chapter 1 as electromagnetic energy which is undesirably coupled out of an emitter or into a receptor by means other than conduction. As stated in Chapter 2, the basic task of testing susceptibility to radiated EMI is that of immersing the EUT in electromagnetic fields of specified levels and of then noting any deterioration in EUT performance in response to this immersion. Figure 13.1 illustrates the basic concept of radiated susceptibility testing, while Fig. 13.2 shows a hypothetical EUT susceptibility profile. The field levels generated to test susceptibility are intended to duplicate those that the EUT might encounter in its normal operation.

Illustrated in Fig. 13.2 is the concept of quality factor, Q, as applied to a frequency at which the EUT is susceptible. As discussed in Section 6.4.1, the Q of the susceptible response limits the speed at which a culprit test signal can be scanned through it. Also implied in Fig. 13.2 is the possibility of using levels in excess of the

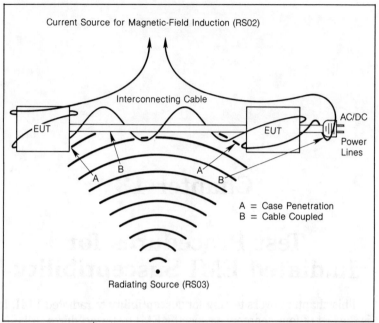

Figure 13.1—Conceptual Illustration of Radiated Susceptibility Testing

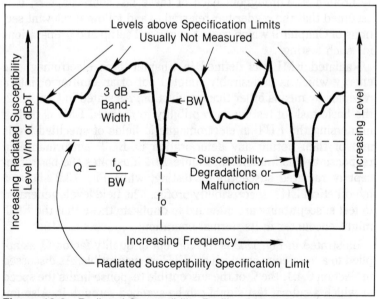

Figure 13.2—Radiated Susceptibility Profile of Hypothetical EUT

limit to permit faster scanning. As discussed in Section 9.4.6, an increase in test level correspondingly increases the allowable scan rate, but at the cost of possible hazard to the EUT. Another option discussed is the establishment of a reduced response criterion for speed scanning.

Caution: Many of the levels which must be generated to test compliance with prevailing radiated susceptibility specifications exceed levels considered safe for human exposure. Some studies indicate possible hazards from continuous exposure to levels as low as $10~\mu W/cm^2$ (6 V/m). Thus, when testing at this and higher levels in a shielded enclosure which may be occupied by test personnel, protection should be provided by interlocks which disable the power amplifiers or radiating antennas until the enclosure is no longer occupied.

13.1 Testing Susceptibility to Magnetic Fields, 30 Hz to 50 kHz

This procedure is complementary to that of Section 11.1.1 for emission testing of magnetic fields at close proximity to a radiating source. It is generally applied to military equipment which must operate near other equipment and sources likely to radiate magnetic fields in the 30 Hz to 50 kHz frequency spectrum. The typical specification limit for susceptibility testing calls for the test coil to be only 5 cm from the EUT, as compared to the 7 cm spacing called for in the procedure for testing comparable emissions. However, the coils are of different design as shown by a comparison of Figs. 11.1 (Chapter 11) and 13.3. The susceptibility test often is performed at a test level 20 dB above the limit to identify potentially susceptible frequencies.

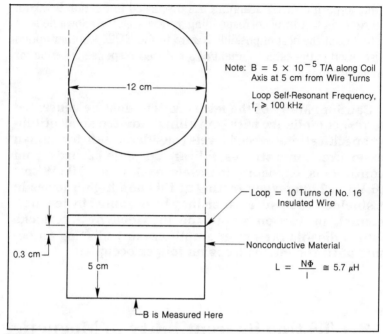

Figure 13.3—Magnetic Coil for 5 cm Susceptibility Testing

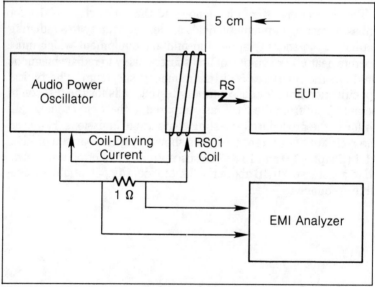

Figure 13.4—Setup for Testing Susceptibility to Magnetic Fields at 5 cm

13.1.1 Test Preparation and Setup

Since the susceptibility test limit typically is stated in units of dBpT, it is convenient to convert these units to dBμV as developed and measured across a 1 Ω test resistor through which the current feeding the coil is made to flow. This is shown in Fig. 13.4. As discussed Section 5.2.3.1, the flux density, B, along the axis of this coil at the 5 cm distance, per ampere of current flow is (in dBT/A):

$$B = 20 \log (5 \times 10^{-5}) = -86 \qquad (13.1)$$

Adding 240 dBpT/T to convert to terms of pT:

$$B = 154 \text{ dBpT/A} \qquad (13.2)$$

Since the measurement being made is of the voltage across a 1 Ω resistor, the voltage is numerically equal to the current, and:

$$B = 154 \text{ dBpT/V} \qquad (13.3)$$

Subtracting 120 dBμV/V to convert to terms of μV:

$$B = 34 \text{ dBpT/}\mu\text{V} = -34 \text{ dB}\mu\text{V/pT} \qquad (13.4)$$

Thus, subtract 34 dB from each level of the limit in dBpT to convert to its corresponding level in dBμV. Labeling the ordinate of the graph of the specification limit versus frequency in these terms will facilitate assessment of the measured data.

A typical military specification for this test requires that the measured test signal level for susceptibility be normalized, based on a 6 dB signal-to-noise ratio (S/N = 6 dB) and a 1 Hz bandwidth. Thus, to correct for the S/N ratio actually used, subtract from the measured susceptibility level, B_o, the number of dB by which that S/N ratio exceeds 6 dB; i.e., subtract (10 log S/N − 6). Then, since the noise level to which the signal is being compared will be increased by the use of a bandwidth greater than 1 Hz and decreased by a bandwidth less than 1 Hz, correct for the bandwidth difference by subtracting 10 log BW, where BW is the overall 3 dB bandwidth affecting the measurement noise level. Thus, the net level, B in dBpT, to be compared to the specification limit is:

$$B = B_o - (10 \log S/N - 6) - 10 \log BW \qquad (13.5)$$

13.1.2 Test Procedure

To test susceptibility to low-frequency magnetic fields, refer to the setup shown in Fig. 13.4 and proceed as follows:

1. Position the field-radiating loop 5 cm from the surface of the EUT with the plane of the loop parallel to the plane of the surface. As implied by Fig. 13.3, commercially available loops for this type of test incorporate a spacer which is butted against the EUT surface to produce the required 5 cm spacing.
2. Supply the test loop with sufficient current to produce magnetic flux densities approximately 20 dB greater than the applicable specification limit at the test frequencies.
3. Move the loop over the surface of the EUT and its signal I/O cables and connectors to determine locations of the maxima of any observed susceptibility. Note that this step of the procedure is the most time consuming because the EUT must be scanned in both frequency and loop location. It is possible that test time can be shortened considerably by analyzing the EUT to determine its most vulnerable components and by then providing justification in the test plan for restricting the loop positions to those nearest those components. When such an approach is not feasible, an initial location of the loop in the center of one of the EUT faces is suggested.
4. With the frequency and loop position both optimized for maximum susceptibility, reduce the loop current until the EUT is no longer affected by the applied field. Record the resulting level as the susceptibility threshold.
   a. For the class of EUTs defined as having an audio output, adjust the loop current until the EUT gives a reading on an audio voltmeter or suitable EMI analyzer which is 20 dB greater than its internal noise If a 20 dB value cannot be obtained, use a 6 dB interference-to-noise ratio. Correct the measured level for S/N and BW in accordance with Eq. (13.5).
   b. For EUTs with outputs other than an audio output, the degree of degradation must be defined in the test plan.

    c. For EUTs with both audio and other outputs, the test
      is performed to meet both steps 4a and 4b.
5. Repeat steps 1 through 4 at the test frequencies approved
   in the test plan or as determined in step 3.

13.2 Testing Susceptibility to Induced Power Frequencies and Spikes

The purpose of induction-field testing is to determine the degree of susceptibility of the EUT to fields generated by nearby power lines, through the flow of normal power currents and from transient spikes generated by switching of equipment connected across the line.

13.2.1 Test Preparation and Setup

Typically, two distinctively different types of signal are applied to test susceptibility to magnetic induction fields:

1. A spike waveform, the same as used for conducted susceptibility and shown in Fig. 12.5 (Chapter 12), is applied. Typical amplitude as applied to the radiating turns is 200 V, and typical width is either 10 μs (as shown in Fig. 12.5) or 0.15 μs, depending on the specifying agency and its applications for the EUT.
2. An ac power signal is applied to the radiating turns at the frequency used in the operational system, typically at a 20 A current level.

Shown in Fig. 13.5 is a typical setup for performing the above tests on the EUT and its cabling.

The following notes apply to the setup:

1. The ac power input and output leads are exempt from the cable test.
2. The intention of the cable test is to test groups or bundles of wires, not individual wires or pairs.
3. Current-carrying wires for cable testing are to be kept 15 cm from the cable connectors.

13.7

4. All cables should be kept at least 5 cm above the ground plane.
5. To minimize test time, test as many wire bundles at the same time as practical.

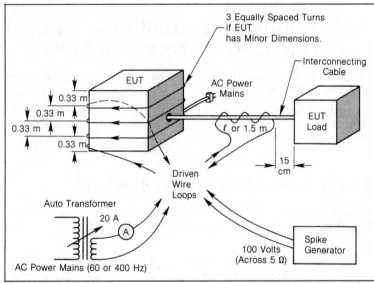

Figure 13.5—Setup for Testing Susceptibility to Magnetic Induction

13.2.2 Test Procedure

The test procedure consists of applying the appropriate spike and power-frequency voltages to all EUT modules and interconnecting leads while monitoring the EUT for any performance degradation. Use both positive and negative spike polarities, and adjust levels in accordance with the applicable specification.

13.3 Radiated Susceptibility Testing with Helmholtz Coil

The technique covered in this section is useful for determining susceptibility to magnetic fields generated by power transmission lines and power stations. Although typically applied to automotive electronic modules, subsystems and systems, it is generally applicable to such testing of any EUT over the range of 60 Hz to

30 kHz. The fields from the power generating sources and lines consist of the fundamental signal (60 Hz) and its odd harmonics which typically taper off in amplitude at the rate of about 12 dB per octave. The intent of the test is to simulate and subject the EUT to levels to which it might be exposed, based on a flux density of 160 dBpT at 60 Hz.

13.3.1 Test Preparation and Setup

Figure 13.6 is a block diagram of the test setup using the Helmholtz coil to generate the test field as discussed in Section 5.2.3.2. The radius of the coil will be determined by the need to produce a uniform magnetic field encompassing the size of the EUT as shown in Fig. 13.7. The boundary for a field, B_p, within 1 dB of that at the center between the two coils, B_c, is an ellipsoid of revolution having a major diameter of 1.6R and a minor diameter of 1.4R. For $B_p = B_c$, the volume shrinks to a sphere with diameter 1.2R. Coils are commercially available in a wide range of sizes which produce a frequency-dependent magnetic flux density of 180 dBpT at 60 Hz and a decreasing rate of 12 dB/octave. The relationships among the coil dimensions, the number of turns and the current required to produce the desired flux density are given in Section 5.2.3.2.

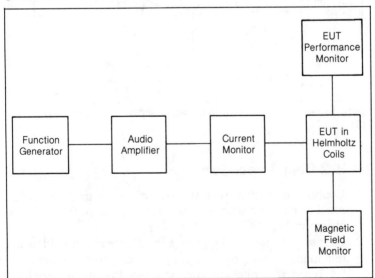

Figure 13.6—Block Diagram for Helmholtz Coil Susceptibility Testing

The audio power amplifier shown in the block diagram, Fig. 13.6, should be capable of producing approximately 200 W; all items of test instrumentation should have an operational frequency range from 60 Hz to 30 kHz with the ability to handle the required current.

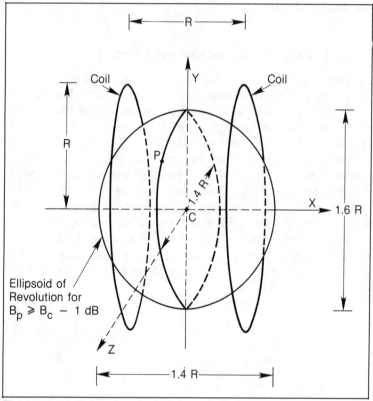

Figure 13.7—Helmholtz Coil Configuration Showing Uniform Field Within 1 dB

13.3.2 Test Procedure

1. Connect the system with the sensor for the magnetic field monitor installed between the coils in place of the EUT as shown in Fig. 13.6.
2. Calibrate the system by generating the required field at a minimum of three frequencies per octave (see Section 9.4.3) and recording the current needed to produce each

level. If the coils are precisely made, this calibration will be required no more often than for other antennas.

3. Place the EUT between the coils. Generate the required field and note any degradation of EUT performance, as specified in the test plan. In the event of deteriorated performance, reduce the level to eliminate the condition and then increase the level until the condition recurs. Note and record the threshold level of flux density which induces the susceptible condition.

13.4 Testing Susceptibility to Radiated Electric Fields, 14 kHz to 40 GHz

Susceptibility to electric fields is tested over a wide range of frequencies to determine the ability of the EUT to operate properly in its prospective electromagnetic environment. With relatively few exceptions, to be noted in Sections 13.4.5 and 13.4.6, these tests are performed with the EUT in a shielded enclosure or inside a field-producing structure or test cell. This reduces or eliminates problems related to establishing the required field strengths (1 V/m up to 200 V/m) on an open-area test site.

It should be noted that whenever far-field conditions exist, the generation of an E-field simultaneously produces a known H-field. Thus, the performance degradation of an EUT under such conditions could equally well be caused by H-field susceptibility. However, since the wave impedance at the EUT is not usually a known parameter in E-field testing, this H-field aspect is disregarded except as specifically noted below.

13.4.1 Choosing the Field-Producing Transducer

Worthwhile information on the various antennas and structures available for generating electric fields is contained in Section 5.2.2 and summarized in Table 5.2. Similarly, the application of TEM cells, reverberation chambers and mode-tuned enclosures to radiated susceptibility testing is discussed in Section 7.4. Table 13.1 summarizes the applicability of various structures, chambers and antennas for developing the fields needed to test EUTs of the sizes noted. Lack of an entry in the frequency-range columns for a field-producing device indicates that it is not usable or not recommended for the respective frequency range.

**Table 13.1—Applicability of Susceptibility
Test Chambers and Antennas**

Chamber/ Antenna	10 kHz to 3 MHz	3 to 30 MHz	30 to 200 MHz	0.2 to 1 GHz	>1 GHz
LF Parallel Plate (Cage)	VS-L				
Long-Wire	VS-M	VS-M			
Parallel-Line	VS-L	S-L			
Parallel-Plate	VS-S	VS-S			
Strip-line	VS	VS	VS		
TEM Cell	VS-L	VS-L	VS-S	VS	VS
Antennas			VS-L	VS-L	VS-L

VS = Very Small EUT: cross sectional area ⩽ 100 cm^2
S = Small EUt: cross sectional area ⩽1,000 cm^2
M = Medium EUT: height ⩽ 1.5 m (single/dual-bay console)
L = Large EUT: multiple-bay racks or consoles

The basic difference between antennas and the other entries in the matrix is that antennas produce the intended field in their radiated pattern, typically at a distance of 1 m, while the other devices create the maximum field within their outline dimensions.

13.4.2 Calibration and Application of Antenna Sources

Figures 13.8 and 13.9 illustrate two typical setups employing both radiating and monitoring antennas. Many variations are possible, depending on parameters such as frequency range, required field strength and test equipment capabilities.

Test field strengths from antennas can be calibrated and controlled by three basic methods:

1. By monitoring at the EUT
2. By monitoring at 180° or some other angle from the EUT
3. By precalibrating and subsequently regenerating the fields

These methods are discussed separately below.

Monitoring at the EUT
This technique uses a field sensor (see Section 5.2.4) located at or near the EUT to monitor the field strength produced by the

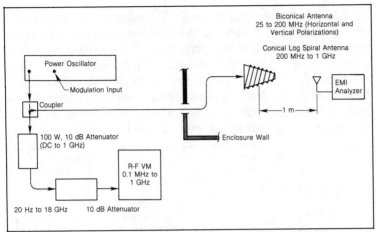

Figure 13.8—Setup for Testing Radiated Susceptibility, 25 MHz to 1 GHz

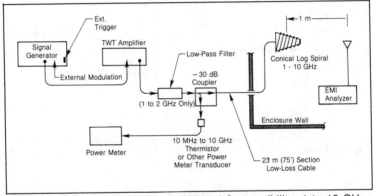

Figure 13.9—Setup for Testing Radiated Susceptibility, 1 to 10 GHz

radiating antenna. This sensor usually employs a broadband detector or active circuitry to which is connected the pickup element, which is a monopole, a dipole or special isotropic design. The output is coupled out of the test enclosure, preferably by isolating (nonconductive) fiber optic cable. It then can be used either to guide manual readjustment of the signal level or in a feedback loop for automatic leveling of the test signal level. Guidance on the use of such sensors is given in Ref. 1.

Monitoring away from the EUT

As shown in Fig. 13.10, the electric field strength can also be monitored by locating a receiving antenna at the same distance from the transmitting antenna as the EUT (typically 1 m), but at a different azimuth. Although not absolutely necessary, it is desirable that the antennas be of the same type. When neither antenna is omnidirectional in the horizontal plane, it is necessary to slew them into boresight alignment as shown in Fig. 13.10. This method should be avoided in shielded enclosure testing, if possible, because of the high likelihood that reflections and other shielded-enclosure effects will produce vastly different levels at the two locations.

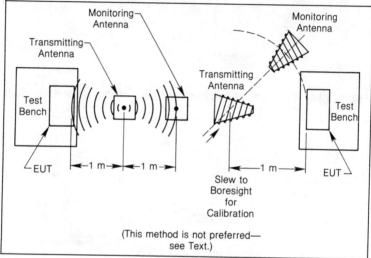

Figure 13.10—Monitoring the Radiated Field Away From the EUT

Precalibrating and Subsequently Regenerating the Fields

This method is superior to the two preceding ones because it provides the theoretically correct field strength calibration, and the test does not have to be interrupted to implement it. Precalibration is accomplished by recording the power or voltage drive, V_t, versus frequency into the radiating antenna needed to produce the desired field strength at a monitoring antenna substituted for the EUT. This procedure determines the transmitting antenna factor, $TAF = E/V_t$, at each frequency as discussed in Section 2.7.1.1. Table 5.1 (Chapter 5) is a guide to the generator output power required to produce field strengths of 1, 3 and 10 V/m at a 1 m distance from a variety of radiating antennas, based on the worst-case TAF over the frequency ranges shown. Each setup must be individually precalibrated because of the wide variations in configurations within the shielded enclosure.

13.4.3 Structures and Chambers as E-Field Sources

As shown in Table 13.1, one type or another of test structure or chamber is best suited for radiated susceptibility testing at frequencies from 10 kHz to over 1 GHz, depending on the size of the EUT. It is clear from the TAF comparison in Table 5.2 that structures and chambers are 15 to 30 dB more economical, in terms of input power, than competitive antennas in generating fields in their respective frequency ranges of coverage. Differences as great as 100 to 1 in required input power clearly imply huge cost savings or cost penalties.

Another significant advantage of test structures and test cells is that their TAFs typically are flat over their ranges of frequency coverage, in contrast to antennas, for which the TAFs typically show wide variations. This shortens calibration time and permits the testing to proceed much more rapidly. Application of TEM cells and reverberating/mode-tuned enclosures to radiated susceptibility testing is discussed in Section 7.4. Figure 13.11 shows a setup using a parallel-plate line for radiated susceptibility testing of a three-module EUT over the frequency range 14 kHz to 30 MHz.

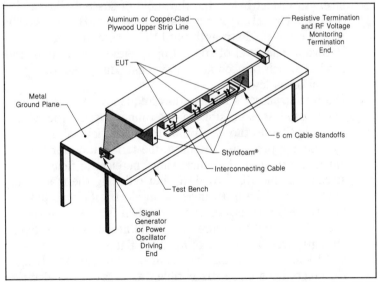

Figure 13.11—Parallel-Plate Line Setup for Testing Multiple-Module EUT

13.4.4 Test Procedure

1. Before beginning the test, check that the EUT and the test setup have been properly prepared in accordance with the recommendations in Chapter 9 with regard to EUT layout (Section 9.2.2), lead arrangement (9.2.2.1), bonding (9.2.2.3), loading (9.1.3.1) and excitation (9.1.3.2).

2. Establish the required electric field strength at 10 kHz (or another lowest required test frequency) using one of the field-producing structures described in Section 5.2.2. Select the type of modulation for the test signal to which the EUT is most likely to be susceptible (see Section 9.1.7.). If the bandwidth of the desired modulation exceeds 50 percent of the RF carrier, delay imposing it until the RF carrier frequency is twice the modulation 3 dB bandwidth.

3. Begin scanning the frequency of the test signal at a suitable rate in conformance with the principles established in Section 9.4.6. Look for a susceptible condition in the EUT and record the test frequency.

4. At each susceptible test frequency, reduce the field strength to just below the threshold of susceptibility and note this level. Lower the level another 10 dB, then slowly increase the field strength until the condition recurs. Record as the level of susceptibility either this level or the level at which the condition previously disappeared, whichever is lower.

5. If a test structure such as a low-frequency parallel-plate line is used, it is possible to determine whether the EUT is susceptible to the electric or magnetic field component by a simple procedure. Remove the termination for the antenna structure, thus increasing the electric field strength at the EUT by 6 dB, but reducing the magnetic field to zero. The 6 dB increase in electric field assumes that the EUT is located not more than 0.075λ from the open-circuit end to assure a 1 dB flatness of electric field strength over the distance; for 2 dB flatness, the distance is 0.104λ, and for 3 dB flatness it is 0.125λ, or $\lambda/8$. If the EUT continues to be susceptible, the cause is the electric field, whereas if correct operation is restored, the magnetic field is the culprit.

Before restoring the field-generating structure to its normal operation and proceeding with the test, it might be efficient to investigate possible remedies for the susceptibility problem noted. Clever use of foil shielding tapes (for electric-field shielding) or of special alloy sheets or steel wire mesh Zippertubing® (for magnetic shielding) can point the way to a permanent solution.

6. Proceed with the testing until the upper frequency of the range to be tested is attained. At some frequency (see Table 13.1), it will be necessary to change over to a conventional antenna to produce the field, such as shown in Figs. 13.8 and 13.9. When this is done, increase the radiated level by 3 dB over that required and position the antenna so that it radiates equal horizontally and vertically polarized fields. If the antenna is circularly polarized, the 3 dB adjustment is not necessary.

7. Repeat steps 2 through 6 for other EUT faces and other EUT operating modes as required. During step 4 adjust the antenna to maximize the susceptible response and record the polarization angle from horizontal of the antenna.

13.4.5 Performing Radiated Susceptibility Tests in an Anechoic Chamber

Use of an anechoic chamber, such as discussed in Section 7.3, becomes a viable option at frequencies above 200 MHz. In this range, TEM cells and other structures become too small for many EUTs, but the absorbing material for lining the enclosure walls becomes more effective. The basic design objective is to create an indoor EMI test facility which simulates open-field testing without its concomitant constraints from weather and FCC-regulated limitations on permissible emissions. The use of an enclosure with shielding is especially important if swept testing is required. This is because open-area testing, as discussed below, usually must be licensed for operation at discrete frequencies. Reference 2 discusses in detail the various aspects of anechoic chamber testing of large automotive systems per SAE J1507.[3]

13.4.6 Radiated Susceptibility Testing on Open-Area Sites

Despite their obvious limitations, open-area sites are the preferred choice for radiated susceptibility tests of very large EUTs. A typical example is a tractor-trailer combination, for which a suitable anechoic chamber is either impractical or unreasonably costly.[4] This section briefly discusses the unique aspects of this type of testing, i.e., the need for licensing to transmit at selected frequencies, special antennas for the VLF through HF range and some aspects of the test fields. All of these topics and more are covered in much greater detail in Ref. 1.

License

It is imperative that the organization performing the tests have an experimental license before any radiated susceptibility tests are performed. Any organization with a legitimate requirement can obtain such a license from the FCC. As detailed further in Refs. 1 and 4, obtaining the license is relatively easy, provided the request is reasonable and does not seek the use of frequencies the FCC is not authorized to grant. Both references provide guidelines to the selection of frequencies which the FCC will be able to grant.

Special Antennas

Available off-the-shelf antennas cannot illuminate a whole vehicle with the required high levels of field strength in the frequency range from 10 kHz to about 25 MHz. Therefore, special antennas must be designed and built. The types of antennas suggested are a modified Beverage antenna, a parallel-plate line and a pair of vertical rod antennas, all of which produce the vertically polarized electric fields most commonly encountered in the electromagnetic environment. The modified Beverage antenna and the parallel plate line are covered in Sections 5.2.2.3 and 5.2.2.2, respectively, in Chapter 5 of this Volume, as well as in Refs. 1 and 4. Although not regarded as a particularly efficient radiator of test energy in its generic form, the **rod**, or **whip**, antenna is enhanced for this application by extending its length to 2 or 3 m and improving its matching to the signal source.

Test-Field Considerations

Two major concerns in exposing a vehicle to susceptibility test fields on an open-area site are how to generate a uniform field and how to calibrate it accurately. Reference 1 provides methods for calculating the field strength produced at various positions and identifies the optimum devices, such as isolated probes, for calibrating the fields actually produced.

13.5 Testing Susceptibility to Radiated EMP Field Transients

The purpose of the test discussed in this section is to determine the susceptibility of the EUT to a relatively high-magnitude radiated electromagnetic pulse (EMP) which results from an atmospheric nuclear detonation. This radiated test is typically applied to items which will be installed in a relatively exposed location; EUTs designed for installation in shielded locations are more likely to be subjected to the conducted susceptibility tests of Section 12.5.[5]

CAUTION: All of the tests that simulate a response to conducted and radiated EMP involve potentially hazardous levels of voltage and current. Every reasonable effort should be made to protect personnel from contact or exposure.

Figure 13.12 shows the radiated pulse typically specified for this type of testing. At least 10 such pulses typically are to be applied

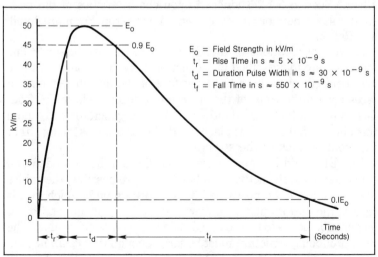

Figure 13.12—Radiated Pulse for Testing EMP Susceptibility

for each EUT operating mode and each orientation of the EUT. The pulse occurrence rate shall be not faster than once per second nor slower than once per minute. The high-level currents induced on the EUT surface by application of this radiated waveform can disrupt EUT operation by penetration to critical elements within the EUT, either by flowing through intentional apertures such as ventilation ports or by the leakage of their accompanying magnetic fields through the walls of the EUT case or cabinet.

As with most susceptibility testing, the equipment is to be tested in normal operation. Satisfying this requirement assumes greater importance and becomes more difficult to implement in this test because peripherals which are essential to EUT operation, but not part of the actual test, must be protected from high levels of applied energy. Also, test instrumentation and leads which are not involved in the normal EUT installation must be protected, either by placement at a sufficient distance from the test field or by locating them in a separate shielded enclosure. All EUT cabling which is to be included in the test must receive the same degree of protection accorded it in its intended installation, such as surrounding it with metal conduits.

13.5.1 Test Preparation and Setup

The setup recommended for military testing is shown in Fig. 13.13.[5] Section 5.1.2.3 touched upon characteristics of the transient pulse generator and other items in the setup. For more detail, see Ref. 5.

All test orientations of the EUT within the parallel-plate line structure are to described in the test plan. Typically, at least three are required: one where the front face of the upright equipment faces toward the front of the structure, a second where the front face is turned 90° toward either the load or generator end, and a third in which the EUT is placed so that its top side is facing either the front or back of the structure.

The EUT and its cables under test all are to be grounded and connected as in the actual installation. Where possible, the cables under test are to be positioned 5 cm above ground, which in this case is the bottom plate. Similarly, any EUT instrumentation or termination box is to be grounded as in the operational system. The field-producing structure must be large enough that clearance between the upper plate and the EUT, including its associated cables

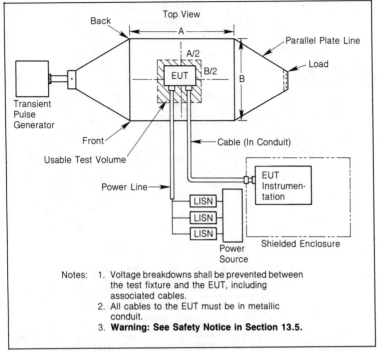

Figure 13.13—Setup for Testing Radiated Susceptibility to EMP

and conduits, is at least as great as half the total spacing between the plates. Examples of large structures are shown in Ref. 5.

13.5.2 Test Procedure

Before inserting the EUT into the parallel-plate line, calibrate the transient pulse generator output by adjusting it to produce the specified waveform such as that shown in Fig. 13.12. As shown in the diagram of the calibration setup of Fig. 13.14, a D-dot sensor (see Section 5.2.4) is oriented for maximum response and positioned between the horizontal parallel plates at the proposed EUT location. This sensor responds to the vertical component of the electric field and produces an output proportional to its derivative; its associated integrator, located in the shielded enclosure, feeds the reconstructed pulse to the 200 MHz oscilloscope for viewing and measurement. Self-integrating probes such as those described in Ref. 6 also may be used.

13.21

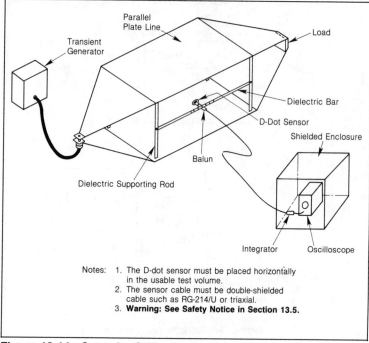

Figure 13.14—Setup for Calibrating Radiated Transient Test Field

1. With all power off, install the EUT within the parallel-plate structure and orient it at its first position. Check out the EUT to confirm proper operation.
2. Starting at the minimum output level of the transient pulse generator, apply the test signal. Gradually increase to the specified test level, noting any deterioration in EUT performance as the level increases. Note and record any such degradation and the level at which it occurs.
3. Repeat step 2 for all other orientations of the EUT.

13.6 References

1. Bronaugh, E.L., and McGinnis, W.H., "Whole-Vehicle Electromagnetic Susceptibility Tests in Open-Area Test Sites: Applying SAE J1338," *SAE Transactions*, Vol. 92.

2. Bronaugh, E.L., "Highlights of Forthcoming SAE J1507 and a Practical Realization of Its Procedures for Radiated Testing of Automotive Systems," *SAE Transactions*, August 1985, pp. 476-481.
3. SAE J1507, "Information Report on Anechoic Test Facility for Radiated Susceptibility, 20 MHz to 18 GHz, Electric Field" (Warrendale, PA: Society of Automotive Engineers).
4. SAE J1338, "Open Field Whole-Vehicle Radiated Susceptibility 10 kHz-18 GHz, Electric Field," (Warrendale, PA: Society of Automotive Engineers, 1981).
5. MIL-STD-462 Interim Notice 5 (Navy), 1 April 1986.
6. Spiegel, R.J.; Booth, C.A.; and Bronaugh, E.L., "A Radiation Measuring System with Potential Automotive Under-Hood Application," *IEEE Transactions on EMC*, Vol. EMC-25, No. 2, May 1983, pp. 61-69.

13.7 Bibliography

SAE ARP 1972 (January 1986), "Recommended Measurement Practices and Procedures for EMC Testing," (Warrendale, PA: Society of Automotive Engineers), prepared by SAE AE4 Committee on Electromagnetic Compatibility.

MIL-STD-461C "Electromagnetic Emission and Susceptibility Requirements for the Control of Electromagnetic Interference," 4 August 1986.

MIL-STD-462, "Electromagnetic Interference Characteristics, Measurement of," 31 July 1967.

SAE J1113, "Electromagnetic Susceptibility Measurement Procedures For Vehicle Components (Except Aircraft)," (Warrendale, PA: Society of Automotive Engineers), draft of January 28, 1987.

Index

Index

Index

Other Books Published by ICT

1. Carstensen, Russell V., *EMI Control in Boats and Ships*, 1979.
2. Denny, Hugh W., *Grounding for Control of EMI*, 1983.
3. Duff, Dr. William G., *A Handbook on Mobile Communications*, 1980.
4. Duff, Dr. William G. and White, Donald R.J., Volume 5, *Electromagnetic Interference Prediction & Analysis Techniques*, 1972.
5. Feher, Dr. Kamilo, *Digital Modulation Techniques in an Interference Environment*, 1977.
6. Gabrielson, Bruce C., *The Aerospace Engineer's Handbook of Lightning Protection*, 1987.
7. Gard, Michael F., *Electromagnetic Interference Control in Medical Electronics*, 1979.
8. Georgopoulos, Dr. Chris J., *Fiber Optics and Optical Isolators*, 1982.
9. Georgopoulos, Dr. Chris J., *Interference Control in Cable and Device Interfaces*, 1987.
10. Ghose, Rabindra N., *EMP Environment and System Hardness Design*, 1983.
11. Hart, William C. and Malone, Edgar W., *Lightning and Lightning Protection*, 1979.
12. Herman, John R., *Electromagnetic Ambients and Man-Made Noise*, 1979.
13. Hill, James S. and White, Donald R.J., Volume 6, *Electromagnetic Interference Specifications, Standards & Regulations*, 1975.
14. Jansky, Donald M., *Spectrum Management Techniques*, 1977.
15. Mardiguian, Michel, *Interference Control in Computers and Microprocessor-Based Equipment*, 1984.
16. Mardiguian, Michel, *Electrostatic Discharge—Understand, Simulate and Fix ESD Problems*, 1985.
17. Mardiguian, Michel, *How to Control Electrical Noise*, 1983.
18. Smith, Albert A., *Coupling of External Electromagnetic Fields to Transmission Lines*, 1986.
19. White, Donald R.J., *A Handbook on Electromagnetic Shielding Materials and Performance*, 1980.
20. White, Donald R.J., *Electrical Filters—Synthesis, Design & Applications*, 1980.
21. White, Donald R.J., *EMI Control in the Design of Printed Circuit Boards and Backplanes*, 1982. (Also available in French.)
22. White, Donald R.J. and Mardiguian, Michel, *EMI Control Methodology & Procedures*, 1985.
23. White, Donald R.J., Volume 1, *Electrical Noise and EMI Specifications*, 1971.
24. White, Donald R.J., Volume 2, *Electromagnetic Interference Test Methods and Procedures*, 1980.
25. White, Donald, R.J., Volume 3, *Electromagnetic Interference Control Methods & Techniques*, 1973.
26. White, Donald R.J., Volume 4, *Electromagnetic Interference Test Instrumentation Systems*, 1980.
27. Duff, William G., and White, Donald R.J., Volume 5, *Prediction and Analysis Techniques*, 1970.
28. White, Donald R.J., Volume 6, *EMI Specifications, Standards and Regulations*, 1973.
29. White, Donald R.J., *Shielding Design Methodology and Procedures*, 1986.
30. *EMC Technology 1982 Anthology*
31. *EMC EXPO Records 1986, 1987, 1988*

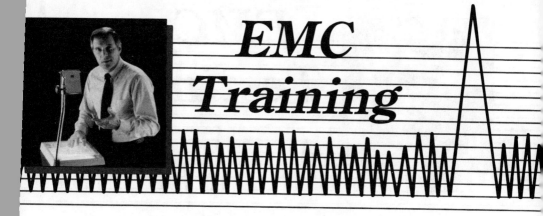

EMC Training

Interference Control Technologies, Inc. (ICT) is the premier EMI/EMC and TEMPEST training organization in the world. Founded in 1970 as Don White Consultants, Inc., ICT has educated over 45,000 degreed electronic engineers, technicians, scientists and managers from over 49 countries, representing over 1300 organizations.

All ICT seminars are designed to provide the latest pragmatic insight and methodology to *real-world* interference control and noise suppression issues. Our goal is to equip each student not only with the appropriate theory but with field-tested, proven solutions.

ICT achieves this objective in two ways. First, by providing an instructor who is both a seasoned communicator and a practicing expert in his field. Collectively our staff brings over 600 years of international work experience from diverse industrial, commercial, military and regulatory backgrounds.

Secondly, ICT updates its extensive student handout materials regularly to ensure clarity and relevancy. All students receive a notebook with a copy of every transparency presented, as well as, hardbound handbooks, computer software, an *EMC Technology* magazine subscription and other related materials.

Seminars can be taught in one of seven different languages and are regularly scheduled throughout the Unites States, Europe, the Middle and Far East, South America and Austrailia.

ICT also offers any one of its more than 25 standard seminars as is, or we can tailor any class to meet the clients specific need. These seminars can then be taught at the client's facility and at a time most conducive to the client's schedule.

Course Titles Inclide:

Grounding & Shielding
Practical EMI Fixes
EMC Design & Measurement
Intro to EMI/RFI/EMC
TEMPEST: Design & Measurement
TEMPEST: Facilities Design
Plus 15 other EMI control courses!

for more information ...

Interference Control Technologies
PO Box D
Gainesville, Va 22065
703-347-0030

ICT–

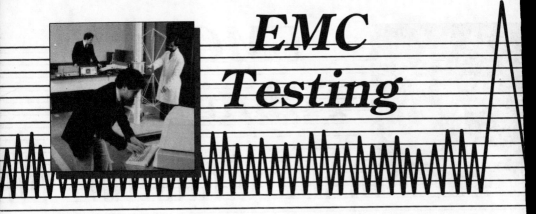

EMC Testing

THE MEASURE OF SUCCESS

Electro Service Corporation has assembled a staff of the *Right People*. People with the *need-to-know* to get your product to the marketplace quickly.

Years of work and millions of dollars in development money can go to waste when regulatory delays occur, often because of a simple problem: not knowing the correct regulations and procedures to obtain approvals in the shortest time. ESC can prevent those regulatory delays because we understand the system, inside and out, and guide you through the maze to compliance accecptance.

FULL SERVICE CAPABILITY

ESC will ensure your product gets the careful consideration it deserves. We specilaize in obtaining product approvals from these regulatory agencies:

Canadian Standards Association
Electrical Testing Labs
Canadian Dept. of Communicatons
Dept. of Health & Human Services
FederalCommunictions Commission
TUV Rheinland USA
Underwriters Laboratories
Verband Deutscher Elektrotechniker

MEETING YOUR TESTING NEEDS

ESC uses sophisticated testing equipment and procedures, RF screen rooms, test sites, and ground planes to provde RFI/EMI test capabilities from 10 kHz to 60 GHz. ESC can meet your testing needs if you manufacture or market any of the following similar devices:

* Business/Industrial Equipment
* Computers/Computer Peripherials
* Home Appliances
* Industrial Radio Systems
* Multi-Band Receivers
* Office Equipment
* Public Broadcast Receivers
* Radio-Controlled Devices
* Satellite Receivers
* Security Systems
* Telephones/ Auto Dialers
* Transformers
* Transmitters/ Receivers
* Video Games

for more information ...

Electro Service Corporation
2 Davis Drive
Belmont, CA 94002
415-592-5111

-ICT-